D1452131

Practical Seismic Interpretation

Michael E. Badley

INTERNATIONAL HUMAN
RESOURCES DEVELOPMENT
CORPORATION
Boston

Cover and interior design by Outside Designs

Library of Congress Cataloging in Publication Data
Badley, Michael E., 1947–
    Practical seismic interpretation.

    Bibliography: p. 257
    Includes index.
    1. Seismic reflection method.   I. Title.
TN269.B23   1985   622'.159   84–22507
ISBN 0–934634–88–2

[ISBN 90–277–2100–9   D. Reidel]

Printed in the United States of America

Contents

Preface

This book is about the practical aspects of reflection seismic interpretation, written by a working explorationist for explorationists. It is neither mathematical nor theoretical and does not claim to give a comprehensive treatment of the seismic-reflection method. The more geophysical topics, such as acquisition, processing, modeling, and so on, are not dealt with in any detail. The book does deal, however, with many of the everyday practicalities and problems facing the working interpreter; and, as such, has a geological bias. The book is aimed especially at those new to interpretation, who, when confronted with a pile of fresh seismic sections, wonder where to start the interpretation, what to pick, how to recognize multiples, and so forth.

Reflection seismic has made great inroads into the field of exploration over the last twenty years, and in many respects technology has advanced faster than developments in interpretation techniques. From modest beginnings, seismic reflection is now an indispensable exploration technique. This is especially true in marine areas where wells are generally relatively few in number and usually widely spaced. Continued improvement in the quality of seismic data has not only increased their importance, but has also increased the volume of data being collected, both during data acquisition and in the density of the grids. The advent of 3-D surveys has brought with it the new problem of how to cope with the vast volume of data produced. Nowadays there are few people in exploration who do not have direct contact with seismic data. Increasingly, seismic interpretation is the common ground between the geologist and the geophysicist. However, this was not always the case. Over twenty years ago Dobrin (1960) in his book *Introduction to Geophysical Prospecting* felt the need to write:

The variable-density and variable-area sections give a particularly convincing illusion that they are actual pictures of geologic formations below the surface. Manufacturers of these devices (plotters producing the sections) have often suggested that such sections could be turned over to the geologist or to management as a final presentation of the geophysical data in geological

v

terms. Such a practice would represent an abdication of the geophysicist's responsibilities. Unless the record sections are carefully interpreted by the geophysicist before being turned over to the geologist, their introduction may have to be looked upon as a backward step in the exploration process.

This was written at a time when exploration departments were polarized into two camps, namely, the geologists and the geophysicists. How relevant are such sentiments today? Certainly seismic sections have improved dramatically and look more and more akin to geological cross-sections. But some of Dobrin's words of caution still hold good: careful interpretation is still of paramount importance! What has changed most is the interpretation of sections and, indeed, the interpreters. Seismic interpretation, in common with many other modern high technologies, for example, computing, has with technological advance moved away from the realm of the specialist geophysicists into the domain of a wider geological public. No longer are seismic sections 70% noise and artefact with primary events peeping through; indeed, the reverse is now usually true. Previously the interpreter's main task was to extract the real data from the welter of noise. This required not so much geological knowledge, as detailed knowledge of the seismic system itself. Today, assuming that the interpreter has a basic understanding of the seismic method and its limitations, an interpretation is rooted more in basic geological principles, but with the details of acquisition and processing still retaining an important role.

So what does the new situation demand of the interpreter who is no longer, of necessity, a geophysicist? Firstly, as before, the interpreter must have a thorough grasp of the seismic method so that both its potential and its limitations can be appreciated. Secondly, the interpreter must have a more comprehensive geological background if the full potential of the seismic method is to be realized. To meet these requirements, this book is divided into two halves. The first half covers the areas of knowledge that every interpreter needs to have before starting an interpretation; the second half deals more with the practicalities and techniques of the interpretation itself.

There is a saying that the best geologist is the one who has seen the most rocks. Perhaps this is also true of interpreters. The best interpreter is the one who has seen the most seismic sections: it is all a question of experience. Although we should perhaps replace "most" with "greatest variety from different areas" and add the extra qualification "and has been around long enough to see the drilling results and find out if the interpretation was right, wrong, or (more usually) somewhere in between."

Good picking!

Acknowledgments

Thanks are expressed to the authors, companies, and professional associations who have allowed the use of their material in this book. The book has evolved from the manual accompanying the IHRDC course Practical Seismic Interpretation—a Workshop Course. Special thanks are extended to David Donohue for giving me the opportunity to launch the course, to Nigel Anstey for supplying both inspiration and encouragement, and to the IHRDC staff for their support and help. However, neither the course nor the book would have been possible without the great help and assistance that I have received from Merlin Profilers Ltd., and in particular Mike Doherty. I am also very grateful to Norsk Hydro and their staff for help in obtaining material for both the course and the book. The help of Tom Egeberg, Harald Nordberg, Kjell Arne Oppeboen, Christian Rambech Dahl, and Paul Bosc is especially appreciated. The assistance of Mike McCullagh in the preparation of the section on mechanical contouring is gratefully acknowledged. Numerous other individuals attending the course have helped with their comments; and the help and comments of my colleagues John Price and Mike Ashton have been invaluable, as has the assistance of Margaret Hudson, for typing, John Mackey, for drafting, and Gay Blanchard, for proofreading. Finally, I must thank my wife, Pam, for making a very hectic life fun.

Chapter 1

Introduction

Usually, it all begins with a bang generated, for example, by a dynamite explosion on land or an air gun offshore, which sends a short, sharp pulse of sound into the ground. The sound wave rushes down and down until it meets a new rock layer of hardness (hardness in the sense of the rock's resistance to being squeezed) different from the hardness of the rocks in which it is traveling. A replica of the downward-traveling sound wave echoes back toward the surface from the boundary between the two rock layers. The original pulse continues its downward journey, gradually becoming weaker, sending echoes back to the surface every time it encounters a change in rock hardness. The greater the hardness change, the stronger is the echo. Listening devices (geophones on land and hydrophones offshore) hear the echoes as they return to the surface. There are usually so many echoes that, once they start arriving, they often overlap to form a continuous stream of sound. On a typical commercial seismic survey, the geophones listen for echoes for six seconds after the initial bang. The last echoes to arrive are normally very weak, often one hundred thousandth of the strength of the early echoes; and so the geophones that detect them must be very sensitive.

The basic concept of the seismic method is illustrated in figure 1.1. Before progressing it is perhaps worthwhile to review briefly how the seismic-reflection method is applied in practice and to introduce some of the jargon that inevitably evolves with any technique.

DATA ACQUISITION

The initial bang is called the *shot;* its geographical location, the *shotpoint;* and the resulting sound, the *source pulse* or *source wavelet.* Rock hardness is called *acoustic impedance,* and is defined by the product of sound velocity in the rock and the rock's density. The echoes are called *reflections.* The stream of reflections arriving at, and recorded by, the geophone during the listening time is called a *trace.*

The boundary across which hardness changes is called an *acoustic-impedance boundary* or *seismic reflector.* The latter term is usually reserved for boundaries that

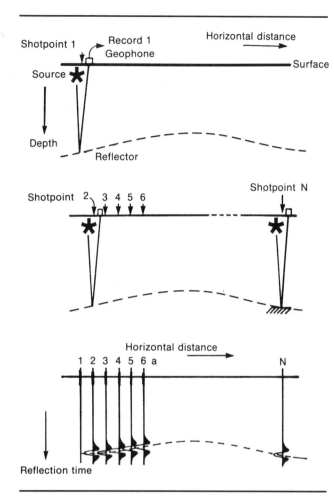

FIGURE 1.1 *The basic concept: a reflection-time measurement at regular intervals along a line, and the representation of those measurements in the form of a seismic section. Reprinted by permission of IHRDC Press from Anstey, 1982.*

produce recognizable reflection traces on seismic sections. Not all reflections produce recognizable events on seismic sections because they are too weak to be detected, are lost through interference with other reflections, etc. The type and relative size of the acoustic-impedance change is defined by the *reflection coefficient.*

Reflections resulting from sound waves that make an extra return trip, either between reflectors or down from the surface and back again, are called *multiples.* If the overlying layer is softer than the underlying layer (i.e., has lower acoustic impedance), the reflection is *positive;* if the upper layer is harder, the reflection is *negative.*

If a positive reflection on a seismic section has a certain shape (consisting of a series of wiggles about a central axis), then a negative reflection has the same shape but is reversed—every peak a trough, every trough a peak. The manner in which this (i.e., a peak or trough for a positive reflection) is displayed on a seismic section is known as *polarity.*

Sound waves travel down to a reflector and back again; therefore, the time taken from the initial bang to the recording of a reflection is called *two-way time.*

Details of the trace are analyzed in terms of: *amplitude,* a measure of reflection strength; *frequency* (measured in *hertz*), the number of oscillations per second; *bandwidth,* the range of frequencies present; and *phase,* which describes the relative shape and time position of a reflection.

In the simplest seismic system, consisting of a source and one geophone, reflections are assumed to originate from subsurface points midway between the two. However, such a system is very susceptible to *noise* (i.e., all forms of unwanted sound, such as multiples, wind noise, etc.); and it was soon found that recording reflections from the same subsurface point for different source-to-geophone spacings (*offset*) not only improved the strength of primary reflections but also resulted in a significant decrease in noise. This was termed as an improvement in the *signal-to-noise (S/N) ratio.*

A setup by which reflections are recorded from the same subsurface point with different source-to-geophone offset is known as *common-depth-point (CDP)* or *common-midpoint (CMP)* shooting. Each common midpoint consists of two or more traces, the number of which determines the *coverage* or *fold* of the seismic record. For example, two traces for a common depth point produce 2-fold or 200% coverage; 96 traces, 96-fold coverage.

Whether on land or offshore, it would be cumbersome to record all of the data for each common midpoint before proceeding to the next, and so data are acquired in the most time-efficient manner. This results in a jumble of data which has to be reordered during processing.

PROCESSING

Once all the data have been collected we arrive at the processing stage where we try to produce the perfect seismic section. The first task is to edit and reorder the data so that the series of samples corresponding to each geophone are brought together. This process is called *demultiplexing* and results in a separate trace for each shot-point, sampled at whatever interval has been used during recording (often 4 ms). After the data have been demultiplexed there follow several processing steps before the data are assembled into an acceptable seismic section. Some of the more common processing steps are described below.

Static corrections or *statics* are corrections made to compensate for differences in land elevation (hills and valleys along the seismic line), velocity effects of the upper weathered-rock layer, depth of the hydrophones, etc.

Deconvolution: The seismic pulse starts out as a short duration burst of sound; but, as it passes through the Earth, repeated echoes eventually produce an overlapping series of reflections lasting for several seconds, a process called *convolution*. As its name suggests, deconvolution is a mathematical procedure for unscrambling the convolution effects to reveal only those reflections that stem from real reflectors.

Next, the traces are grouped together into families from common midpoints, and are then known as *CMP or CDP gathers.* Once the traces are grouped into CMP gathers, information on subsurface velocity can be obtained by a process known as *velocity analysis,* an essential processing step. Velocity analysis provides the *normal-moveout (NMO) velocities.* Since the same reflection on each CMP trace will have been recorded at progressively greater times for increasing offsets because of the ever-lengthening travel paths, the appropriate NMO velocity applied to a reflector has the effect of bringing the reflection to the same time for all traces in the CMP gather.

Following NMO correction the traces are ready for the next, and main, step in the processing sequence, in which all the values corresponding to a particular reflection time on each trace are added together. This process, called *stacking,* not only enhances the reflections from true reflectors but also usually leads to a reduction in noise.

Commonly, a second deconvolution operation is applied after stacking, in an attempt to remove unwanted reflections and perhaps also to change the shape of the pulse to some more desirable form.

By now, the seismic section is almost in its final form, and one of the last processing steps is to remove unwanted frequencies from the data. Due to attenuation by the Earth the frequency of the seismic pulse decreases with depth. It is possible to estimate the maximum frequency to be expected at a particular depth. Removal of frequencies above those that can be reasonably expected is not just a cosmetic exercise, but improves the signal-to-noise ratio. Removal of unwanted frequencies is accomplished using a filter whose passband becomes of lower frequency with increasing depth—*a time-variant filter (TVF)*. A seismic section that has undergone this processing sequence is commonly called a *filtered-stack section.*

A basic assumption of the CMP method is that reflections originate in the subsurface from the midpoint between source and geophone. However, if the reflector has sizeable dip, the assumption is no longer valid; the position of the reflection in the seismic section is then displaced downdip and the dip of the reflector is underestimated. To restore the reflections to their correct subsurface positions, the data must be *migrated*. After migration the section is, not surprisingly, called a *migrated section.*

This brief discussion has described just about the absolute minimum number of steps necessary to produce a seismic section, and additional processing procedures are often used to get the best possible results.

INTERPRETATION EQUIPMENT

Once the final processed seismic sections have landed on the interpreter's desk, the next step is interpretation. The actual requirements and equipment needed to carry out a seismic interpretation are extremely basic—namely, knowledge; some colored pencils; and, last but not least, an eraser! However, to carry out an interpretation in an efficient manner, the following requirements should be met.

Firstly, adequate space and a good, even source of lighting. Seismic interpretation requires lighting with twice the candle power usual for office work. This is essential to ensure that the sections can be viewed for normal work periods without inducing eye strain. Although, it must be said, even with the best of lighting some seismic sections induce not only eye strain, but brain strain as well.

Secondly, a table large enough to enable the sections to be unfolded and laid flat for a length of at least 130 cm. This is important because throughout the interpretation the seismic sections should be viewed both from above and obliquely along their length. Viewing the sections obliquely has a foreshortening effect on the reflector pattern and enhances lateral continuity of events. Often reflector configurations that are obscure when viewed from above become obvious when the sections are viewed in this way.

Thirdly, pencils. Marking on the seismic sections must be clear, precise, and delicate. This requires, above all, sharp pencils and a light, steady hand. The lines on seismic sections should always be thin, so as not to dominate the reflection wiggles, and should leave the section with an uncluttered appearance. Heavy, thick lines make it impossible to review the interpretation subsequently, as

4

the eye is always drawn to the colored lines and the original reflection pattern fades into the background. It is a favorite old trick in poor data areas to put lots of thick colored lines on the sections—they can look very convincing until compared with an uninterpreted example. The other reason for thin lines is accuracy. An untidy, thick colored line can span up to 40 ms on a half-scale section (5 cm, or 2.5 inches, to 1 second two-way time), and introduce totally unnecessary inaccuracy into the interpretation. This point can be especially critical if the lines are to be digitized by someone other than the interpreter. A good practice is to use a soft (e.g., HB or No. 2) pencil to mark the horizons initially, only adding color in a uniform code later, as the interpretation progresses. For fine lines, 0.5-mm mechanical pencils have been found ideal. Colored leads are widely available; obtain the softest leads possible. If colored crayons are to be used throughout the interpretation, choose relatively soft, wax-based crayons that erase easily.

This brings us, finally, to an absolutely essential piece of equipment, the eraser. This should be as large as possible: mistakes, or changes of mind, are inevitable and the eraser will see plenty of action during an interpretation. A final refinement is an artist's horsehair brush to sweep away the erasings; you are then set up for many happy hours of seismic interpretation.

Chapter 2   Essential Theory

In this chapter we will investigate the fundamental processes of the seismic-reflection method, an understanding of which is essential for the interpreter.

THE NATURE OF REFLECTIONS

It all starts with a bang: an explosion, either in a shothole in the ground or below the surface of the water, produces an expanding compressional wavefront. Once the wavefront has left the chaos of the immediate vicinity of the explosion, it can be seen to consist of a seismic pulse with a duration of several tens of milliseconds. This seismic pulse is called the source wavelet. A simplified example of a seismic pulse and the basic elements of the seismic reflection method are shown in figure 2.1. Let us follow the course of a seismic pulse as it travels down into the ground. The seismic pulse is transmitted through the rocks as an elastic wave which transfers energy by the movement of rock particles. The dimensions of the elastic wave, or seismic wave, are very large relative to the vibration displacements of individual rock particles. Nevertheless, the seismic wave motion can be specified in terms of particle velocity and particle pressure caused by the vibrations induced by its passage. The speed in rock, typically several thousands of meters per second, at which the particle motion transports the seismic energy determines the seismic wave velocity. These high velocities contrast with those of the individual rock particles, which have velocities magnitudes of order lower, being measured in millionths of meters per second only. For each rock type, or lithology, when it is impinged by a seismic wave, there is both a particular intrinsic susceptibility to particle motion and characteristic velocity for the passage, by particle vibration, of the seismic wave through the rock.

The predictable and characteristic acoustic properties of a rock are defined as its acoustic impedance (Z), the product of density (ρ) and velocity (V).

$$Z = \rho V. \tag{2.1}$$

Velocity is usually more important than density in controlling acoustic impedance. For example, porosity varia-

Time

(a)

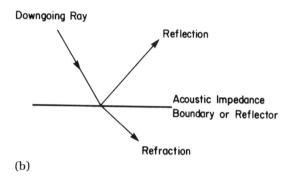

Downgoing Ray

Reflection

Acoustic Impedance
Boundary or Reflector

Refraction

(b)

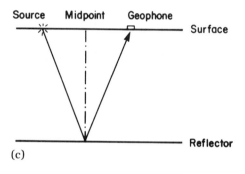

Source   Midpoint   Geophone

Surface

Reflector

(c)

FIGURE 2.1 *The basic elements of the seismic-reflection method.* (a) *Diagrammatic source wavelet.* (b) *Reflection and refraction at an acoustic-impedance boundary.* (c) *Reflection geometry for a horizontal reflector.*

tion or the content of the pore fluids (e.g., gas in a sandstone) has a much more significant effect on velocity than on the density of the rock.

The relationship between particle velocity, particle pressure, and acoustic impedance is most easily explained by analogy with electricity (see Anstey, 1977, pp. 2–7). Using the analogy we can illustrate two fundamental relationships:

1. In electricity,

voltage = current × resistance,

which in acoustic terms is equivalent to

pressure = particle velocity × acoustic impedance.

2. In electricity,

power = current × voltage,

which in acoustic terms is equivalent to

intensity = particle velocity × pressure,

where acoustic intensity represents the energy flux across unit area in unit time.

To convey a more tangible meaning to the concept of acoustic impedance, Anstey (1977) likened it to acoustic hardness. "Hard" rocks, for example, limestone, granite, etc., have high acoustic impedance, whereas "soft" rocks, for example, clays, are relatively squeezable and have low acoustic impedance. Alternatively, we could say that a given pressure would produce a large particle velocity in a low-acoustic-impedance rock (e.g., clay) but a small particle velocity in a high-acoustic-impedance rock (e.g., limestone).

We can now return to the seismic pulse, which we left forming part of the expanding compressional wavefront after the initial explosion. It will continue its downward journey into the Earth with constant velocity so long as the acoustic impedance of the rocks does not change. Typically, however, the sedimentary sequence consists of successive layers of differing lithologies which also, as a rule, have differing acoustic impedance. This need not always be the case, as acoustic impedance is the product of two variables, velocity and density. It is quite common, for example, that a claystone and a relatively porous sandstone, although having quite different lithologies, have identical values for acoustic impedance. When, however, the seismic wave encounters a rock layer with different acoustic impedance from the rock in which it is traveling, the wavefront splits. Part is reflected back toward the surface and part is transmitted and refracted to continue the downward journey (figs. 2.1 and 2.2). The wavefront split occurs exactly at the boundary between the different rocks and is caused by the abrupt change in acoustic impedance.

The seismic-reflection method is based on the recording and measurement of reflections from such boundaries. It is, therefore, important to understand why reflections arise in the first instance and what information is coded in the reflection.

Using, as an example, a thick clay interval overlying a horizontal limestone, we would expect a vertically downward propagating wave to induce a large particle motion as it passes through the clay, but only a small particle velocity in the limestone. If all of the energy in the wavefront were transmitted into the limestone, we would have a situation at the interface of a large particle velocity in the

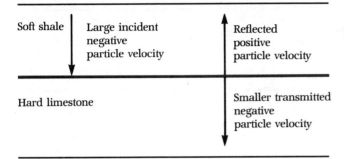

| Soft shale | Large incident negative particle velocity | Reflected positive particle velocity |
| Hard limestone | | Smaller transmitted negative particle velocity |

FIGURE 2.2 *Continuity of particle velocity at a soft-to-hard interface. The arrows indicate the raypath direction (i.e., direction of travel). Reprinted by permission of IHRDC Press from Robinson, 1983, fig. 3.15, p. 144.*

clay, whereas just on the limestone side of the interface the particle velocity would be small. Without there being a reflection, a difference in particle velocity across an interface can only occur if the two lithologies separate along their boundary. Separation along a boundary due to the passage of a seismic wave is impossible deep in the subsurface where overburden pressure is many orders of magnitude greater than the particle pressure of the seismic wave.

In order to balance the particle velocities on either side of the acoustic-impedance boundary, there must be a reflection (fig. 2.2). Not all of the incident energy in the clay can be transmitted into the limestone, and the amount that is reflected provides an exact balance between the particle velocities on either side of the interface. From this we can infer, as of course we would intuitively expect, that no energy is lost at the acoustic-impedance boundary and that the sum of the transmitted energy and reflected energy is equal to the incident energy.

We can also conclude that the strength of the reflection must be directly related to the contrast in acoustic impedance across the boundary. The greater the contrast, the stronger the reflection required to balance the difference in incident and transmitted energy.

The strength of a reflection generated at a boundary can be quantified in terms of the boundary's reflection coefficient (*RC*); at normal incidence this is

$$RC = \frac{Z_2 - Z_1}{Z_2 + Z_1}, \tag{2.2}$$

where

Z_1 = acoustic impedance in the upper layer.
Z_2 = acoustic impedance in the lower layer.

The reflection coefficient can be positive or negative depending upon whether "softer" rocks overlie "harder" rocks, or vice versa.

We do not actually measure directly the contrast in acoustic impedance across a boundary but deduce it from the amplitude of the recorded reflection. The greater the amplitude, the stronger the reflection and, by inference, the greater the acoustic-impedance contrast. Onland geophones respond to particle velocity amplitude; offshore hydrophones respond to acoustic pressure amplitude. In terms of amplitude the reflection coefficient is the ratio of amplitude of the reflected wave to that of the incident wave. For example, if the reflected wave has one third the amplitude of the incident wave, the reflection coefficient is 0.33. A reflection coefficient of 0.33 is relatively large; usually reflectivity is much lower. Fortunately, the energy reflected is approximately proportional to the square of the reflectivity. In the above example for a reflector with an *RC* of 0.33, only one ninth of the energy is reflected while eight ninths continues the downward journey. So, in most cases, the fraction of energy reflected is minute and, fortunately, almost all the energy is transmitted and available to generate reflections from deeper interfaces.

Recording the amplitudes of the reflections as they return to the surface enables us to assess the magnitude of the acoustic contrast causing reflection. This can have geological significance, but it would be even more useful if we could also determine whether the reflection coefficient is positive or negative and so deduce whether the change in acoustic impedance is from softer to harder or harder to softer rocks. To see if this is possible we need to examine further the nature of the measured parameters and their relationship to the reflectors. On land, geophones respond to particle velocity, while offshore hydrophones measure pressure. For a plane wave in a lossless earth, both produce an identical response to the seismic wave (fig. 2.3). A geophone located above the source shot would register an initial upward motion, or positive particle velocity; or, if the shot were in water, a hydrophone would register a positive pressure. If the same measurement were made below the shot, to record the downgoing wave, the hydrophones would again register a positive pressure but the geophone would register a negative particle velocity because the initial motion of the seismic wave is downward.

On land, where the geophone responds to particle velocity, the incident particle velocity affecting an underlying reflector is negative (i.e., the initial motion is downward). Using the example of clay overlying limestone, particle velocity is relatively large in the clay; and, to balance the lower particle velocity in the underlying limestone, the reflection must have a positive particle velocity (i.e., the initial motion must be upward). See figure 2.2. In water, the hydrophones respond to pressure. Figure 2.4 shows how the small positive pressure of the incident ray must be supplemented by a positive pressure response if the reflection is to balance the larger positive pressure in the limestone.

8

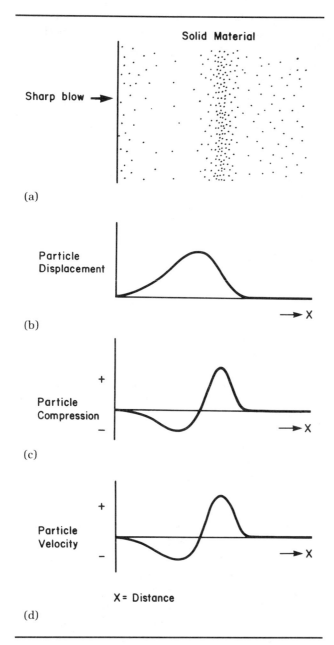

(a)

Solid Material

Sharp blow →

(b)

Particle
Displacement

→ X

(c)

Particle
Compression

+

−

→ X

(d)

Particle
Velocity

+

−

→ X

X = Distance

FIGURE 2.3 *Response of particle compression and particle velocity to the passage of a compressional wave. (a) Diagrammatic representation of particle spacing in a solid material a few milliseconds after being struck by a sharp blow. (b) The maximum particle displacement corresponds with the propagating compressional wave. (c) The particle compression is at a maximum in the propagating wave and a minimum in the rarefactional area behind the compression wave. (d) The particle velocity is positive (i.e., forward) in the compressional part of the wave and negative (i.e., in a backward direction) in the rarefactional part of the wave. The waveforms for particle compression and particle velocity are identical. After Anstey, 1977, by permission of IHRDC Press.*

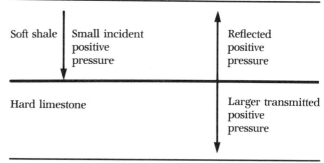

FIGURE 2.4 *Continuity of particle pressure at a soft-to-hard interface. The arrows indicate the raypath direction. Reprinted by permission of IHRDC Press from Robinson, 1983, fig. 3.16, p. 145.*

In both cases the receivers (geophones or hydrophones) would have registered a positive reflection from the contrast between clay and limestone. Note that there is a difference between the situation on land, where we start with a negative input signal (the initial motion is downward), and offshore, where the input signal is positive. The situation for an acoustic boundary with a negative reflection coefficient, for example, limestone overlying clay (harder to softer), is also shown in figure 2.5. This time both geophones and hydrophones register a negative reflection.

We can conclude that a reflection, whether measured by a geophone or a hydrophone, will always have the same response. If $Z_1 < Z_2$ (i.e., a soft rock overlying a harder rock), the reflection will be positive. If $Z_2 < Z_1$, the reflection will be negative.

We are now in a position to conclude that by recording reflections it is possible, theoretically, to relate the amplitude of the reflection to the size of the acoustic-impedance change and determine whether the reflection originates from an interface with a positive or negative reflection coefficient. Both the magnitude of the reflection coefficient and its sign are influenced mainly by geological factors, that is, lithological change (with some notable exceptions), and form the basis for providing a predictable link between reflections and geology. Last, but not least, we are able to measure the traveltime of a seismic pulse to the interface and back to the surface again (i.e., the two-way traveltime). If the velocity of the seismic wave through the rocks is known, or can be estimated, the two-way time can be converted into depth using

$$\text{depth} = \frac{\text{two-way time} \times \text{velocity}}{2}. \tag{2.3}$$

At this stage we should introduce the concept of polarity. Instead of describing reflections as positive or negative, it is more usual to use the term *polarity*. Use of the word polarity is merely a recording and display conven-

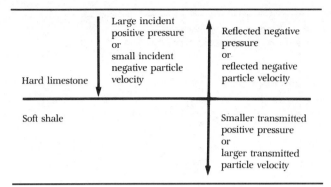

FIGURE 2.5 *Continuity of particle pressure and compression at a hard-to-soft interface. The arrows indicate the raypath direction.*

tion and has no special significance in its own right. The Society of Exploration Geophysicists (SEG) defines normal polarity in this way:

1. A positive seismic signal produces a positive acoustic pressure on a hydrophone in water or an upward initial motion on a geophone on land.
2. A positive seismic signal is recorded as a negative number on a tape, a negative deflection (downswing) on a monitor record, and a trough (white) on a seismic section.

Using this convention, in a seismic section displayed with SEG normal polarity we would expect:

A reflecting boundary to appear as a trough in the seismic trace if $Z_2 > Z_1$

A reflecting boundary to appear as a peak in the seismic trace if $Z_2 < Z_1$

Figure 2.6 shows normal and reverse polarity displays for minimum- and zero-phase pulses, two common seismic-pulse types.

REFLECTIONS: SOME LIMITATIONS AND PROBLEMS

In a typical sequence of sedimentary rocks, seismic reflections will arise at each lithological boundary across which the acoustic impedance changes. These boundaries are called seismic reflectors. All acoustic-impedance changes have the potential to produce reflections. However, whether or not these changes are significant enough for their reflections to be recognized and recorded will depend upon the sensitivity of the seismic recording and processing system. Invariably, many reflections that arise from the acoustic-impedance changes present in sedimentary sequences are too small to be recorded by the methods currently available.

Figure 2.7 shows a layered sedimentary sequence and corresponding logs of velocity, density, and acoustic impedance. The rock sequence includes common sedimen-

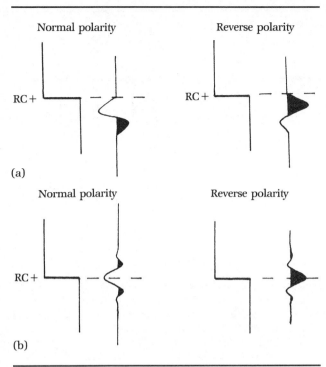

FIGURE 2.6 *Examples of idealized normal and reverse polarity for* (a) *minimum- and* (b) *zero-phase wavelets at an acoustic-impedance boundary with a positive reflection coefficient.*

tary rocks and typical acoustic-impedance contrasts. Two of the boundaries are especially instructive in showing the relationship between velocity, density, and acoustic impedance. At the boundary between the gas-filled and water-bearing sands there is a sharp acoustic-impedance change which is an example of a nonlithologic acoustic-impedance change. The presence of gas in porous sand greatly reduces the seismic velocity and thereby the acoustic impedance. The other interesting boundary is between claystone and salt. The velocity log indicates a significant velocity increase at the top of the salt. If we were to rely solely on velocity as an indicator of acoustic impedance, we would expect the boundary to generate a strong reflection. However, the density shows a significant decrease from the claystones into the salt—a change in the opposite direction to that of the velocity. As acoustic impedance is the product of velocity and density, the changes in velocity and density largely cancel each other to produce only a small change in acoustic impedance at the top of the salt. A reflection from the top salt will be much weaker than we would have expected had we based our expectations of reflection strength on the velocity increase.

On the right side of figure 2.7 is the simplified seismic trace that would be produced by the acoustic-impedance changes. This could represent just one of many traces on a seismic section.

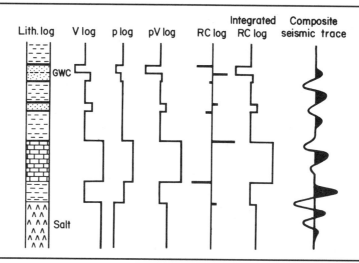

FIGURE 2.7 *The derivation of the reflection coefficient log and the resulting composite trace for a minimum-phase, normal-polarity (SEG) wavelet. The lithological sequence shown at the left consists of: a basal salt section overlain by a thick shale, massive limestone, and a shale sequence containing two sands. The lower sand is water saturated, while the upper sand contains gas overlying water-saturated sand. The velocity is shown under V log; with high velocity in the salt and limestone, a velocity in the water-wet sands slightly higher than in the shales, and a major depression of velocity in the gas sand. The density log is shown under ρ log. The salt density is very low, and the porosity in the lower sand causes the density to be coincident with that of the shales. The density in the gas sand is depressed. The acoustic-impedance log, shown under ρV log, is the product of velocity and density. For most lithologies it has similar form to the V log, excepting cases where velocity and density change in opposite directions. This occurs in the upper water sand, and is not significant; but in the salt the changes in velocity and density almost cancel. The reflection coefficients of the acoustic-impedance boundaries are shown under RC log, which shows the sign and expected strength of reflections. A composite seismic trace that would be produced by convolving a minimum-phase, normal-polarity (SEG) wavelet with the RC log is shown. The integrated RC log shows the effect of making a running sum of all values in a moving window down the RC log; this restores the ρV log. After Anstey, 1980a, and Robinson, 1983, by permission of IHRDC Press.*

Before going further, it is worthwhile to look at an example that shows many of the features discussed above. It is taken from a normal-polarity seismic section which passes across the Troll Field, a giant gas/oil accumulation offshore Norway (fig. 2.8). The reservoir is formed by a sequence of heterogeneous clastics some 250 ms (about 400 m) thick and overlain by shales. Several very interesting features related to acoustic-impedance changes are present. The changes in acoustic impedance between the water-filled sands, gas-filled sands, and shales are all large enough to produce strong reflections. Acoustic impedance is highest in the water-bearing sands and lowest in the gas-bearing sands. The shales have an intermediate value of acoustic impedance. From these relationships it is possible to predict the anticipated reflections on the normal-polarity section. In the water-bearing interval the reservoir top is marked by an increase in acoustic impedance and should produce a trough on the seismic trace (arrow *A*). However, in the gas zone the impedance decrease across the boundary and the reservoir top should produce a black peak (arrow *B*). At the gas-water contact the polarity of the reservoir top reflector should change from a peak to a trough (arrow *C*).

Within the sands the gas-water contact should produce a strong trough defining the contact (arrow *D*). This gas-water contact is horizontal, but its reflection shows gentle westward dip across the structure. This is a velocity effect. The dip of the "flat spot" is caused by lower velocities in the gas sands. The greater the thickness of overlying gas sand, the longer the traveltime of the seismic pulse through it, and so the deeper the flat spot appears to lie.

The seismic section shows a response to the acoustic-impedance changes in line with our predictions, but there is a further interesting effect in the seismic section, which gives some measure of the dependence of the system on the magnitude of acoustic-impedance change. The water-bearing reservoir interval appears to be quite homogeneous. No internal reflections are present—the interval is seismically transparent. However, well results show the interval to consist of massive sands separated by more shaly intervals. Although changes in small acoustic impedance occur at lithological boundaries, evidently they are too small to be detected by this seismic system. By contrast, the gas-filled reservoir interval does show some internal reflections, which dip into the flat spot and disappear. The ability of the seismic system to see internal structure in the gas-filled part of the reservoir is a direct result of the gas. The gas-filled sands have significantly

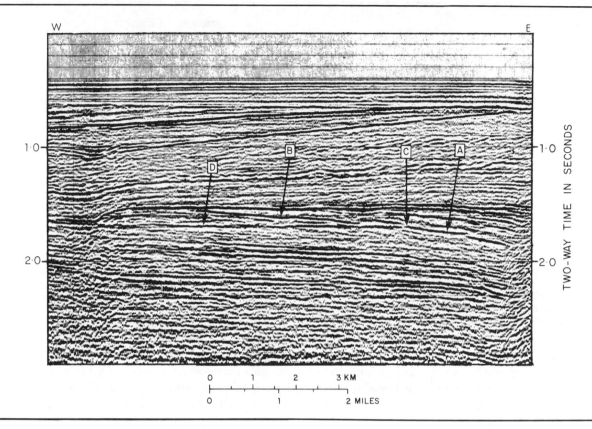

FIGURE 2.8 *Seismic section across the Troll Field, offshore Norway. Minimum-phase normal-polarity (SEG). See text for explanation. Courtesy Norsk Hydro.*

lower acoustic impedance than the argillaceous zones, which have a much lower gas saturation. The changes in acoustic impedance at the lithological boundaries are now sufficiently large to be detected by the seismic system and so reveal the reservoir's internal structure.

Figure 2.8 demonstrates that the seismic system does respond in a predictable manner. We need now to investigate further the capabilities of the method when it is used to investigate rock units in the subsurface. The example in figure 2.8 will be used to illustrate these problems. We have to contend with the selective manner in which the seismic method recognizes boundaries in the subsurface. They are visible to the seismic system only if there is an acoustic-impedance contrast *and* if the contrast is great enough to produce a reflection that can be detected. This can be a serious shortcoming of the method if, for example, there is no acoustic-impedance contrast between a reservoir sandstone and an overlying claystone seal. Lithologically, such a boundary would be clear cut and sharp to the geologist examining either a core of rock from a well or wireline logs. But to the seismic method the reservoir top would be quite invisible: no acoustic-impedance contrast, no reflection. The seismic system "sees" in a different way. What may be obvious to the

naked eye is invisible to seismic system if there is no acoustic-impedance contrast. The absence of reflectors within the water-bearing sandstones of figure 2.8 demonstrates that even if there are acoustic-impedance contrasts, in order to appear on a seismic trace as reflections these contrasts must be above a certain threshold level.

Even when readable reflections are generated, there may still be problems. Figure 2.7 shows the seismic response to a typical rock sequence. No vertical scale is indicated. If a scale is added, we will perhaps be in for an unpleasant surprise. In figure 2.9 the trace of a sonic-log curve* has been added. The sonic-log curve gives a very detailed impression of the interbedded nature of the rock sequence. In most cases the sequence can be subdivided into lithological units using the sonic curve, and further subdivision internally of some thicker units may be possible. Assuming that for most boundaries the change in velocity is a good guide to likely change in acoustic impedance we can compare sonic-log and seismic responses

* A sonic log is made with an instrument, lowered on a cable into a borehole. It measures the compressional wave velocity of the rock units adjacent to the borehole. In favorable circumstances it is able to detect and display beds with thickness down to about 20 cm. The sonic log curve shows the varying velocities of the individual beds and if we assume this is primarily due to lithological changes (except the gas sand), then the curves can be considered as a crude depiction of the bedded nature and vertical variability of the rock sequences.

12

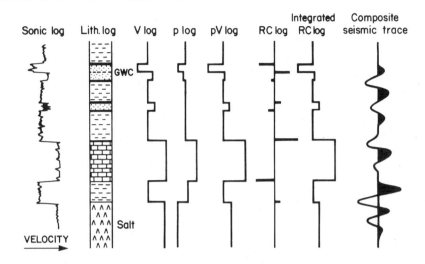

Sonic log   Lith. log   V log   p log   pV log   RC log   Integrated RC log   Composite seismic trace

GWC

VELOCITY

Salt

FIGURE 2.9 *Diagram showing the difference in resolution between a wireline sonic log and a seismic trace. After Anstey, 1980a, by permission of IHRDC Press.*

for the same sequences. The comparison is not too favorable. There is an incredible contrast in scale for information displayed in well logs and seismic traces. Geologists are familiar with using well logs at scales of 1:200, 1:500, 1:1000, etc., but the scales for seismic records are in the order of 1:10000 and upwards. Bridging the gap between the level of detail seen in well logs and the relative lack of detail in seismic records is a major problem. There is no tool or method that falls between the two. Well logs give great detail at isolated locations but provide no information about the geology between wells. Seismic traces show what happens laterally, but in a very limited and selective way.

INTERFERENCE

The above examples show clearly that one main problem facing the seismic method is interference between the seismic responses from closely spaced acoustic-impedance boundaries. The seismic trace in figure 2.9 is a composite of the seismic response at each acoustic-impedance contrast. The composite trace cannot be interpreted simply, as there is not a straightforward one-to-one relationship between the seismic trace and the acoustic boundaries. Because the seismic pulse is longer than the separation between some of these contrasts, the reflections interfere.

Interference always occurs when the reflections from different reflectors overlap. Interference is controlled by the length of seismic pulse in milliseconds and the spacing of acoustic-impedance boundaries in time, which is a function of the interval velocity.

Interference can be constructive or destructive (fig. 2.10). Obviously there are many possible combinations of

acoustic-impedance spacing that produce interference. The length of the seismic pulse is critical. Ideally, the pulse would be a spike whose reflections would be similar spikes of lesser amplitude (fig. 2.11a); particle motion would be instantaneous and wavelength infinitesimal; and we would have almost perfect resolution. Typically, however, the input pulse consists of one or two peaks and one or two troughs and has a duration (length in the seismic section) of 20–100 ms (fig. 2.11b). The fact that the wavelet often comprises several cycles (follow half-cycles) rather than the desired spike, means that a single reflecting horizon can generate a reflection consisting of the primary event followed immediately by one or more follow half-cycles (fig. 2.11c). This can give a false impression of interbedding.

For the interpreter to evaluate the pulse shape it is necessary to know at which basic pulse shape the processing was aimed. This is not necessarily the same as the input pulse, since transformations to a new pulse shape are often made during processing. In an extremely simplified way seismic pulses displayed on seismic sections can be grouped into two main types, minimum phase and zero phase (fig. 2.6). (Although this is a reasonable simplification for the interpreter it may not be for the processing geophysicist or the modeler).

A minimum-phase pulse has its energy concentrated at its front, and is thought to be typical of many seismic signals. The pulse is said to be "front loaded," with its onset at the acoustic-impedance boundary. However, detailed analysis of pulses of the minimum-phase type reveals many different varieties. The first peak or trough need not have the greatest amplitude, and processing usually results in the first follow half-cycle having a comparable amplitude followed by a strongly attenuated tail. Quite often the lead event can be much weaker than the

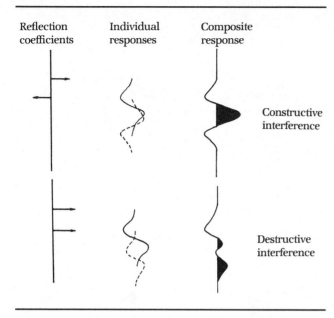

FIGURE 2.10 *Constructive and destructive interference affecting a minimum-phase normal-polarity wavelet.*

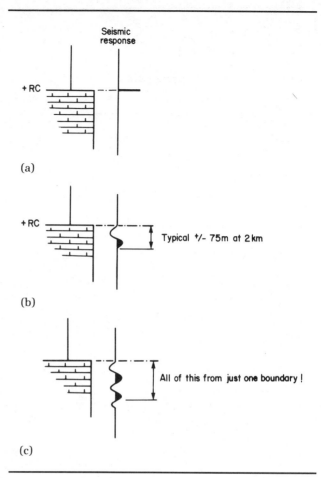

FIGURE 2.11 *Seismic response at a positive acoustic-impedance boundary. (a) Idealized situation where the seismic response is a spike at each acoustic-impedance boundary. (b) Idealized normal-polarity minimum-phase response of a good seismic system. (c) Response of a poor seismic system that produces a reflection consisting of several cycles from a single boundary.*

first follow half-cycle in data processed and displayed to minimum phase.

Zero-phase pulses, a product of wavelet processing and land Vibroseis data, have become more common in recent years. Zero-phase pulses consist of a central peak and two side lobes of opposite sign and lesser amplitude. Here the boundary is located at the central peak and not at the wavelet onset as is the case for minimum-phase pulses. Although a zero-phase pulse is only theoretical and is not physically realizable—since it requires that particle motion begin before the wavefront reaches the surface of the impedance contrast—this type of pulse offers the following advantages:

1. Given the same amplitude spectrum, a zero-phase signal is always shorter and always has greater amplitude than the equivalent minimum-phase signal; it therefore has a greater signal/noise ratio.
2. The maximum amplitude of zero-phase signals always coincides with the theoretical reflectivity spike. The maximum amplitude of a minimum-phase signal is delayed with reference to the reflectivity spike.

Figures 2.12 and 2.13 illustrate the contrasting interference effects for a variety of bed configurations on minimum- and zero-phase wavelets. The figures not only show the dramatic effect of interference on the composite response but also the marked differences between the responses of minimum- and zero-phase pulses to the same geological configuration. The differences are due to interference effects caused by the different shapes of the zero-

and minimum-phase wavelets. The zero-phase wavelet is centered around each acoustic-impedance boundary, and so has scope for interference with wavelets from nearby boundaries both below and above. The minimum-phase wavelet, however, extends down from the boundaries and so can only interfere with wavelets from underlying boundaries.

VERTICAL RESOLUTION

Having encountered the problem of interference we can now ask:

1. How thick must a bed or unit be before there is no interference between the reflections from acoustic-impedance contrasts at the unit's top and base?
2. How thin can a bed or unit be before its top and base are no longer resolvable?

14

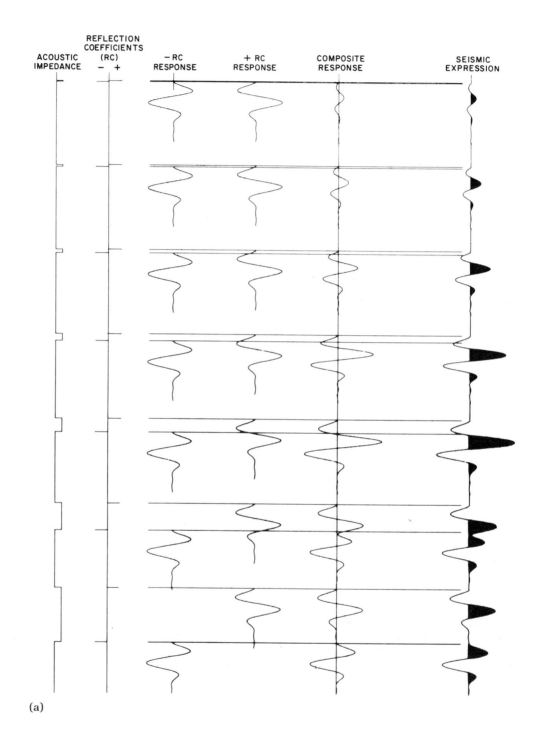

(a)

FIGURE 2.12 *Examples of interference on a minimum-phase normal-polarity wavelet for a range of bed thicknesses and bed spacings. Courtesy Norsk Hydro.*

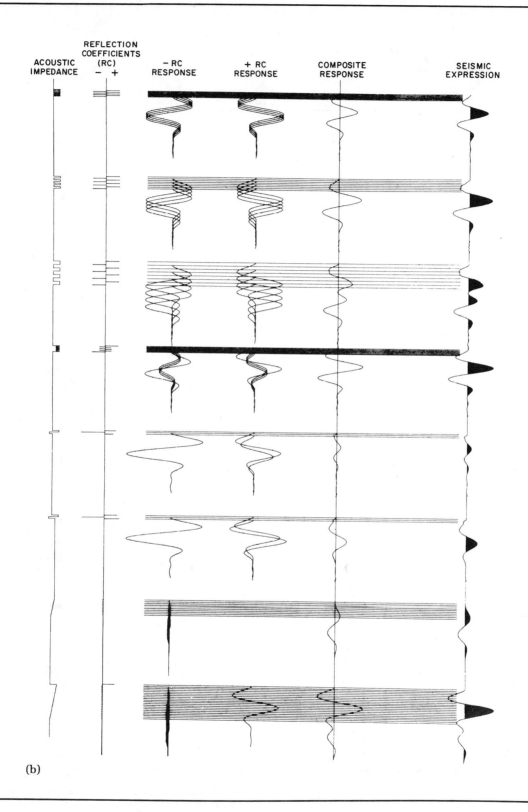

(b)

16

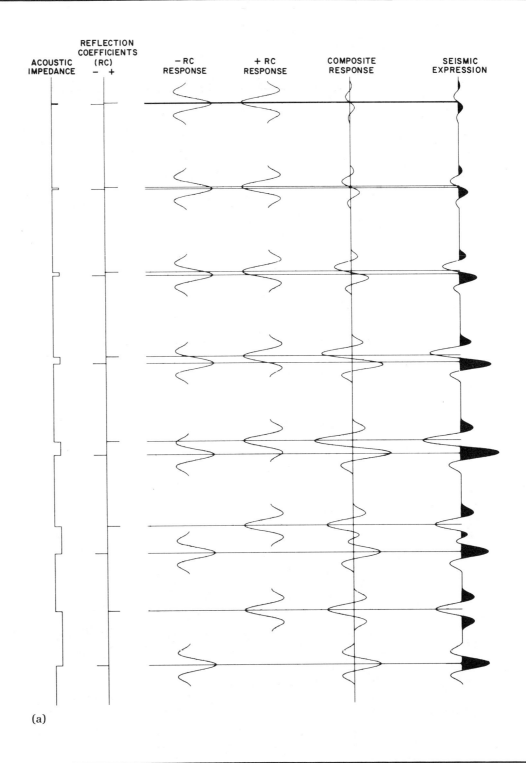

(a)

FIGURE 2.13 *Examples of interference on a zero-phase normal-polarity wavelet for a range of bed thicknesses and spacings. Courtesy Norsk Hydro.*

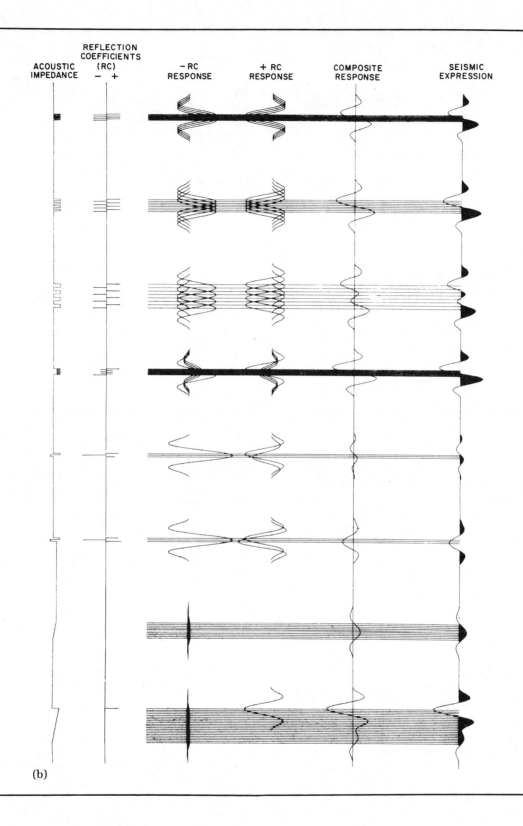

ACOUSTIC IMPEDANCE

REFLECTION COEFFICIENTS (RC)
− +

− RC RESPONSE

+ RC RESPONSE

COMPOSITE RESPONSE

SEISMIC EXPRESSION

(b)

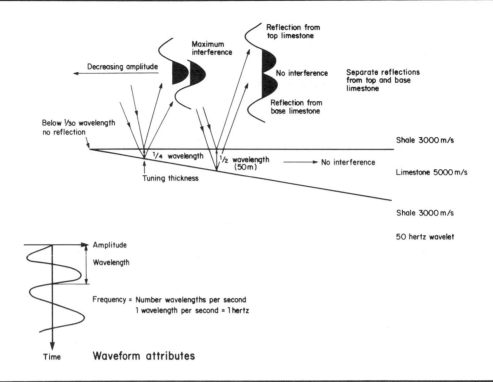

Figure 2.14 is an example of a wedge-shaped limestone unit (high velocity) encased in claystones (lower velocity). An expanding wavefront, in this case a minimum-phase wavelet, is reflected from the top of the limestone. The polarity of the incident wavelet is preserved on the reflected wavelet. The reflection from the base limestone, however, has its polarity reversed, as we would expect from a change from higher to lower acoustic impedance.

The two reflected wavelets of opposite polarity will be separated in time so long as the time thickness of the limestone is equal to, or greater than, half the wavelength of the seismic wavelet. Potentially, we can resolve top and base limestone, so long as the limestone thickness is greater than half the wavelength. If the limestone is thinner than half the wavelength, the two opposite polarity reflections begin to overlap and interfere. When the two-way transit time of the limestone reaches half the wavelet width (i.e., the limestone thickness equals one-quarter of the wavelength), as shown in figure 2.14, the two wavelets constructively interfere to form a single wavelet of anomalously high amplitude. This thickness is known as the tuning thickness. For a limestone velocity of 5000 m/s and seismic-wave frequency of 50 Hz, maximum constructive interference or tuning would occur at a limestone thickness of 25 m. When the limestone thins to less than the tuning thickness, the unusually high amplitude of the combined top and base limestone reflections decreases, and the combined reflections appear nearly the

FIGURE 2.14 *Interference effects associated with a high acoustic-impedance wedge encased in lower acoustic-impedance shale. The limestone must be thicker than half the seismic wavelength for no interference between reflections from its top and base. Maximum interference and amplitude of the resulting reflection occurs at a limestone thickness equivalent to one quarter of the seismic wavelength—the tuning thickness. For limestone thicknesses below one-quarter wavelength, the reflection remains the same shape but decreases in amplitude. Once the limestone is about one-thirtieth wavelength or less, reflections from the top and base effectively cancel and there is no detectable seismic response.*

same as for a single interface (fig. 2.14). This single reflection does not thin as the bed thins.

The relationship between frequency, velocity, and wavelength is straightforward:

$$\text{wavelength} = \frac{\text{velocity}}{\text{frequency}}.$$

For example, if the frequency of our seismic wave was 50 Hz, or alternately expressed, had a period of 20 ms, at the depth where the limestone with a velocity of 5000 m/s occurred, then the limestone would have to be at least 50 m thick (half the wavelength of 100 m) to enable resolution of its top and base by the seismic trace. If, on the other hand, the frequency of the seismic wave was only 20 Hz, then the limestone would have to be at least 125 m thick for its top and base to be resolved. In the shallow

FIGURE 2.15 *Estimating the dominant frequency or period of the seismic wavelet from a seismic section. Isolated high-amplitude, continuous reflections should be chosen to reduce the risk of interference effects. It is assumed that on minimum-phase processed sections, individual reflections consist of a lead and follow half-cycles (the first and second half-cycles). Zero-phase data is assumed to have a waveform consisting of lead and follow half-cycles symmetric about a higher-amplitude central peak or trough. The dominant frequency is Hertz = 1/period(s). The seismic section here is processed to produce a minimum-phase waveform and is displayed with reverse polarity (SEG).*

Reflection A: duration 12 ms; frequency 83 Hz
Reflection B: duration 15 ms; frequency 67 Hz
Reflection C: duration 25 ms; frequency 40 Hz

The estimated frequencies should always be calculated for several reflections in a particular time range and the estimates compared with the time-variant filter (TVF) limits given in the seismic section label. The estimated value must fall within the range of the time-variant filter.

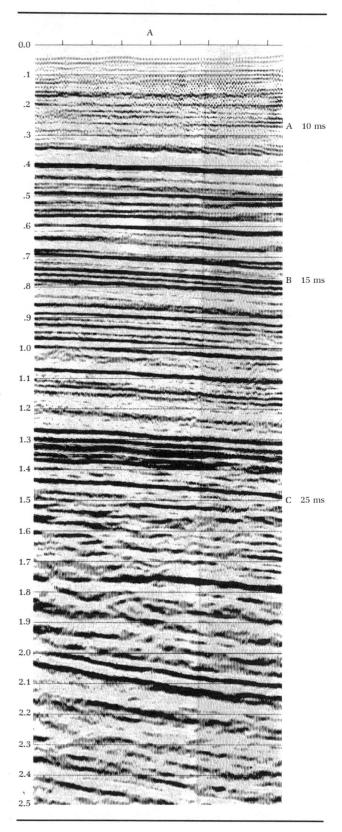

section where velocities are usually low and frequencies are high, wavelengths of around 40 m are common, with a corresponding resolvable thickness of 10 m and a detectable limit of bed thickness to produce a reflection of about 1.3 m. Deeper in the section, where velocities are higher and frequencies lower, these resolvable and detectable limits are higher. In the example above, for example, with a velocity of 5000 m/s and a frequency of 20 Hz, the resolvable and detectable limits are 62.5 m and 8.3 m, respectively. It is difficult to determine directly from the seismic trace the wavelength of the seismic pulse in meters. However, if the wavelet's period and the interval velocity of a unit can be estimated, wavelength is readily determined from the relationship.

$$\text{wavelength} = \frac{\text{velocity}}{\text{period}}. \qquad (2.4)$$

The dominant wavelength or period of the seismic pulse at a particular depth can be estimated by first finding a reflection that is likely to be free from interference effects and then by measuring the duration in milliseconds of the lead and follow cycles (fig. 2.15). The tuning effect is most marked if the reflection coefficients have opposite signs at the top and base of a unit. If they are the same, for example from a wedge that has an acoustic impedance intermediate between the acoustic impedances above and below, the waveforms tend to a minimum at the quarter-wavelength thickness; and this produces a dimming of the reflection at the top of the wedge (fig. 2.16). In this case there is still a reflection after the wedge has pinched out due to the contrast in acoustic impedance between the overlying and underlying units. The detectable limit, the minimum thickness for

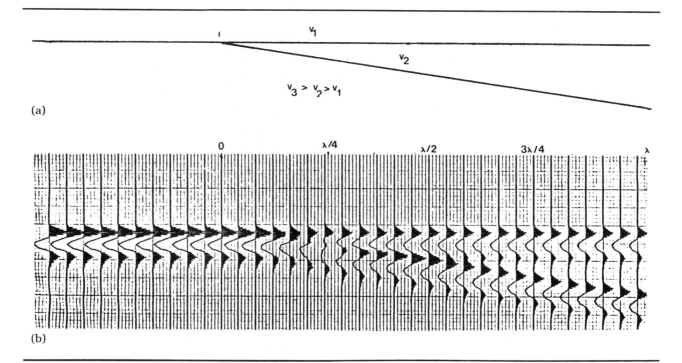

(a)

(b)

FIGURE 2.16 *Reflection from a wedge of acoustic impedance intermediate in magnitude between that of the over- and underlying units. The thickness of the wedge is indicated as a fraction of the dominant wavelength. Note that there is still a reflection beyond the limit of the wedge due to the contrast in acoustic impedance between the over- and underlying layers.* (a) *Model.* (b) *Seismic section. Reprinted by permission of the EAEG from Sheriff, 1975, fig. 6.9, p. 128.*

a layer to give a reflection, is of the order of $\frac{1}{30}$ of the wavelength.

In situations where it is necessary to estimate bed thickness for beds thinner than one-quarter wavelength, modeling techniques can be used to relate amplitude and thickness. Theoretically, the thickness of thin beds below the quarter-wavelength threshold can be estimated from variations in reflection amplitude. Figure 2.17 shows the build-up in amplitude at the quarter-wavelength thickness and the decrease in amplitude as the wedge thins. The main problem with the technique is the need for an amplitude reference (usually from well data) and a detailed control on the amplitude. This usually limits the technique to marine seismic data. The technique requires modification for situations where the reflection coefficients at the top and base of the thin interval have the same sign (see fig. 2.16). In addition to these specialized applications, tuning effects are commonly observed as they affect reflections truncating beneath an unconformity or as they affect onlapping reflections. With knowledge of the likely seismic frequency and interval velocity it may be possible to attempt an estimate of bed thickness at the one-quarter wavelength or tuning thickness in such situations.

HORIZONTAL RESOLUTION

Although it is often convenient to visualize seismic reflections as single rays emanating from a point (e.g., fig. 2.1) actual reflections result from the interaction of a reflecting boundary and a seismic wavefront. The wavefront impinges not just upon a single point, but upon a considerable area of the reflector surface. The resulting reflection is actually produced from a circular zone of quite large diameter. The extent of the area producing the reflection is known as the *Fresnel zone*. This is the portion of the reflector from which energy returns to the geophone or hydrophone within a half-cycle (i.e., one-quarter wavelength) after the onset of the reflection. Contributions from this zone sum constructively to produce a reflection (fig. 2.18). On an unmigrated section, horizontal resolution is determined by the size of the Fresnel zone.

Figure 2.19 shows a model of Fresnel effects. The model shows a continuous bed to the left and three isolated units with lateral extents expressed in terms of Fresnel zones. Each unit thins and pinches out over a shorter distance. The model indicates the following predicted responses:

1. A diffraction is associated with each bed termination.
2. The amplitude of each diffraction decays rapidly away from its apex.
3. The diffractions show polarity reversed on opposing limbs.
4. The gaps between the units are largely masked by the diffractions.
5. A unit of only ½ Fresnel zone produces a seismic re-

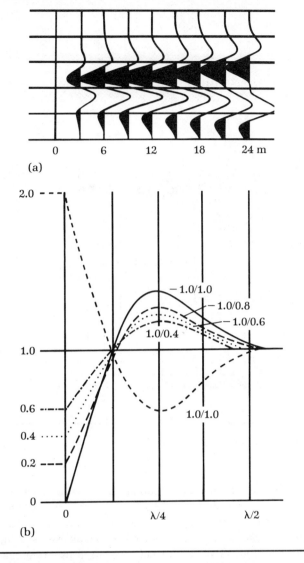

(a)

(b)

FIGURE 2.17 *Reflections from a wedge, enclosed in material of constant acoustic impedance. (a) Reflection waveshape; the wedge thicknesses are given in meters for a velocity of 1525 m/s. (b) Maximum peak-to-trough amplitudes where reflectivity at top and base of the wedge has ratios 1.0/1.0 [conditions for dim spot at one-quarter wavelength], −1.0/1.0, −1.0/0.8, −1.0/0.6, −1.0/0.4. The −1.0/1.0 curve applies to the wedge in (a). Thickness is given in wavelengths. Reprinted by permission of IHRDC Press from Sheriff, 1980a, fig. 8.6, p. 169; after Neidell and Poggiagliolmi, 1977.*

FOR SPHERICAL WAVES:

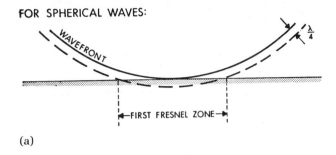

(a)

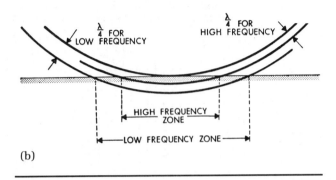

(b)

FIGURE 2.18 *Fresnel zone. (a) The first energy to reach a geophone from a plane reflector is from the point where the reflector is first tangent to the wavefront. The area of the reflector that produces the reflection is limited by the area that the wavefront one-quarter wavelength later makes with the reflector. The energy arriving within this interval sums constructively to produce the reflection. (b) The Fresnel zone is larger for low-frequency components than for high-frequency ones. Reprinted by permission of the AAPG from Sheriff, 1977, fig. 7, p. 11.*

sponse that is indistinguishable from a diffraction from a point source. Even with a width of one Fresnel zone the seismic response can only be distinguished with difficulty from that of a simple diffraction.

The magnitude of Fresnel zones can be approximated from the relationship

$$rf = \frac{V}{2}\sqrt{\frac{t}{f}} \qquad (2.5)$$

where

rf = radius of the Fresnel zone.
V = average velocity.
t = two-way time in seconds.
f = dominant frequency in hertz.

For example, a reflection at 1.7 seconds with a 35-Hz component corresponds to a Fresnel-zone radius of 275 m (equivalent to an area of 0.237 km²), for an average veloc-

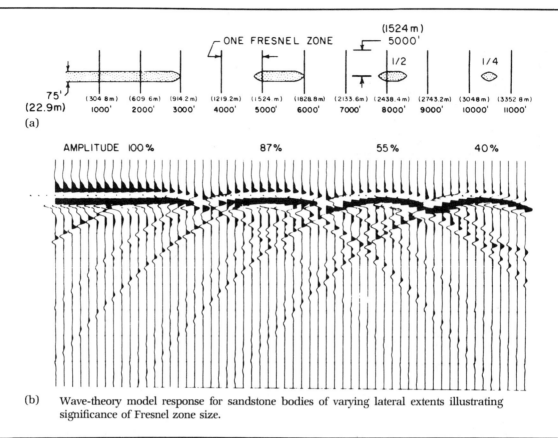

(a)

(b)   Wave-theory model response for sandstone bodies of varying lateral extents illustrating significance of Fresnel zone size.

FIGURE 2.19 *Reflections from reflectors of varying limited extents. (a) Cross-section of model: vertical lines are spaced at the Fresnel-zone size. (b) Seismic section over the model. The peak amplitudes of the four reflections are, respectively, 100%, 87%, 55%, and 40%. Reprinted by permission of the AAPG from Meckel and Nath, 1977, fig. 5, p. 421; after Neidell and Poggiagliolmi, 1977.*

ity of 2500 m/s; and a reflection at 3.5 seconds with a 20-Hz component corresponds to a Fresnel-zone radius of 732 m (equivalent to an area of 1.68 km^2), for an average velocity of 3500 m/s.

Horizontal resolution decreases with depth, increasing velocity, and lower frequency. A deep feature has to have a larger areal extent to produce the same effect as a smaller, shallower feature. If, for example, there is a hole in a reflector smaller than the Fresnel zone, the Fresnel zone extends onto the reflector surrounding the hole so that the reflection appears to be continuous across the hole. Such a hole might represent a channel cut into horizontal beds. There are, however, changes (such as in the amplitude) that can be used to distinguish the situation.

Another illustration of the effect of the Fresnel zone is shown by the box model of figure 2.20. The box could represent, for example, a pinnacle reef. A seismic line to the side of the box shows a reflection from the box (as well as the continuous reflection from the main reflector), because part of the Fresnel zone extends onto the box. The reflection from the top of the box produces a spurious event on section 4, a sideswipe reflection. Sideswipe is the most detrimental of the Fresnel zone effects. Conventional 2-D migration, which repairs much of the horizontal resolution loss due to the Fresnel zone effect, is unable to reposition correctly sideswipe reflections.

Fresnel-zone effects are often seen in the vicinity of faults. Figure 2.21 shows how the amplitude of a reflector decreases in the vicinity of a fault because only part of the Fresnel zone is available to produce a reflector.

THE EFFECT OF DEPTH

The above discussions on resolution and interference have highlighted the influence of frequency and velocity on our ability to interpret features in the seismic section. Unfortunately, both velocity and frequency show an overall change with depth that causes a gradual decrease in resolution. This is rather unwelcome, for if any of the factors vary, so will our perception of the reflection pattern. This can have a major effect on our ability to interpret the seismic section.

Velocity tends to increase with depth due to compac-

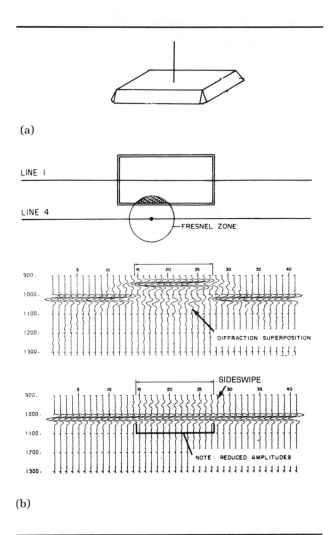

(a)

(b)

FIGURE 2.20 *Reflections from a box model. (a) Isometric diagram of the model; the length:width:height:depth ratios are 10:5:1:10. (b) Plan showing Fresnel-zone dimensions relative to box dimensions. Line 1 passes over the box. Line 4 passes to the side of the box, but close enough for part of the Fresnel zone to impinge on the box. Reprinted by permission of IHRDC Press from Sheriff, 1980a; after Neidell and Poggiagliolmi, 1977.*

---

tion and diagenetic effects. Frequency decreases due to attenuation of the seismic wave—there is an almost constant fractional energy loss per cycle of the seismic wave; and higher frequencies are attenuated more than lower frequencies for a particular path length. From this we can conclude that with increasing depth vertical and lateral resolution decreases, and interference effects become more pronounced as the pulse length increases (due to lower frequency). The loss of frequency with depth makes it less likely that a bed's thickness will exceed the minimum one-quarter wavelength for potential resolution

of reflections from its top and base, or even the half-wavelength required for no interference between reflections from a unit's top and base.

The fact that there is an overall decrease in strength of contrasts in acoustic impedance as burial depth increases in a further problem that results in weaker reflections. This comes about through the gradual convergence of acoustic-impedance values for different lithologies with increasing compaction. Although acoustic impedance increases as both velocity and density increase, not all lithologies are affected to the same degree. Whereas limestone may show only modest increases in acoustic impedance with burial, a clay, as it compacts and converts into a claystone, will show a significant increase in acoustic impedance. The net effect of this process is to produce generally lower acoustic-impedance contrasts and thereby reduced reflection coefficients. Lower reflection coefficients, combined with the ever-decreasing energy and lower frequency of the seismic wave, ultimately limits the ability of the seismic reflection to detect and resolve boundaries. Figure 2.22 illustrates how the seismic response varies with depth, even for the same pair of lithologies. Limestone is overlain by clay, producing a large positive reflection coefficient in the shallow subsurface. The seismic wavelet here is also of relatively high frequency and the seismic response is a sharp, high-amplitude reflection. As the lithologies become more deeply buried, the clay compacts and converts to shale and the limestone gradually reduces in porosity. Acoustic impedance increases for both lithologies—but at a greater rate in the shale. This results in a real decrease in acoustic-impedance contrast with increasing burial. By the time the shale and limestone are buried to 5000 m or more, the difference in acoustic impedance may not be especially large. The decrease in acoustic-impedance contrast results in gradually weaker reflections from the same lithology pair with increasing depth. The reflections not only become weaker; they also change their shape. The Earth preferentially attenuates the higher frequency part of the seismic signal with increasing traveltime, resulting in a gradual increase in wavelength with depth. This wavelength increase changes the shape of the reflection (fig. 2.22).

Figure 2.23 shows the effect of different wavelet length (frequency) on interference effects. Looked at in another way, the four seismic traces shown in figure 2.23 could be used to model the seismic response for the lithological column *a* at different burial depths. At the shallowest depth, *f*, in figure 2.23 the seismic response has the highest frequency, but this decreases with depth resulting in poorer resolution. Responses *e*, *d*, and *c* would represent the changing waveform as frequency decreases with increasing burial.

24

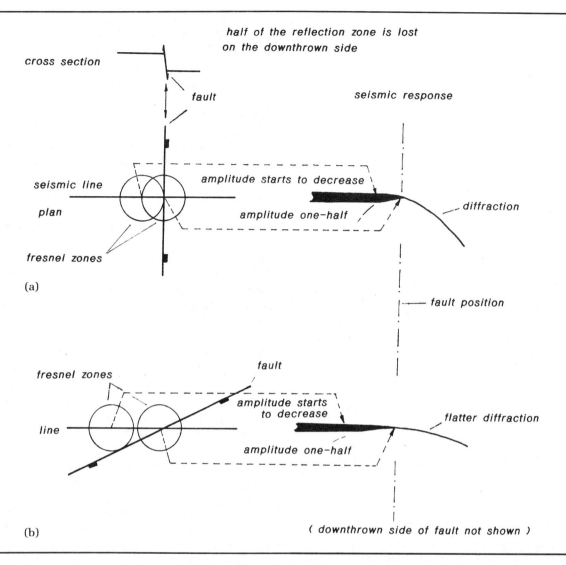

(a)

(b)

Finally, figure 2.24 shows part of a real seismic section. In the interval down to 2 s the reflections are strong and lots of geological detail is indicated. The interval below 3 s is quite different. There are fewer strong continuous reflectors and the overall appearance suggests a much simpler geology. But beware, this could be an unwarranted conclusion. The loss of detail and change of reflection character of the deeper section is unlikely to be due to simpler geology, but rather to effects of lower seismic pulse frequency and lower reflection coefficients in the deeper geology.

FIGURE 2.21 *Effect of Fresnel zones on reflection amplitude near to a fault. (a) Fault perpendicular to the seismic line that juxtaposes a reflector against material of constant acoustic impedance. Reflection amplitude is constant until the Fresnel zone passes over the fault. Reflection amplitude decreases and reaches half of its former value when the center of the Fresnel zone is coincident with the fault. (b) Fault oblique to the seismic line. The decrease in reflection amplitude is spread over a larger portion of the seismic line. After Anstey, 1980a, by permission of IHRDC Press.*

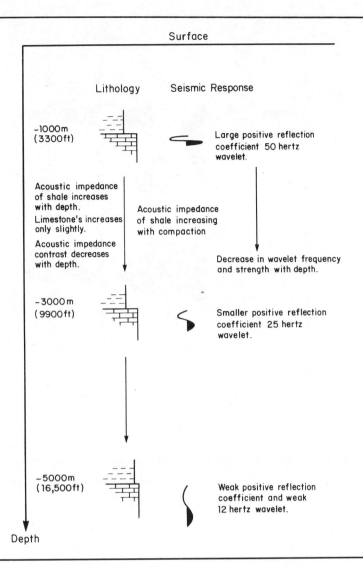

Surface

Lithology   Seismic Response

-1000m
(3300ft)
Large positive reflection coefficient 50 hertz wavelet.

Acoustic impedance of shale increases with depth.
Limestone's increases only slightly.
Acoustic impedance contrast decreases with depth.

Acoustic impedance of shale increasing with compaction

Decrease in wavelet frequency and strength with depth.

-3000m
(9900ft)
Smaller positive reflection coefficient 25 hertz wavelet.

-5000m
(16,500ft)
Weak positive reflection coefficient and weak 12 hertz wavelet.

Depth

FIGURE 2.22 *Sketch showing the effect of increasing depth, through changes in acoustic impedance and seismic-wavelet frequency, on the seismic response from an acoustic-impedance contrast between clay and limestone. The effects of burial, especially compaction, affect clays more than limestone. Although both show an overall increase in acoustic impedance with depth, the rate of increase is greater in the claystones. This results in weaker reflections with depth. The Earth attenuates the seismic signal, preferentially removing the higher frequency components. The gradual loss of frequency with depth changes the wavelength and shape of the seismic wavelet. The combined effect of decreasing frequency and acoustic-impedance contrasts produces a change from shallow, strong, sharp reflections to weak, long reflections at depth.*

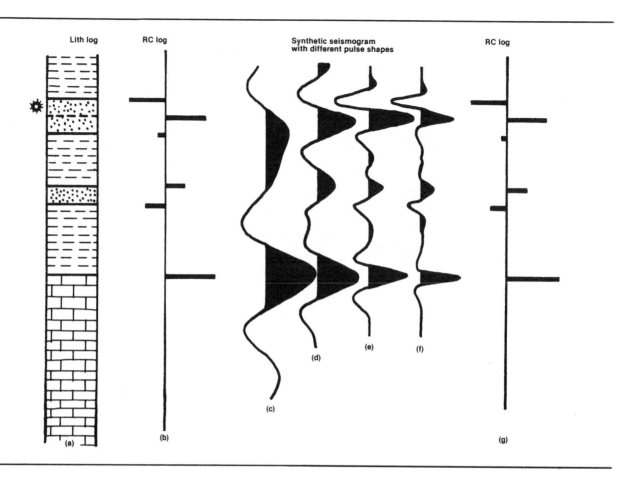

FIGURE 2.23 *The effect of wavelet frequency on the seismic response. Reprinted by permission of IHRDC Press from Anstey, 1980a.*

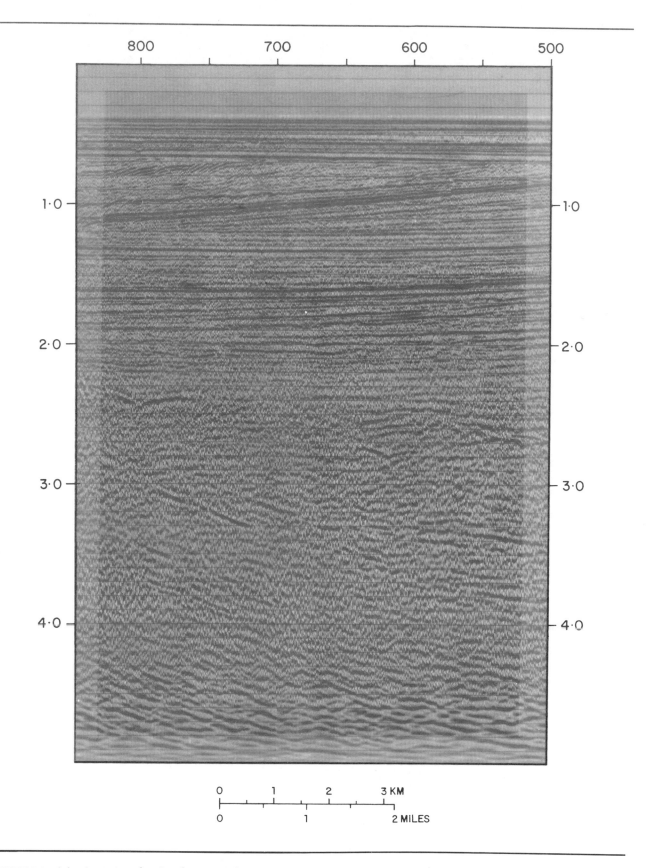

FIGURE 2.24 *Seismic section showing decreasing frequency (increasing reflector spacing) and reflection strength with depth. Courtesy Norsk-Hydro.*

Chapter 3

The Real World

The seismic method has been treated in an extremely simple manner to highlight its main theoretical capabilities and limitations and to provide the minimum understanding of the seismic system required of an interpreter. However, even if everything works successfully, the interpretability of the section will be influenced by:

1. phenomena arising from basic assumptions made by the method and the way in which it is implemented—artefacts of the method; and
2. distortions caused by using time as a scale and not depth—velocity distortions and artefacts.

Before proceeding to draw geological conclusions from seismic data the interpreter must be able to recognize, evaluate, and disregard reflections and configurations that result from the causes described above. This chapter will illustrate these system- and velocity-generated effects.

NOISE

Noise is a term covering all phenomena unrelated to geology that have to be recognized and disregarded in an interpretation. Common sources of noise are multiples, reverberations, diffractions, etc. Even after perfect processing some degree of noise will still be present in a seismic section. Initially, separating primary reflections from noise may be a problem for new interpreters; but after a while it can become difficult to see noise, as the mind becomes trained simply to ignore it. Noise is any part of the seismic signal not related to primary reflections. Random noise forms no particular pattern, lacks coherence, and generally degrades the quality of the section. On shore, the geophones can pick up random noise from wind, traffic, animals, power lines, moving sand grains, etc. Offshore random noise is generated by other boats surveying in the area (this noise can come from hundreds of kilometers away), waves, fish shoals, wrecks, etc. Noise from a specific point (e.g., a wreck on the sea bed or a sea cliff) can produce a long, dipping reflector which will have its point of origin at the noise

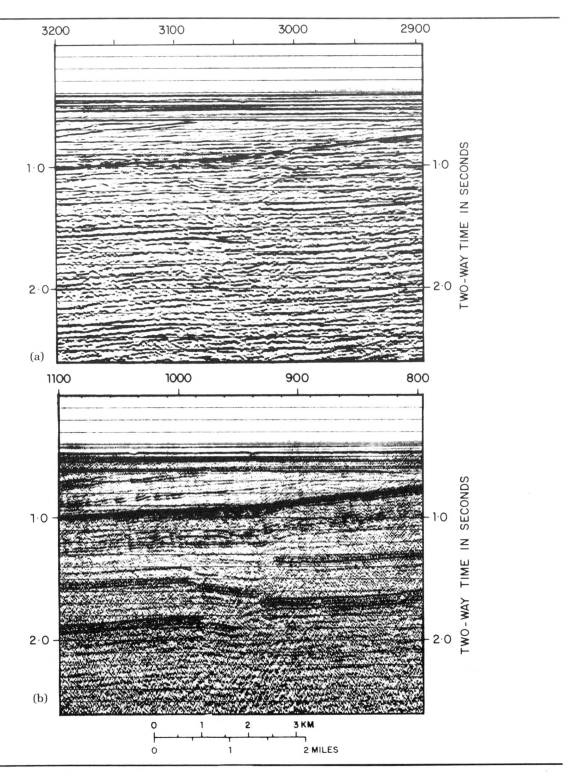

FIGURE 3.1 *Two seismic profiles shot over the same location. Line (a), shot in 1982, is poorly processed, and has a very poor signal-to-noise ratio. Line (b), shot in 1980, is excellent. Reflectors A, B, and C, and the faults X and Y, so clear on line b, can only be followed with great difficulty on line a. Courtesy Norsk Hydro.*

source. Offshore seismic data obtained during weather conditions marginal for data acquisition will be poorer than data from the same area acquired under good conditions. The difference between the two will be the higher level of noise in the data obtained during the bad weather. Noise cannot be avoided altogether, and much of the acquisition and processing effort is directed toward reducing noise to an acceptable level: a seismic section with a good signal-to-noise ratio is the goal. Both acquisition and processing procedures can be designed to tackle these problems. In addition there are other processing steps which can be thought of as largely cosmetic; that is, they are designed to give the data a better appearance or make it more easily interpretable. In the early days, it was soon found that using a simple setup of a source and a receiver, such as that shown in figure 1.1, often gave very poor results and was plagued by noise. Even with modern sophisticated systems, however, processing rarely, if ever, manages to remove all noise; and it is important that the interpreter be able to recognize the different types of noise.

In some areas seismic sections are mainly noise, and the relative proportion of real reflection to noise is often referred to in a nonquantitative way as the signal-to-noise ratio. Poor processing also results in noisy sections. Figure 3.1 shows parts of two seismic sections, from different surveys, that have identical locations. The difference in quality is startling. The upper section, shot in 1982, is very noisy and difficult to interpret—multiples of all types abound. The lower section, shot in 1980, is excellent and very interpretable. The figure illustrates that the newest data is not always the best. Pity the poor interpreter who has the task of interpreting the seismic record from the 1982 survey shown in figure 3.1.

THE COMMON-DEPTH-POINT METHOD

Around 1960 it was found that there was considerable advantage to be gained by repeatedly sampling the same subsurface point using different travel paths of the wavefront. This can be achieved simply by increasing the spacing between source and receiver about a common midpoint and recording successive data in an overlapping manner to provide a duplication of subsurface coverage (fig. 3.2). This is known as the common-depth-point (CDP) or common-midpoint (CMP) technique. Moving both the source and receiver an equal distance to either side would also record a reflection path having the same midpoint to provide twofold coverage (fig. 3.2). The reflection time is greater because the seismic pulse has traveled further. A third source and receiver spacing (offset) would produce a third recording of reflection with the same midpoint, increasing coverage to threefold coverage, etc. Gradually, with the advance of computer technology, the fold or coverage employed to make

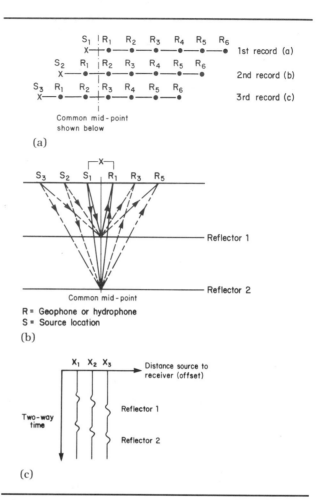

(a)

(b)

R = Geophone or hydrophone
S = Source location

(c)

FIGURE 3.2 *The common-midpoint (CMP) or common-depth-point (CDP) method. (a) Plan view of the acquisition procedure: Receivers, spaced equidistantly, are arranged in line behind the shot location. After recording the shot, the source is moved forward a distance equal to the spacing between the receivers. In this manner, each receiver moves forward one position; that is, for the second record, the position of receiver 2 (R2) is the same as that occupied by receiver 1 (R1) for the first record. (b) Geometry of the common-depth-point gather for the subsurface location midway between the source and receiver 1. This subsurface location is sampled by source-to-receiver spacings (or offsets), S2 and R3, S3 and R5, S4 and R7, etc. (c) Diagram of source-to-receiver spacing (offset) and two-way time. Reflections from reflectors 1 and 2 have progressively longer traveltimes for increasing offset due to the longer travel paths.*

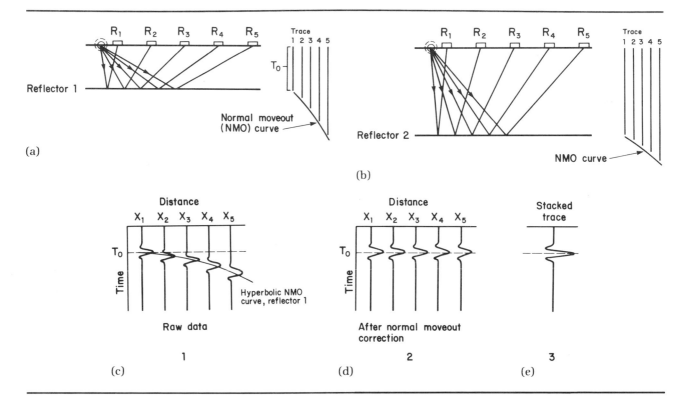

(a)

(b)

(c)

Raw data

1

Hyperbolic NMO curve, reflector 1

(d)

After normal moveout correction

2

(e)

Stacked trace

3

FIGURE 3.3 *Normal-moveout effects of the common-midpoint method.* (a) *A shallow reflector has a relatively steep curve on a time versus offset plot, due to the large differences in traveltimes through the low-velocity layer between the short and long source-to-receiver offsets.* (b) *A deeper reflector has a less steep curve on a time versus offset plot, due to the decreasing difference in the total travel paths between the small and large offsets.* (c) *The normal-moveout velocity can be calculated from the hyperbolic curve of reflection arrivals on a time versus offset (distance) plot.* (d) *The correct normal-moveout (NMO) velocity brings a reflection to the same time for all offsets.* (e) *Addition of the corrected NMO traces results in a stacked trace.*

seismic sections has increased from 12 to 24 to a present-day common configuration of 96 fold or more.

It would be extremely cumbersome, time consuming, and expensive to obtain data for each common-midpoint location in the way shown in figure 3.2. Not surprisingly, techniques have been devised to optimize data acquisition both on land and offshore. On land, geophones are usually located either side of the source in the direction of the seismic lines. Once data are recorded for a particular source position, the seismic is extended by picking up geophones from the back of the geophone line and moving them up to the front—a continuous leap-frog process. On land, two types of source are commonly employed, dynamite and Vibroseis. Vibroseis has become a popular source in recent years as it is both speedy and produces little environmental damage. Instead of producing a sharp sound pulse by an explosion, Vibroseis puts a specific range of frequencies into the Earth using a vibrating plate in contact with the ground beneath. The plate is vibrated for several seconds over a sweep of frequencies. The raw data are uninterpretable. Only after the raw data have been correlated with the input sweep signal during the processing do interpretable data, in a form similar to that obtained by other means, emerge.

Offshore, the seismic line is recorded by towing a cable containing hydrophones behind a boat. This configuration is an end-on spread (e.g., fig. 3.2), and the shot spacing is a function of the firing rate and boat speed, whereas the receiver spacing is a function of the hydrophone spacing in the cable.

All of these techniques, both on land and offshore, produce a jumbled set of raw data that have to be reorganized into different source-to-receiver combinations that have the same CMP. Once the data has been reorganized into a CMP gather, the traveltime for the common reflection point will vary with the source-to-receiver spacing; small spacings or effects will have the shortest traveltimes with progressively longer traveltimes for larger offsets (fig. 3.3). In practice, many traces are involved, up to 96 and more, and the delay in reflection time caused by longer travel paths causes the reflection to form a curved event. The principle of seismic velocity measurement is that the extra distance of the offsets divided by the extra traveltime gives the velocity. This velocity can be used to correct the delay in arrival time of a reflection with a long

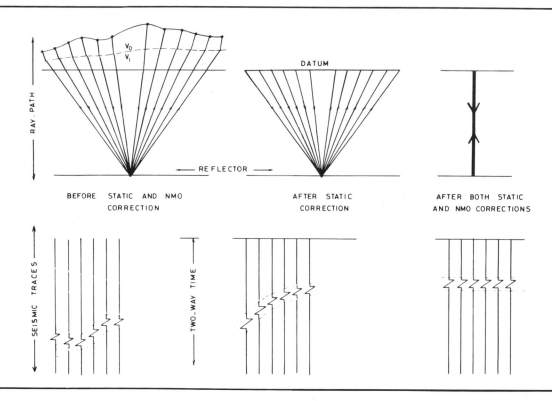

FIGURE 3.4 *Static corrections: The raypath diagram* (above) *and seismic traces* (below) *show static and dynamic corrections to a CMP gather. Reprinted by permission of Birkhäuser Verlag from Al-Sadi, 1980.*

travel path compared with the shortest, and bring the reflection to the same time on both traces. The velocity required to bring the reflection to the same time on all the traces is called the normal moveout (NMO) velocity. Bringing a reflection to the same time on each trace of a CMP gather is known as NMO correction. As the far trace represents a longer travel path in the shallower rocks, the amount of NMO is related to the interval velocity of the rock layer. The amount of NMO always decreases with reflection time (fig. 3.3a, b), but it also depends on the velocities; low velocities produce steeper NMO curves. The change in steepness of the curve from a shallower to a deeper reflection can be related to the interval velocity of the rock layer.

After NMO correction, the traces are summed to give one stacked trace for each CMP location. Stacking not only boosts the strength of primary reflections but also attenuates random noise events that do not add together during the stacking process, and so increases the signal-to-noise ratio.

STATIC CORRECTIONS

Static corrections are probably the most critical processing step for land data. They are especially important in areas of rough terrain and where the near-surface velocity is highly variable—either laterally or horizontally—because they affect reflection continuity, resolution, the accuracy of velocity analysis, and structural form. Figure 3.4 illustrates the problem.

Usually before land data is analyzed for NMO velocities and stacked, corrections have to be made to account for anomalous effects caused by significant elevation or near-surface velocity changes caused by the water table, by alluvial and glacial fill, and by weathering. Poor static corrections result in poor reflector continuity and poor velocity control. Accurate static corrections can make the difference between an outstanding section and one that is not usable (fig. 3.5). Static corrections are a processing problem over which the interpreter has little control, other than to request reprocessing. However, there are some pitfalls in static corrections that can, in some circumstances, produce good-looking but structurally incorrect sections; and, as a rule of thumb, beware of reflections that bear a relationship to the surface shape.

Static corrections for marine data involve correcting for the depth of source and hydrophones below the sea-level datum—the theoretical mean sea level—and are less of a problem. However, if incorrect they can cause considerable problems for ties of well to seismic and in tying data from surveys with different static corrections.

MULTIPLES

Multiples are reflections that have undergone more than one bounce. Figure 3.6 shows a simple situation where some of the energy reflected back to the surface from a

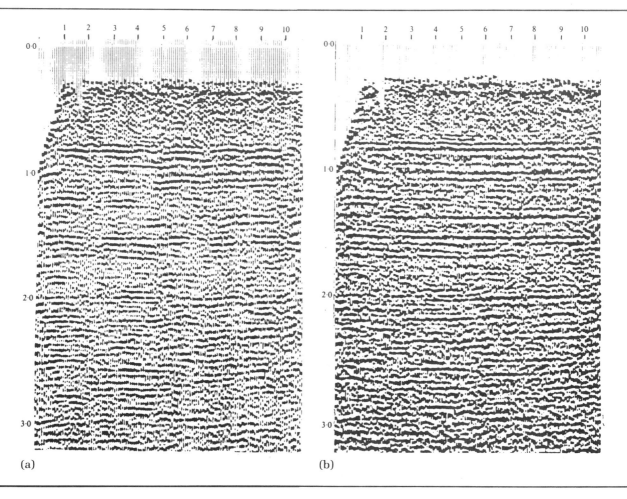

(a)   (b)

FIGURE 3.5 *Static corrections applied to a seismic section to eliminate the effects of variations in elevation, weathering thickness, or weathering velocity. (a) Before static corrections, the reflections appear discontinuous and the entire section is noisy. (b) After static corrections. Reprinted by permission of Cambridge University Press from Telford et al., 1976.*

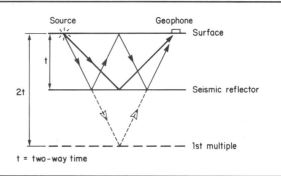

FIGURE 3.6 *A simple multiple: A reflection from the reflector, is reflected back into the ground from the air/water or air/ground interface, and makes a second journey to the reflector and back. The resulting reflection, a simple multiple, occurs at twice the time of the primary reflection.*

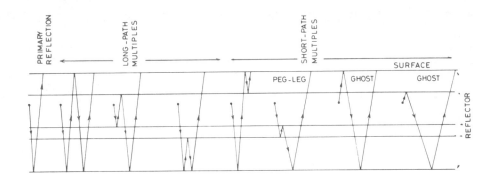

SURFACE

PRIMARY REFLECTION

LONG-PATH MULTIPLES

SHORT-PATH MULTIPLES

PEG-LEG   GHOST   GHOST

REFLECTOR

FIGURE 3.7 *Common types of multiple reflections. Reprinted by permission of Birkhäuser Verlag from Al-Sadi, 1980.*

reflector bounces back into the subsurface again from the interface between the air (or water) and sediments. The downward-traveling ray will again be reflected by the deeper reflector and return to the surface to be recorded by the geophones. The geophones thus receive signals twice from the same seismic reflector. The first multiple path is approximately twice the length of the primary raypath, as it has traveled twice there and back through the layer. If the traveltime for the first multiple is t, the traveltime for the multiple will be approximately $2t$. The first multiple will thus appear on the seismic section as a reflection at a time t below the primary event (fig. 3.6).

Common types of multiple reflections are shown in figure 3.7. Data acquisition parameters can be designed to reduce multiple problems (fig. 3.8a, b). However, even with optimum acquisition parameters, multiples will still appear in the data and considerable effort during processing is expended into the removal and attenuation of multiples. Stacking and deconvolution are the two main lines of attack.

Stacking, the combining of the recorded traces after they have been corrected for normal moveout, is the main, and best, form of attack, especially against long-path multiples. Figure 3.9 illustrates how stacking attacks multiples. Velocities for shallower reflections are smaller than those for deep reflectors and consequently, as multiple events are derived from above, their normal-moveout curves should be steeper than those for primary reflections occurring at the same level. Stacking discriminates against multiples provided that the velocity of the multiple is such that, during stacking, it has a normal moveout significantly different from primaries arriving at the same time. This will not be the case when the multiple has had a significant part of its travel path in a high-velocity interval, or if there is a velocity inversion. In both cases, the NMO curves of the multiples may be the same or even flatter than those of primaries recurring at the same time, and will not be attacked by stacking.

Deconvolution is the next line of attack. It is used mainly against short-path multiples and works by combining the recorded trace with another specially designed

trace (operator), which will remove or attenuate repetitions and compress the wavelet. Deconvolution is a time series analysis operation which attempts to undo the filter effects (e.g., attenuation, reverberation, etc.) of the Earth on the propagating wavelet. Deconvolution is used to sharpen the seismic pulse and attenuate multiples. There are many different types of deconvolution and a detailed discussion of the topic is beyond the scope of this book. However, two types are relatively common:

Deterministic deconvolution requires a knowledge of the propagating wavelet, usually from the recorded signature. The method does not assume that the reflection coefficient sequence (the geology) is random and uncorrelated and so is suited to situations where this may not be the case. It is capable of producing a pulse of any desired shape (e.g., zero phase) having the appropriate bandwidth and gives generally predictable results. The difficulty of recording or determining the propagating wavelet is a disadvantage of the method.

Predictive deconvolution uses statistical analysis to calculate the operator. The method attempts to predict event shapes and occurrences in the seismic trace by using past knowledge of event shapes and occurrences obtained by statistical studies. This method is the easiest and cheapest, but it assumes that the geology is random and uncorrelated.

Frequently, deconvolution attempts to produce one of two main wavelet shapes, minimum phase or zero phase. Theoretically, acoustic-impedance boundaries are located at the onset of minimum-phase pulses and centrally for zero-phase. Deconvolution may be applied both before and after stacking.

These are the two main methods of removing multiples, although special problems arise in some situations, in very deep water, for example; and each geophysical company has its own method of tackling the problem.

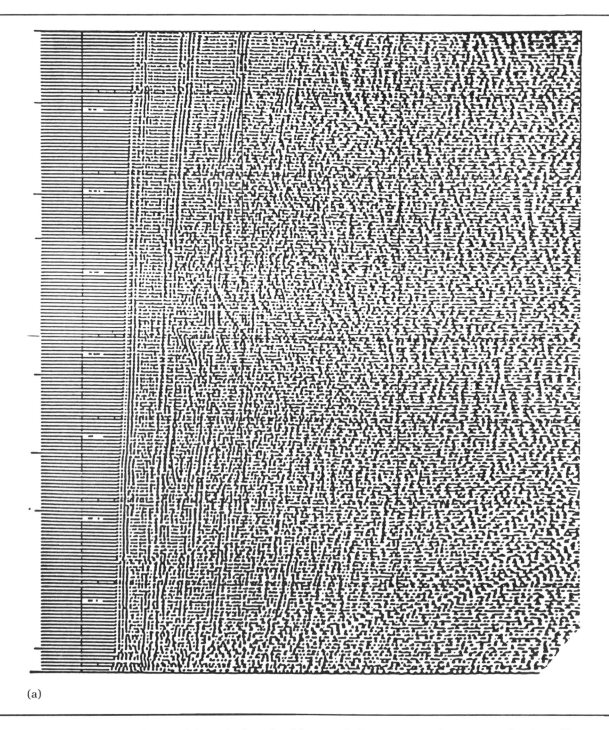

36

(a)

FIGURE 3.8(a) *Seismic section from English Channel produced by a single five-gun array, showing several orders of long-period multiples. Reprinted by permission of IHRDC Press from Sengbush, 1983, fig. 6.13(a), p. 116.*

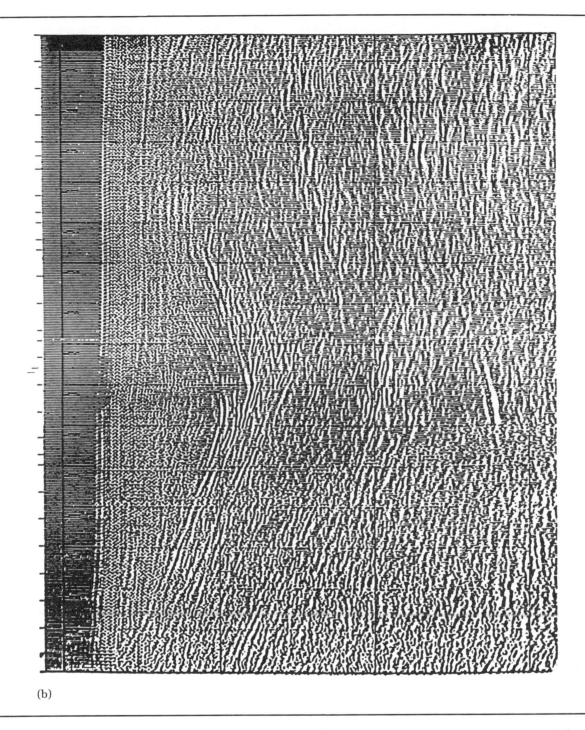

(b)

FIGURE 3.8(b) *Comparison with section* (a) *produced by Shell's super-long array consisting of five arrays, each with five air guns, extending over 350 m. The long-period multiples have been suppressed by the source pattern. Reprinted by permission of IHRDC Press from Sengbush, 1983, fig. 6.13(b), p. 117.*

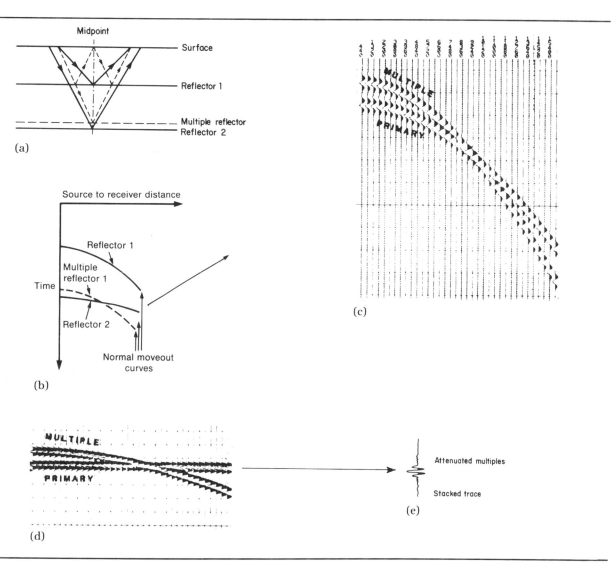

FIGURE 3.9 *Removal of multiples by CMP stacking: (a) Cross-section showing two reflectors and multiple of the upper reflector. (b) Time versus offset diagram showing the NMO curves for reflections from reflectors 1 and 2 and the multiple of reflector 1. The NMO curve for reflection 2 is flatter than that of reflection 1. The multiple of reflection 1 has the same NMO curves as the reflection and crosscuts the flatter NMO curve of reflection 2. (c) A common midpoint gather for the multiple and reflection 2 shown in (b). (d) The CMP gather after normal moveout correction: Reflection 2 has been corrected, bringing the reflection to the same time on all of the traces. The multiple is overcorrected and has a residual moveout. (e) The stacked trace: The primary has been reinforced and the multiple attenuated. Reprinted by permission of IHRDC Press from Sengbush, 1983.*

Optimally, processing will have removed multiples; unfortunately, this is not always the case. Figure 3.10 is an example of a seismic section with a "good" set of multiples. Whatever the type, it is important that multiples are recognized so that they are not interpreted as primary reflections. The effort and success in removing multiples varies between seismic surveys and even within a survey or along an individual section.

A pair of dividers is useful for plotting the expected arrival times of multiples on seismic sections. If a reflection occurs on the section at the anticipated time, it may be a multiple. Further bounces of the seismic signal can cause, second, third, and fourth multiples, etc. (fig. 3.11). These multiples gradually become weaker due to the longer travel path and consequent transmission losses. Multiples can be associated with all acoustic-impedance boundaries, but only those with large reflection coefficients are likely to pose problems.

39

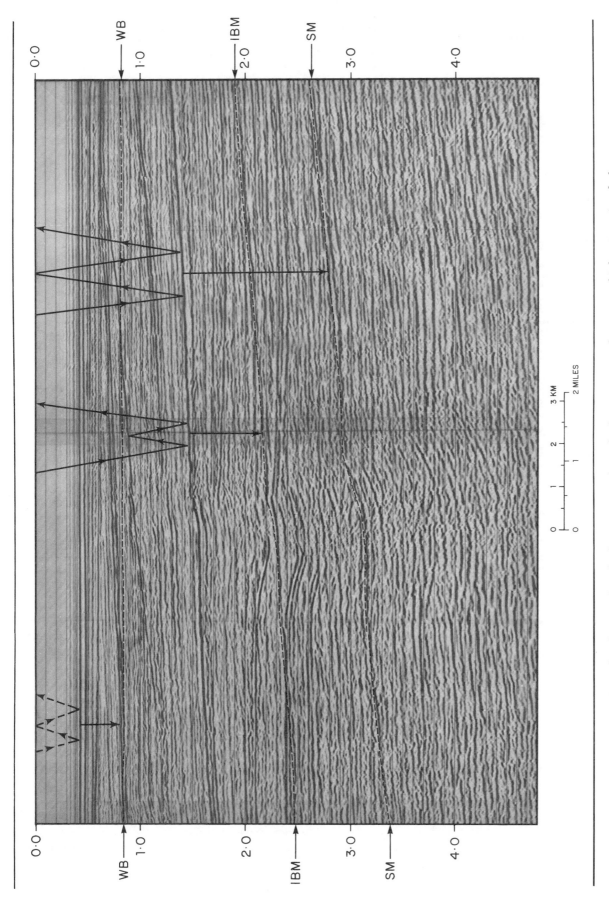

FIGURE 3.10 *A seismic section with a "good" set of multiples. SM, simple multiple; WB, water-bottom multiple; IBM, interbed multiple. Courtesy Societé Nationale Elf Aquitaine.*

40

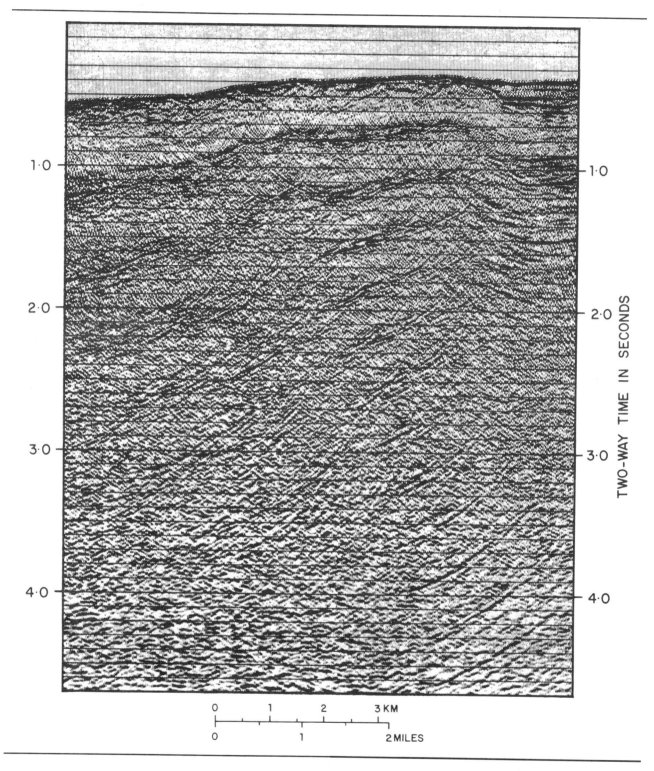

FIGURE 3.11 *Seismic section, with crystalline basement out-cropping at the sea floor, showing water-bottom multiples. The water-bottom multiple is repeated 12 times. Note: The section has been migrated, and this has caused the dipping parts of the multiple to be moved in an updip direction. Courtesy Saga Petroleum.*

Multiples can be divided into two main categories: long-path and short-path. Long-path multiples have travel paths that are long compared with primary reflections from the same deep interfaces; and, therefore, appear as separate reflections. Short-path multiples arrive so soon after the primary reflection from the same interface that they interfere with, and add tails to, the primary reflection, and thus change the waveshape but do not necessarily appear as a separate event.

Water-bottom and Base-weathering Zone Multiples. In offshore areas both the air/water and water/rock interfaces form reflecting horizons; and energy trapped within the water layer may rebound backward and forward, resulting in a water/bottom multiple or reverberation. Largely because of this it was not possible to obtain marine seismic sections until the advent of digital filtering provided a means of tackling the problem. Water-bottom multiples still remain the most common multiple left on seismic sections after processing. Figure 3.11 shows such an example on a seismic line where hard crystalline basement rocks crop out at the sea floor. The seismic signal has bounced several times in the water layer between the sea bed and the surface, and produced a whole train of multiples. In figure 3.11, twelve bounces of the multiple are developed in the primary reflection-free basement. A similar type of reverberation can occur during land shooting when energy is trapped within the weathered zone, rebounding between the surface and the underlying solid rock. Water-bottom multiples not only follow the sea bed; they also often follow a strong reflector and are located at the water-depth traveltime beneath the primary event, but with opposite polarity phase due to the negative reflection at the air/water interface (fig. 3.12).

Simple Multiples. To produce a simple multiple, some of the returning energy reflected back to the surface from an acoustic-impedance boundary will bounce back from the air/sediment or water/sediment interface and travel into the Earth again. The downward-traveling wave will again be reflected by the same acoustic-impedance boundary and return to the surface, where its arrival will be detected at approximately twice the traveltime of the primary reflection (fig. 3.10). In common with water-bottom multiples, a polarity reversal will also occur for all reflections reflected back into the ground from a boundary with a negative reflection coefficient. On the seismic time section, the first multiple appears as a reflection at twice the time of the primary reflection, but with opposite polarity. If the reflection coefficient is very large, it is possible to detect the wavefront making a third or even fourth trip back to the acoustic-impedance boundary. This produces a set of approximately equidistant reflections, each weaker than the one above and with alternating polarity, beneath the primary event.

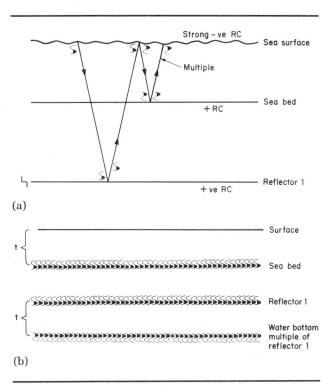

FIGURE 3.12 *Water-bottom multiples. (a) Geological model. (b) Seismic expression (SEG normal polarity). The strong negative reflection coefficient of the air/water interface causes a polarity reversal of the downgoing multiple reflection. The positive sea-bed reflection coefficient does not affect the reflection polarity; therefore, the recorded multiple reflection is opposite in polarity to that of the primary reflection.*

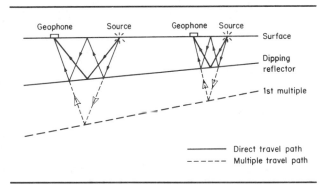

FIGURE 3.13 *Diagram showing how the multiple of a dipping reflector has twice the dip.*

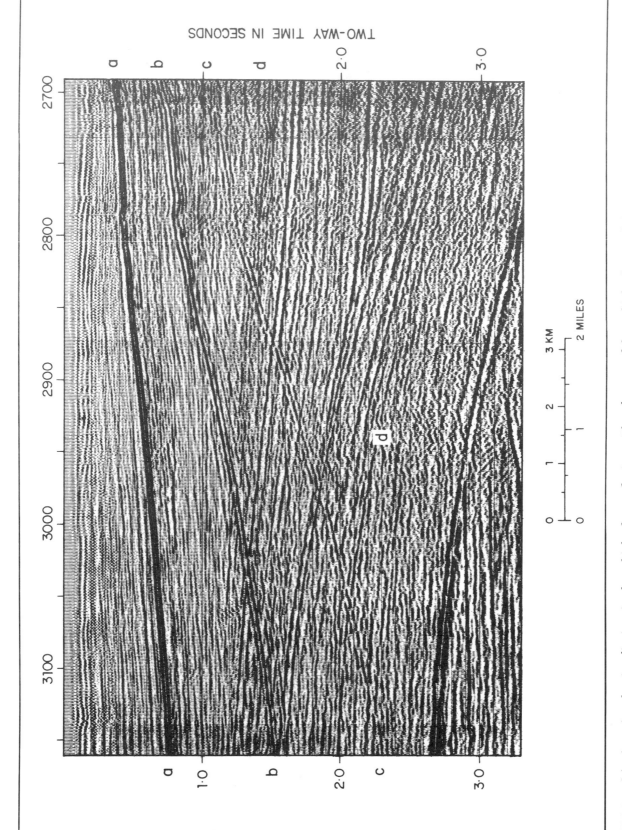

FIGURE 3.14 *Seismic section showing dipping simple multiples from reflection a. Three bounces of the multiples, b, c, and d can be seen. The dip of each successive multiple increases by an amount equal to the dip of the primary reflection a. Courtesy Merlin Profilers Ltd.*

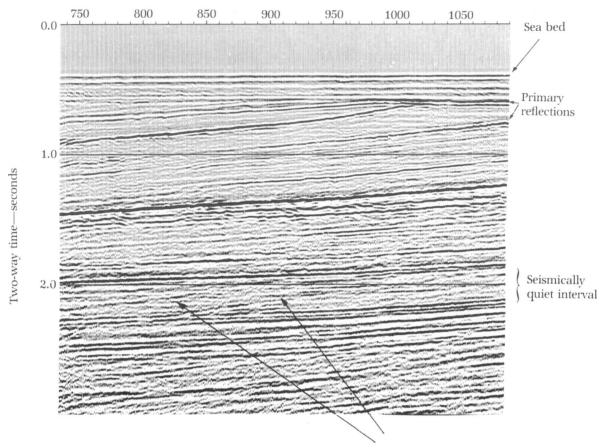

Dipping reflections in a seismically quiet interval—
multiples from the dipping primary reflections above.

Multiples from Dipping Reflectors. When the primary reflector is dipping and the surface layer is flat, the multiple reflection will show twice the angle of dip; since, at any given point, the multiple is twice as deep as the primary event (fig. 3.13). The exaggerated dip of multiple reflections is characteristic and can often be useful in discriminating multiples from deeper primary reflections. The primary reflection (a) in figure 3.14 has a positive reflection coefficient and dips from right to left. The first simple multiple (b) has twice the dip and reversed polarity. The third multiple (c) has three times the dip of (a). The reflection quality of the multiple (c) is too poor to demonstrate a polarity reversal. It should have the same polarity as the primary reflection (a). Remnants of a fourth multiple (d) can just be seen. Simple multiples are most likely to be a problem when especially strong reflectors are present.

Peg-Leg Multiples. A multiple caused by an extra bounce between two reflectors produces a peg-leg multiple (fig. 3.7). Such multiples can be difficult to remove during processing, especially if they originate between divergent reflectors.

FIGURE 3.15 *Multiples that come and go: A seismic section showing dipping multiples in a seismically quiet interval. Amplification of the seismic signal by the automatic gain control has resulted in dipping multiples, from primary reflections above, appearing in the seismically quiet interval. Amplification of the signal has not occurred where the primary reflections are strong. The multiples appear to terminate against the strong reflections at the top and base of the quiet interval. Note how the multiples could be mistaken for clinoforms. Hint! View the section obliquely from the left. Courtesy Norsk Hydro.*

Interbed Multiples. Multiples caused by a repeated reflection in a layer are a special problem because their normal-moveout velocity used for stacking may be higher than the velocity of the primary reflection with which they are associated. This will always be the case if the additional traveltime is through a deep high-velocity layer. Such multiples will not be removed by simple stacking of the CMP gathers.

Multiples That Come and Go. During recording the seismic signal is automatically amplified by the automatic gain control (AGC) to maintain a fairly constant level of sig-

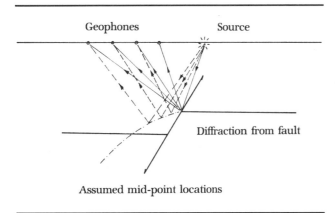

Geophones   Source

Diffraction from fault

Assumed mid-point locations

FIGURE 3.16 *Sketch showing a diffraction from a fault. The hyperbolic form of diffractions arises from the assumption made by the CMP method that reflections arise from mid-point locations between the source and geophone.*

nal. In seismically quiet intervals the AGC amplifies the incoming signal to try to extract primary data. This amplifies not only the weak primary data but also any multiples. If the multiples and primary reflectors are divergent, the resulting reflector configuration can lead to false interpretation. Figure 3.15 is an example where multiples are developed in a seismically quiet zone and appear to be internal structure within the interval. The multiples are absent in the adjacent layers with strong primaries, because the amplification was not sufficiently high to record them. The resulting reflection configuration could be mistaken to be indicative of a sedimentary sequence prograding from right to left.

Ghosts. Ghosts are short-path multiples, common to both land and marine seismic sections, which develop when part of the seismic pulse that initially traveled upward from the shot is reflected downward from the surface or base of the weathering zone to closely follow the main downgoing seismic pulse (fig. 3.7). The ghost will arrive at the geophone slightly later than the direct reflected wave and can either appear as an horizon slightly below the primary reflector or is so close that it joins onto the tail of the primary reflection. On land, the problem can be minimized by drilling shotholes to below the weathering zone. At sea, the problem can be minimized by placing the source at such a depth in the water that the ghost and primary pulse constructively interfere. Otherwise, ghosts can severely degrade the quality of the data. Deconvolution is the main processing attack against ghosts.

DIFFRACTIONS

Diffractions are a common source of noise and can emanate from any abrupt interface in the subsurface (fig. 3.16). Because their curved shape can be mistaken for a

real structure, it is important to identify and disregard diffractions. The commonest sources of diffractions are faults; but chaotic slumping, irregular surfaces (e.g., karst, igneous intrusions, etc.) can also generate diffractions. A sharp contact, for example, the faulted edge of a rock layer, scatters the energy in all directions and is recorded in the form of a hyperbolic trace with the source of diffraction at its apex. Tracing the apex of diffraction can be a useful method to help locate a fault plane on unmigrated seismic sections for horizontal velocity structures. Fault planes can be found by joining successive diffraction apexes (fig. 3.17). Generally, however, diffractions are troublesome and detract from the appearance of the section. They can be removed by migration techniques, which restore the raypaths back to their proper subsurface positions. The diffraction is collapsed back to a point. Diffractions arising from off the line of section may not be properly migrated and remain as remnant diffractions after migration.

REFLECTED REFRACTIONS

Reflected refractions are sound waves that have traveled laterally for some distance in the subsurface before reaching the geophones. They do not normally produce events, because muting before stack is designed to remove far trace arrivals due to refracted rays traveling along a high-velocity layer (Day and Edwards, 1983). However, in certain circumstances they do appear in seismic sections. For example, as an upgoing ray crosses each acoustic-impedance boundary, it is refracted, the angle of refraction increasing across boundaries with increased acoustic impedance. Above a critical angle, the ray is no longer reflected; instead, it is refracted along the higher-velocity layer, which acts like a leaky waveguide; and, therefore, only part of the signal reaches the geophones (fig. 3.18). This results in a reflection whose characteristics are dependent on the interval velocity of the layer and its structure. Alternatively, reflected refractions can also be associated with downgoing rays. Day and Edwards (1983) discuss some possible configurations that could generate reflected refractions and their recognition in seismic sections. Reflections of reflected refractions are often strong and straight, with an associated shadow zone that can easily be misinterpreted as a fault. They are commonly developed in areas of complex structure and caused by a velocity inversion in the sedimentary sequence. The refracting interval must be fairly flat lying, or only slightly undulating, to act as an effective waveguide. Event A in figure 3.19 is a reflected refraction developed in association with a major fault. Event B is the water-bottom multiple of the reflected refraction A. The only artefact likely to be confused with a reflected refraction is the envelope of a series of diffractions. Such a situation could occur where a steeply dipping fault plane generates a large number of diffractions that interfere with each other to produce no

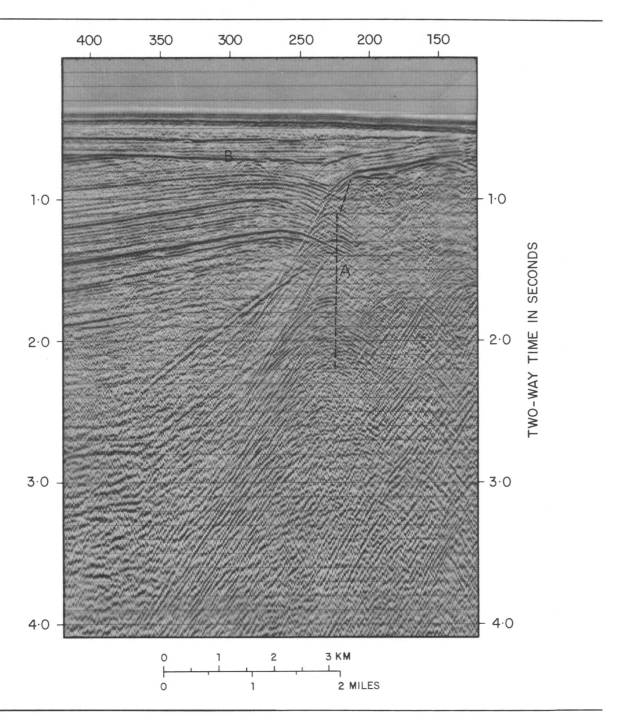

FIGURE 3.17 *Seismic section showing diffractions from a near-vertical fault plane (A). Diffractions can be useful. The fault plane can be located by joining the diffraction apexes. Other diffractions are from small faults affecting a flat-lying reflector (B). Courtesy Norsk Hydro.*

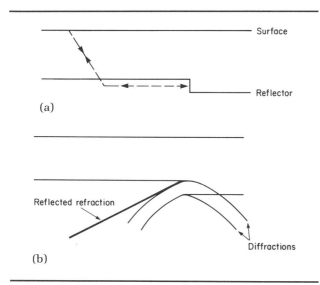

(a)

Surface

Reflector

(b)

Reflected refraction

Diffractions

FIGURE 3.18 *Reflected refractions. (a) Geological model showing how reflections from a steeply dipping surface exceed the critical angle and are refracted along an overlying high-velocity layer. (b) Seismic expression showing the planar dipping reflected refraction. After Day and Edwards, 1983, by permission of the EAEG.*

events, except on the edge of the envelope, where only one diffraction is present (Day and Edwards, 1983). The shape of the envelope will be dependent upon the fault plane dip and the rock velocities. In many cases the flanks of the envelope may be approximately linear.

DIPPING REFLECTORS AND MIGRATION

The seismic system is very sensitive to the attitude of acoustic-impedance boundaries. Most of the cases considered so far have involved reflectors with little or no dip. Once dip is greater than a few degrees, special problems arise. For horizontal reflectors, the geophones will record data originating from a point midway between the source and receiver. However, for dipping reflectors, the subsurface data point is not midway between the source and receiver but is offset in an updip direction (fig. 3.20). The error increases with dip. In structured areas the difference in location between the assumed subsurface data points and actual sampled data points can be considerable and cause smearing of the data when the traces are brought together in a CMP gather (fig. 3.20b). Dip produces reflections that have apparent dips less than the dip of the reflectors; apparent lengths greater than the actual lengths of the reflectors; and apparent locations deeper than, and downdip from the reflectors. On true dip lines, the sample points lie in the plane of the section (fig. 3.21a); but on a true strike line, although the reflectors will appear to be horizontal, the actual sampled points are located off-line (fig. 3.21b). The sampled points in sections along the apparent dip are also out of the plane of

section. The closer the line is orientated to the true dip, the closer the sampled points will lie to the plane of the section. The amount of distortion increases with dip, depth, and velocity.

To counteract dip effects, seismic sections are frequently migrated—a process that attempts to move the assumed subsurface data points updip to their true subsurface locations (fig. 3.22). The effect of the migration is to steepen the dip and shorten the length of the reflection. Diffraction curves collapse to a point that lies at the apex of the diffraction hyperbola.

Anstey (1980a) provides a simple description of the essence of the migration process. If all we have is one observation at SP 1 (fig. 3.23a), and we have nothing to tell us about the dip, then all we know is that we have a reflection at a certain time. In that case, it could have come from anywhere along a surface (which we assume is a circle for the moment) representing that constant time. So in figure 3.23c we actually place that reflection at all its possible sources around the circle. Then in figure 3.23d we do the same for the trace from SP2, SP3 . . . and so on. We find that the circles reinforce in just one zone, and that zone is the true position of the reflector. Figure 3.23e shows the migrated position of the reflection.

Although numerous migration techniques have been developed, three methods are generally applied to data after it has been stacked: Kirchhoff migration, wave-equation or finite-difference migration, and the frequency-domain technique (fig. 3.24). The common idea behind all three methods is the downward continuation technique. This assumes that the stacked section can be regarded as the upcoming wave field recorded at the Earth's surface and that, using the scalar wave equation, it is possible to trace this wave field back to any depth and to find the origin of the waves—the reflected position.

The Kirchhoff method migrates the data by searching for diffractions and moving all energy along the diffraction curve to its apex. This method migrates steep dips well, but does not work so well with noisy data. Noise tends to be organized after migration into characteristic syncline-like reflections (fig. 3.24c).

The wave-equation or finite-difference method uses the wave field observed at the surface to calculate the wave field at various levels. Sheriff (1982) gives a clear non-mathematical description of the method. The method has good performance with low signal/noise ratio. It is adaptable to horizontal velocity gradients, but has difficulty with steeper dips (fig. 3.24b).

Frequency-domain migration, of which there are several variants, transforms the data into a frequency versus wave-number domain. This migration uses an exact operator solution of the wave equation, and then transforms the data back. The method is less demanding of computer time than the other two; has good performance with steep dips, but exaggerates errors caused by poor

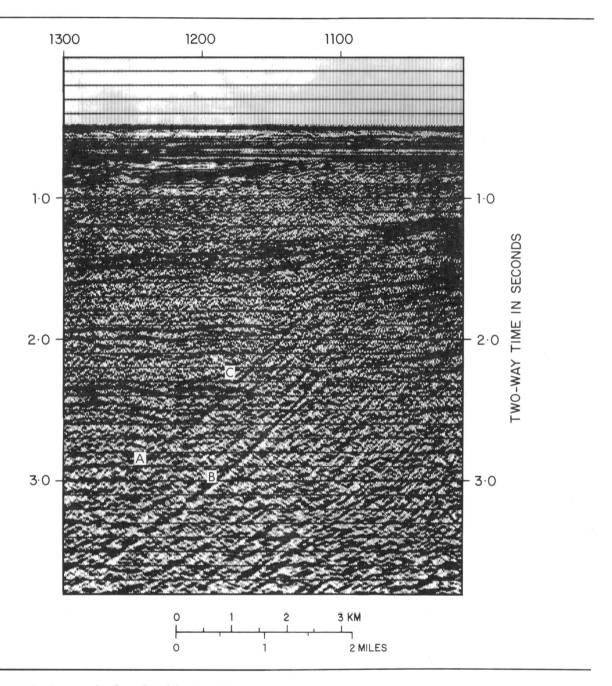

FIGURE 3.19 *Seismic example of a reflected fraction. A: reflected refraction, B: water-bottom multiple of the reflected refraction. Note how the reflected refraction crosscuts a primary reflection at C. Courtesy Norsk Hydro.*

48

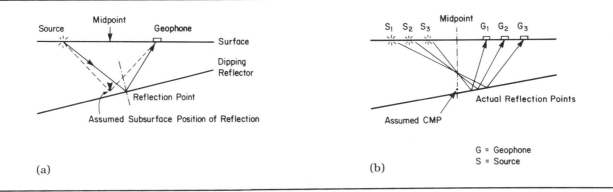

(a)

(b)

G = Geophone
S = Source

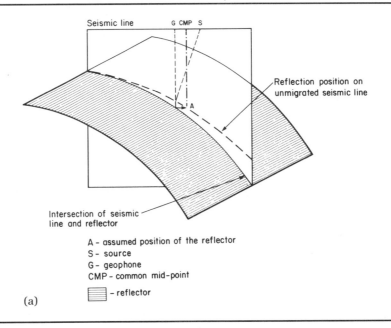

A - assumed position of the reflector
S - source
G - geophone
CMP - common mid-point

▦ - reflector

(a)

FIGURE 3.21 *Relationships between dip, line orientation, apparent reflector position, and actual reflection points.* (a) *Seismic section parallel with the reflector's dip.* (b) *Seismic section parallel with the reflector's strike.*

FIGURE 3.22 *The effect of migration.* (a) *Before migration.*
(b) *After migration. Migration increases reflection dip, moves the reflection updip, and shortens the reflection length.*

FIGURE 3.20 *Effect of a dipping reflector. (a) Diagram showing how the CMP method assumes that the reflection point lies vertically beneath the midpoint between the source and geophone. For a dipping reflection, this assumed reflection point lies downdip of the actual reflection point and above the plane of the reflector. (b) Smearing effect caused by a dipping reflector. The reflection points for different offsets are not coincident for a dipping reflector. This effect can result in smearing when the data are stacked.*

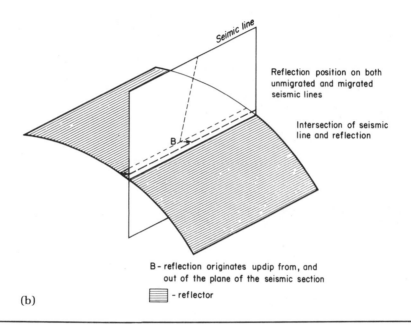

Seismic line

Reflection position on both unmigrated and migrated seismic lines

Intersection of seismic line and reflection

B

B - reflection originates updip from, and out of the plane of the seismic section

⊞ - reflector

(b)

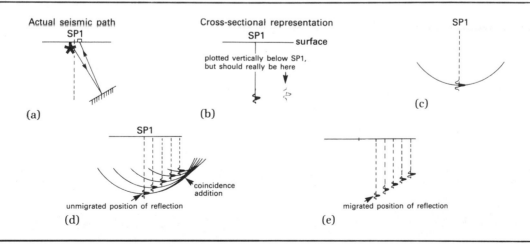

Actual seismic path

SP1

(a)

Cross-sectional representation

SP1 ———— surface

plotted vertically below SP1, but should really be here

(b)

SP1

(c)

SP1

unmigrated position of reflection

coincidence addition

(d)

SP1

migrated position of reflection

(e)

FIGURE 3.23 *A simple view of the process of migration. See text discussion. Reprinted by permission of IHRDC Press from Anstey, 1980a, fig. 4, p. 8.*

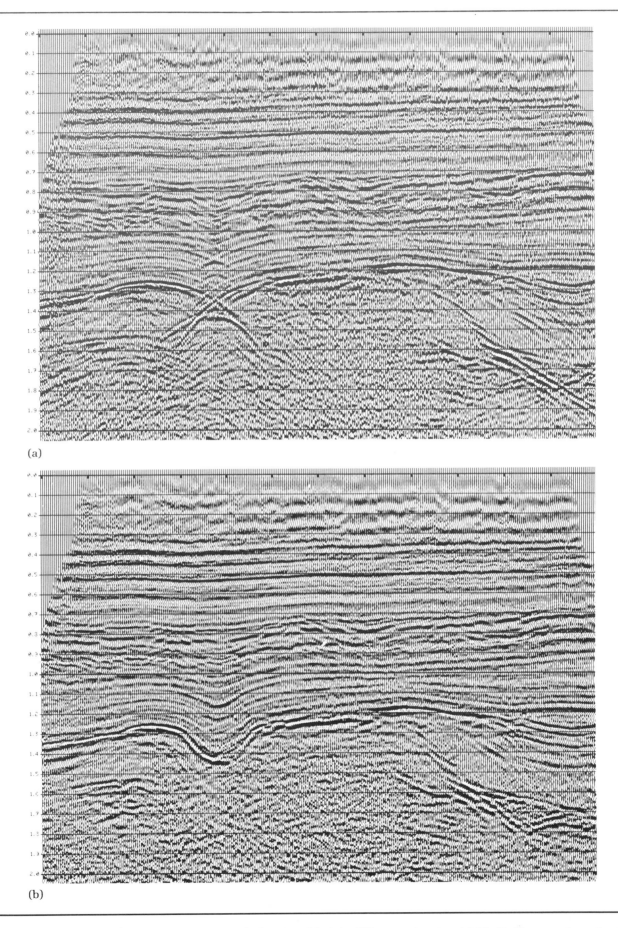

FIGURE 3.24 *Examples of migration.* (a) *Stacked section.* (b) *Finite-difference migration.* (c) *Kirchhoff-summation migration.* (d) *Frequency/wavenumber migration. Courtesy Prakla-Seismos.*

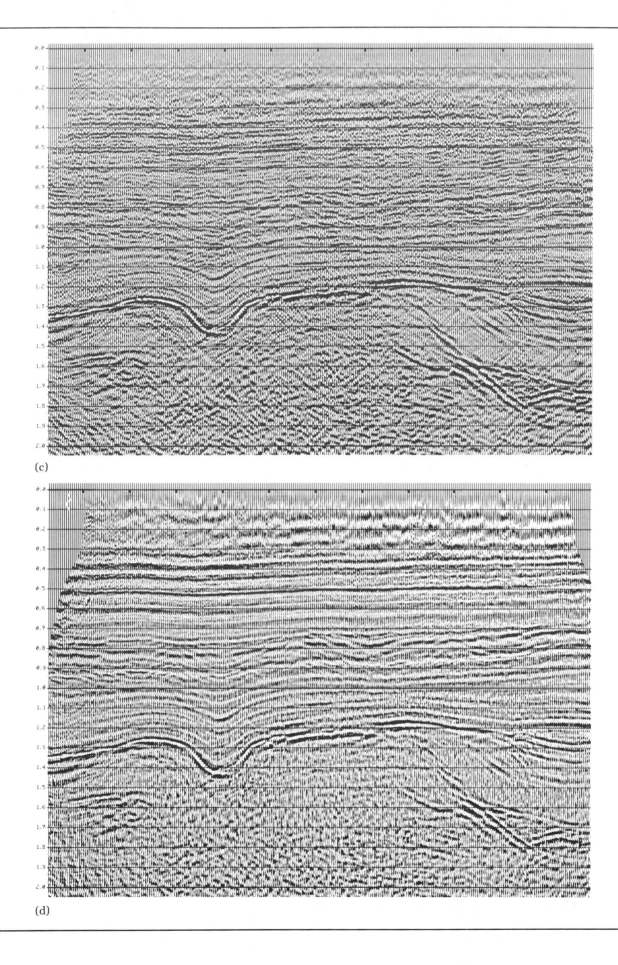

(c)

(d)

52

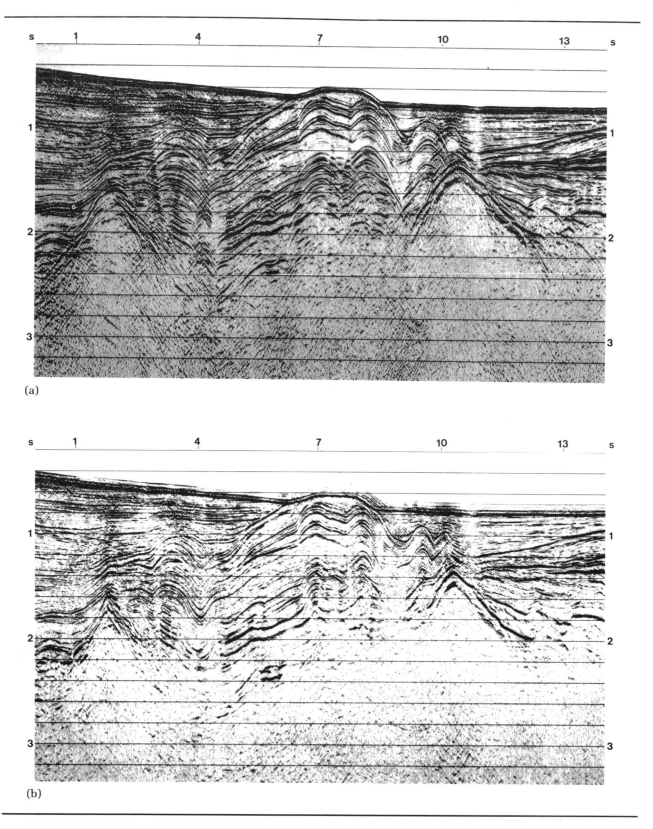

(a)

(b)

FIGURE 3.25 *Seismic example of anticlines and synclines: A complex folded structure from the Santa Barbara Channel, offshore California. (a) Stacked time section. Reflector dips do not exceed about 25°. Horizontal scale in mues. (b) Kirchhoff-summation migration. The migration has steepened dips, narrowed anticlines, broadened synclines, and has resolved some problem areas where there are cross-reflectors on the stacked time section (e.g., in the synclinal axis below the 4-mile point). Courtesy Western Geophysical.*

velocity gradients; and is unable to cope with horizontal velocity gradients.

Each method has its advantages and disadvantages, but if the velocity distribution used for the migration is approximately correct, each of the methods produce about the same results (fig. 3.24). In fact, the various methods are equivalent, or could be, if their practical implementation did not involve making different approximations.

Unless the seismic data are part of a 3-D survey, which uses three-dimensional migration equations (hence the name), the migration will be a conventional 2-D process that is only fully effective on true dip lines. Also, only dipping reflections are migrated. Reflections on true strike lines will be horizontal and, thus, unaffected by 2-D migration. As a result, seismic lines orientated in the dip and strike directions noticeably fail to tie after migration in areas where the dip is about 15° or more.

On sections with a favorable orientation to a structural feature (e.g., perpendicular to a fold axis), even though they are distorted, the reflections will have an easily recognizable form. However, anticlines will appear broader than their true shape (fig. 3.25). The anticlinal crest will be in the correct location because it has subhorizontal dip. Similarly, the axis of an adjacent syncline will be in the correct position, but its flanks will appear steepened and the syncline will appear too steep and narrow (fig. 3.25). If the seismic line is orientated at a high angle to the fold axes, migration will correct these distortions. After migration, anticlines become narrower because their flanks move inward and synclines become broader because their flanks move outward. However, the migration will have no effect on strike lines where reflection will appear to be horizontal and the actual subsurface data points are off-line. Similarly, the fold axes are not moved, because they are areas of near horizontal dip unaffected by migration.

A further reflection characteristic of anticlines and synclines is caused by the focusing or defocusing effect of their curvature. On unmigrated sections, reflection strength often decreases over the anticlinal crests due to effects of defocusing, but increases in synclinal troughs due to a focusing effect. If the syncline is steep and narrow and deep in the seismic section, another effect occurs. The synclinal axis can become a buried focus for the sound waves, which brings the reflections together at a point still in the subsurface (fig. 3.26). There are now three possible reflection paths for a surface generated seismic wave. One from the axial region of the syncline, and additional reflections from the steep flanks. These three raypaths will give rise to three apparent reflectors. The two reflectors originating from the flanks will be underlain by a third curved reflector which looks like a deeper anticline (fig. 3.26). This buried-focus effect produces a bow-tie configuration, which can be unraveled by migration (fig. 3.27).

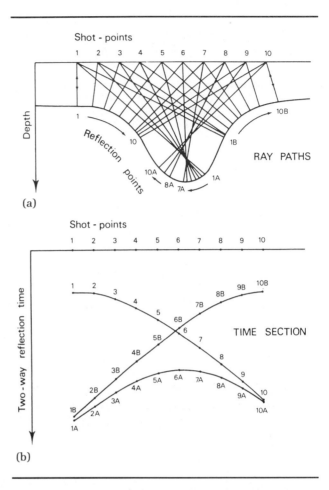

FIGURE 3.26 *The buried-focus or bow-tie effect.* (a) *Geological model showing a reflector with a curvature greater than that of the wavefront. This causes the reflector to be focused below the surface. As a consequence, rays emanating from each of the source locations 1–5 are reflected at up to three different points, all at normal incidence, on the synclinal reflector.* (b) *Schematic seismic section showing the complex pattern of the three reflector curves that resemble the outline of a bow-tie. Reprinted by permission of Graham & Trotman Ltd., London, from* Introduction to Seismic Interpretation, *McQuillin, Bacon, and Barclay, 1979.*

Figure 3.28 shows the beneficial effects of migration on a section that is not characterized by high dips. Note especially how dipping reflections have been moved up-dip, their dip has been increased, diffractions are collapsed, fault terminations sharpened, and the sections generally cleaned up. The differences can be important for the interpretation. For example, in the unmigrated version of the seismic line in figure 3.28, two dipping reflections between 1.8 and 2.1 s, below B, could be interpreted to have been overthrust by the flatter overlying reflections to the right. However, the migrated version of the section clearly shows the structural relationship between the two sets of reflectors to be a normal fault.

54

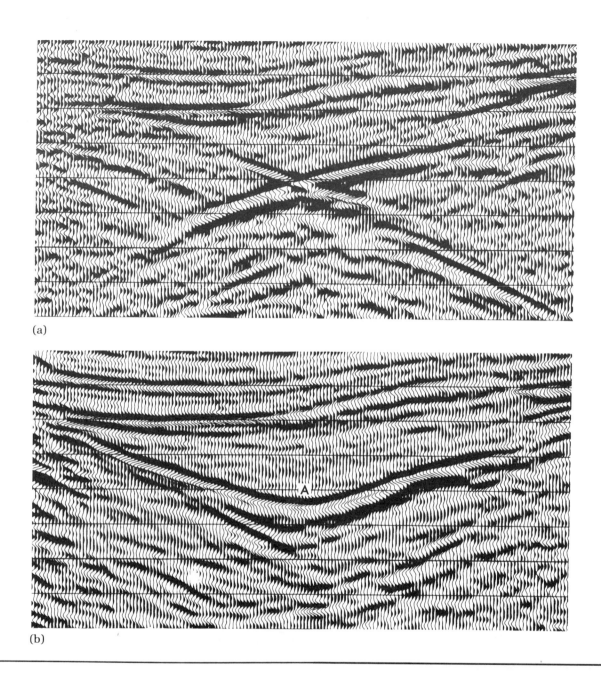

(a)

(b)

VELOCITY DISTORTIONS

Some of the more common spurious effects caused by geology are illustrated in this section. Changes in rock properties include, for example, varying formation thickness and facies change, which can produce subsurface velocity variations. Such variations can cause considerable distortions in stacked time sections when compared with the actual depth and thickness relationships.

The following examples are all variations on the same theme, namely, that lateral and vertical variations in velocity will distort the seismic picture. Their likely effects must be understood and appreciated in order to interpret seismic data properly. Figure 2.8 demonstrated the dis-

FIGURE 3.27 *Seismic examples of a buried focus.* (a) *Stacked section showing the bow-tie effect.* (b) *Migrated section, revealing the true synclinal shape of the reflector. Courtesy Norsk Hydro.*

torting effect of velocity on the seismic picture. In that example, the velocity change was caused by the presence of gas. However, a whole range of more subtle effects can originate merely through the steady increase in velocity with depth, due primarily to increased compaction. Velocity anomalies arise because, on the seismic section, thickness of a unit, displayed in time, is dependent on velocity. The greater the velocity, the thinner the unit.

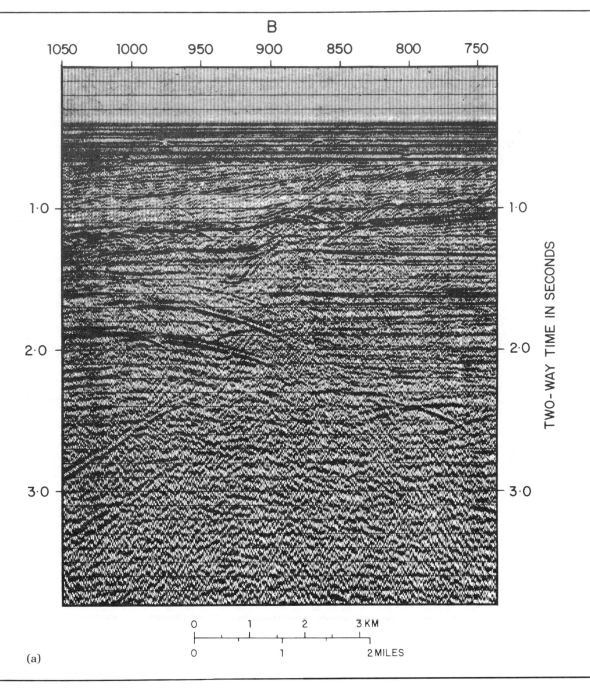

(a)

FIGURE 3.28 *Examples of stacked and migrated seismic sections. (a) Stacked section. (b) Migrated section. Courtesy Norsk Hydro.*

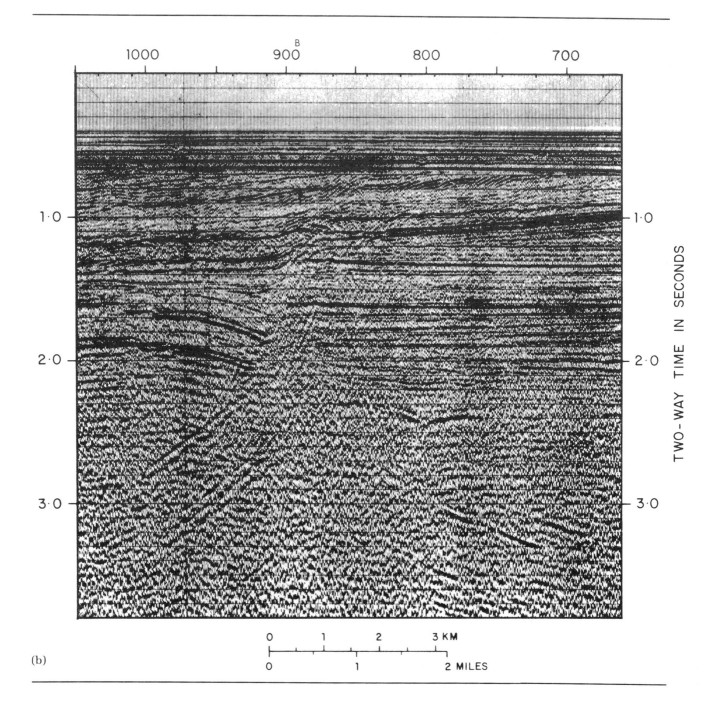

(b)

3. THE REAL WORLD

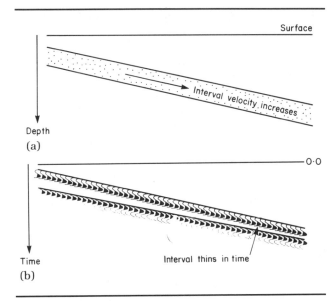

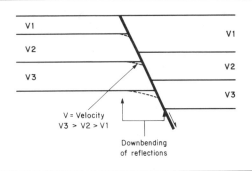

FIGURE 3.30 *Downbending of reflections into a fault. This can occur when low-velocity material is faulted by a dipping fault. In the zone beneath the fault plane, downbending of reflections can occur due to the lower velocities (and, therefore, longer traveltimes) in lower-velocity downthrown rocks.*

FIGURE 3.29 *The effect of increasing velocity with depth on the seismic expression of a dipping unit. (a) Geological model of a thick dipping sandstone unit. The sandstone's interval velocity increases with depth due to diagenesis, but its thickness remains constant. (b) Seismic expression: The sandstone unit appears to thin. It takes less time for the seismic signal to travel through the sandstone as its interval velocity increases.*

APPARENT THINNING DOWNDIP

A typical example of apparent downdip thinning could be a rock unit of constant thickness and lithology that appears to thin on the seismic section as it dips into a basin. The thinning is illusory and the effect is entirely due to a steady increase in interval velocity with depth (fig. 3.29). However, many units commonly thin basinwards, and in these cases the thinning may be exaggerated by the increasing interval velocity with depth. A depth-converted version of the section would remove the apparent thinning. To depth convert requires detailed knowledge of the interval velocities, which are often unavailable. Within well-explored basins, reliable time/depth relationships can be constructed for a variety of lithologies and horizons, enabling good estimates of interval velocity. In undrilled areas reasonable values of velocity (taken from the seismic stacking velocities) can be used to check that the observed thinning falls within the anticipated range. However, this will only work if the target unit is thick enough (at least 100 ms) for an estimation of its interval velocity from seismic data. Where the thinning is greater (or less) than anticipated, alternative geological explanations can be considered.

APPARENT THINNING ACROSS FAULTS

Apparent thinning of a unit from the upthrown side to downthrown side of a fault is sometimes observed on a seismic section. In figure 3.28, reflections X and Y can be

correlated across the major fault below B. The interval between X and Y, however, is 25% thinner in time on the downthrown side than on the upthrown side, although in depth the thicknesses are the same. The apparent thinning is due to increased interval velocity between X and Y in the downthrown block. Some faults have throws that appear to decrease with depth. Both are geologically plausible but are not very common. The most likely explanation for the seismic expression is a variant on the principle of gradual increase in velocity with depth, described above. The units on the downthrown side, being deeper, may have a higher interval velocity and will therefore appear thinner on a time section. The most likely explanation can be investigated by calculating interval velocities for both sides of the fault or, alternatively, checking if the observed thickness change is within reasonable limits of a possible velocity increase. From a single section it may be difficult to determine the cause of the observed thinning in a down-faulted block. The correct interpretation would depend on correlation with other data in the immediate area. This, it is to be hoped, would support either a geological reason for the observed anomaly (e.g., strike-slip faulting juxtaposing different parts of the basin, a period of reverse movement on a normal fault, etc.) or suggest that the relationship could be ascribed to velocity variation.

APPARENT ROLLOVER INTO FAULTS

Seismic reflections in the upthrown block of a normal fault are sometimes observed to bend down toward the fault plane (fig. 3.30). Caution should be exercised in interpreting this apparent rollover, because the observed effect can be explained in several ways—it might be:

a true rollover caused by reverse drag on the fault plane on listric-normal faults;

a portion of a diffraction curve, not entirely removed by

58

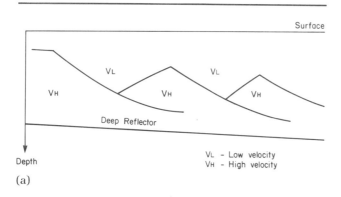

(a)

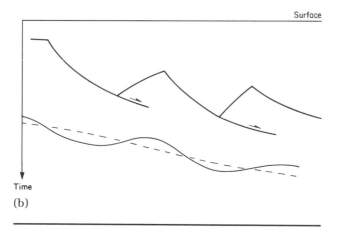

(b)

FIGURE 3.31 *Velocity anomalies beneath detached listric-normal faults. (a) Geological model showing a set of detached listric-normal faults and associated tilted fault blocks. The faults are underlain by a planar dipping reflector. (b) Seismic expression showing velocity pull-up beneath the tilted fault blocks and velocity push-down beneath the intervals of thick low-velocity infill. As a general rule, beware of deeper reflections that mimic the structure of shallower reflections.*

migration, that appears to be in continuity with the reflection; or

a velocity artefact caused by the wedge of lower-velocity rocks above the fault plane, which overlie the up-thrown edge of the fault within the fault zone.

Velocity artefacts associated with reverse and thrust faults are also possible. In all cases care should be taken to ensure that diffractions have been recognized and eliminated. Curvature on reflections lying within fault zones (shadows) should be viewed with suspicion.

VELOCITY ANOMALIES BENEATH FAULTS

Velocity anomalies are common beneath major low-dipping faults such as thrusts or detached listric-normal faults (figs. 3.31 and 3.32). The lateral velocity variations caused by the faulting modify the time structure of deeper reflectors. Figure 3.31 shows how lateral velocity variations associated with listric faults can affect the time structure of a deeper reflector. Figure 3.32 is part of a seismic section from the inner trench slope of the Nankai Trough, southeast of Japan (Aoki et al., 1982). The line shows several thrust slices beneath which reflector *A* clearly shows velocity pull-up.

VELOCITY ANOMALIES ASSOCIATED WITH SALT

Rock salt is inherently unstable because its specific gravity is less than most other sedimentary rocks. It has a tendency to become plastic and flow when loaded beyond a critical point. Bishop (1978) reviews the mechanisms of salt movement. Once movement begins, the salt flows to form pillows, walls, piercements, etc., all of which are features that have marked changes in lateral thickness (fig. 3.33). Although its specific gravity is low, rock salt has a relatively high interval velocity (4570 m/s) compared with its overburden (typically, 2500–4000 m/s). The sound waves thus travel much faster through the salt layer than through the laterally adjacent sediments. In cases where the salt has a higher interval velocity than adjacent sediments, any reflector beneath the salt will, therefore, be recorded sooner on the time section beneath a salt structure than beneath the adjacent area where the salt layer is much thinner or absent (fig. 3.34). If sufficient velocity information is available, depth sections can be constructed to correct for the pull-up. Often, there is insufficient data to preclude the possibility that part of the pull-up could represent genuine structure; in which case, the interpreter can use the shape of the pull-up to come to a decision. If the contact between the salt and the overlying sediments can be seen clearly, and if the presalt structure shows a similar shape, then a velocity pull-up should be suspected. Conversely, if the top of the salt layer cannot be seen clearly, but a velocity pull-up is suspected and sufficient velocity information is available, the degree of pull-up can be used to estimate the salt's thickness and so

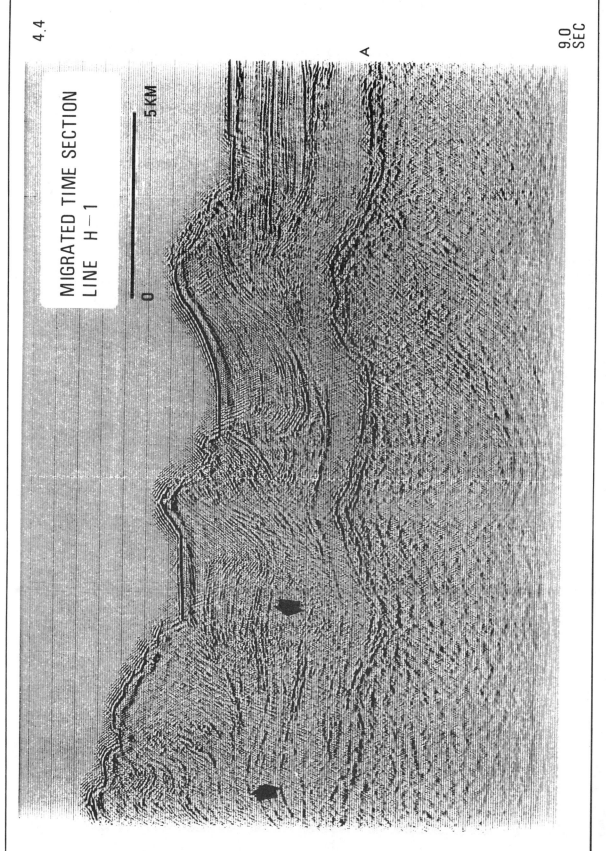

MIGRATED TIME SECTION
LINE H−1

4.4

9.0 SEC

5 KM

0

A

FIGURE 3.32 *Velocity pull-up beneath thrust faults. The seismic section from the inner trench slope of the Nankai Trough, SE of Japan (Aoki et al., 1982), shows marked velocity pull-up of reflection A beneath the thrust slices. The amount of pull-up is determined by the difference in interval velocity between the sediments in the thrust and the adjacent water. Reprinted by permission of the AAPG from Aoki, 1982, fig. 5, p. 315.*

59

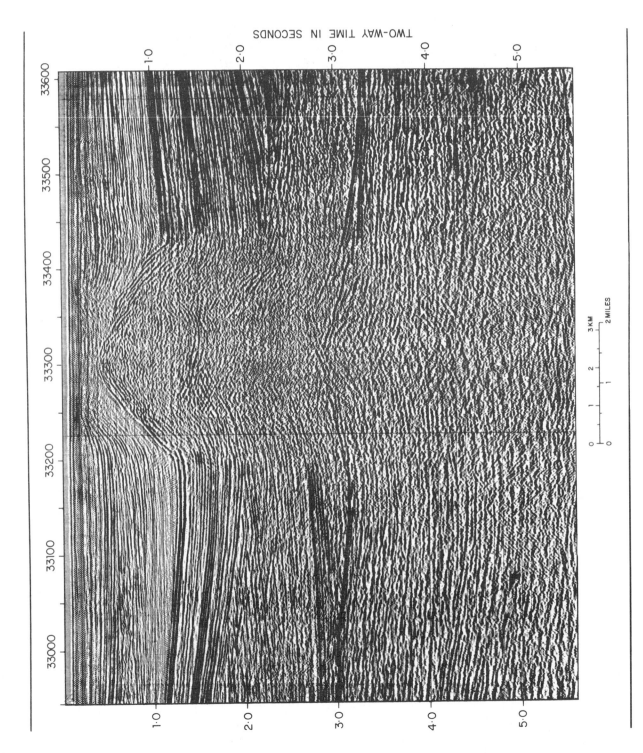

FIGURE 3.33 *Seismic section across a salt diapir. Courtesy Merlin Profilers Ltd.*

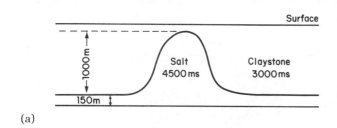

(a)

Travel time through the salt is 1500 ms faster than the surrounding claystone producing a pull-up on the base salt reflection.

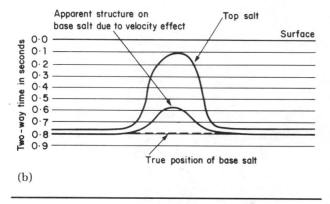

(b)

FIGURE 3.34 *Velocity anomaly beneath a salt diapir. (a) Geological model showing a salt diapir 1000 m high. (b) Seismic expression showing pull-up of 222 ms on the base salt reflector beneath the salt diapir.*

locate its top. The pull-up can be used as an approximate guide to predict the time of the top salt layer where this cannot be seen clearly on the seismic section.

VELOCITY PUSH-DOWN UNDER SHALE DIAPIRS

Thick shale sequences, if undercompacted and overpressured, often show flowage features similar to those of salt, forming domes, walls, etc. The velocity effects, however, are usually the opposite to those of salt, since the shales generally have lower velocity than adjacent sediments. This lengthens the traveltime and the underlying reflectors are pushed down in the opposite sense to figure 3.34. Figure 3.35 shows evidence of major shale flowage from about 800 ms to 1200 ms between shotpoints 1010 and 1170. Subtle push-down beneath the shale flowage affects reflections *A* and *B*. Sometimes, even without flowage, undisturbed overpressured shale intervals can produce velocity anomalies. If accurate velocity data is available, the anomaly can be investigated and removed by depth

conversion. Alternatively, it is possible to resolve the anomaly graphically by plotting the observed thickening against the observed push-down relative to a straight line. If the sag is caused by velocity push-down, the points will approximate to a straight line. Obviously, the phenomena of pull-up or push-down is an extremely useful discriminant criterion for distinguishing between salt or shale diapirs.

VELOCITY ANOMALIES BENEATH REEFS

Carbonate reefs are important reservoir rocks in many parts of the world. Reefs are associated with rapid lateral facies and associated velocity changes, and are so complex that it is difficult to generalize about their detailed attributes. Reef limestones may have higher velocity than the adjacent facies (e.g., back- and forereef shales); or they may have a lower velocity where surrounded, for example, by denser limestones and dolomites. Both situations will give rise to velocity anomalies on a time section (fig. 3.36). Where the reef has a higher interval velocity than the adjacent strata, a velocity pull-up will develop. If the reef is draped by younger sediments, the pull-up could suggest that the overall positive feature is a deep-rooted structure (i.e., prereef in age) and may lead to a pessimistically false geological interpretation. Alternatively, where the reef limestone has lower interval velocity than the surrounding sediments, the velocity anomaly results in a push-down; and the reef base could appear as a low on the seismic time section. This is identical to the shale push-down and the distortion on the time section is open to misinterpretation. If the lower velocity is attributed to exceptional porosity development, a push-down could have great prospective interest.

HIGH-VELOCITY WEDGE-FOCUSING EFFECT

An overlying high-velocity wedge can act as a distorting lens and disrupt the reflection from a continuous surface beneath (fig. 3.37). The figure, taken from Sheriff (1982), shows a geological model and the corresponding predicted seismic response. While the top of the basement on the model is continuous and smooth, the reflection from it has a kink (including some overlap) because of distortion by the overlying high-velocity wedge (which acts as a distorting lens). Two raypaths involving reflecting points *E* and *F* are closely spaced on the reflector (fig. 3.37). The raypath from *E* is shown to miss the high-velocity wedge, whereas the one from *F* may be refracted by the high-velocity wedge so that it actually crosses the raypath from *E*. This causes the basement reflection to be distorted because of the shallower high-velocity wedge. Over the portion of the surface P, the basement reflection is observed twice, once without going through the wedge and once going through the wedge. Such a situation also produces phantom diffractions—they appear in the seismic section but there is no discontinuity in the reflector.

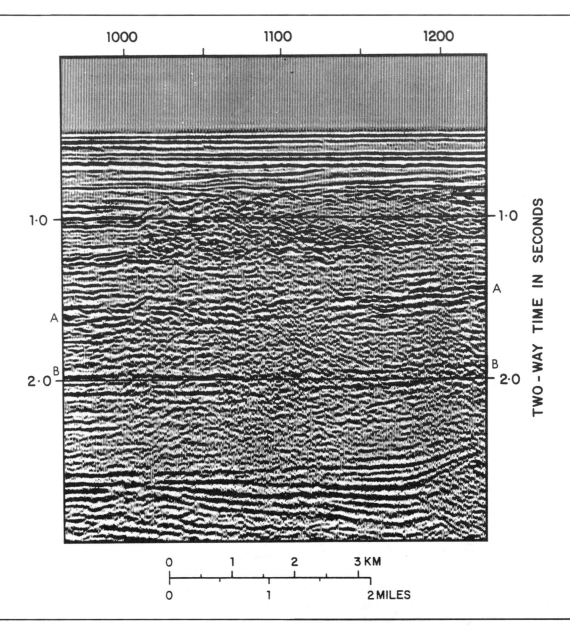

FIGURE 3.35 *Seismic section showing evidence of shale flowage (a zone of chaotic reflections) from about 800 ms to 1200 ms between shotpoints 1010 and 1170. Subtle push-down beneath the shale flowage affects reflections A and B. Courtesy Norsk Hydro.*

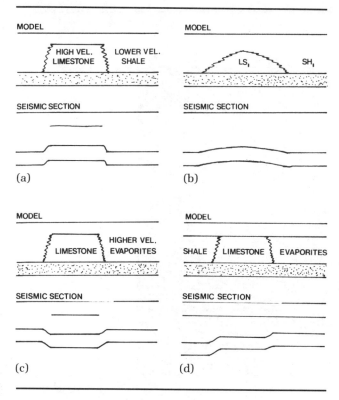

FIGURE 3.36 *Velocity anomalies beneath reefs. (a) A reef composed of high-velocity limestone encased in lower-velocity shales produces a velocity pull-up on underlying reflections. (b) Same as (a), except the reef has a more rounded form. (c) A reef encased in an evaporitic sequence with high interval velocity produces a velocity push-down on underlying reflections. (d) A reef with low-velocity basinal shales to its left and high-velocity backreef evaporites to its right produces a push-down beneath the shales and pull-up beneath the evaporites. Reprinted by permission of IHRDC Press from Sheriff, 1980a, fig. 5.17, p. 115.*

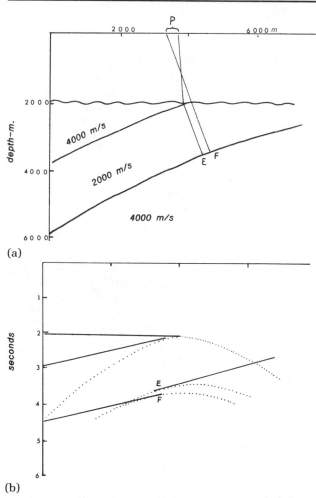

FIGURE 3.37 *Distortion resulting from the focusing effects of a wedge with high interval velocity. (a) Geological model. The raypath from reflection point F just misses the high-velocity wedge. The raypath from E, however, is refracted, so that it crosses the raypath from F. (b) Seismic expression. The earlier arrival of ray E, refracted through the wedge edge, causes two reflections to be seen beneath P. Reprinted by permission of the AAPG; after Sheriff, 1982, fig. 9, p. 13.*

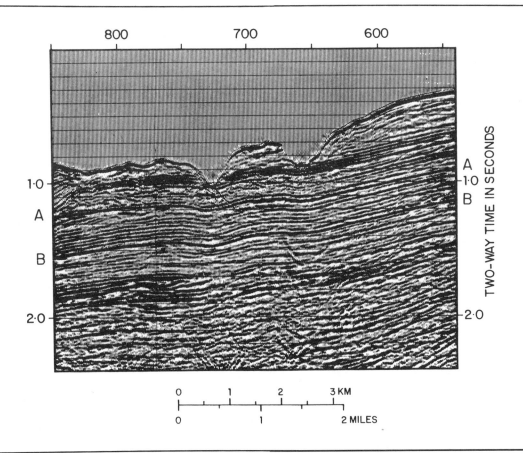

FIGURE 3.38 *Seismic section showing velocity pull-up on reflections A and B beneath two submarine canyons. Courtesy Merlin Profilers Ltd.*

VELOCITY ANOMALIES ASSOCIATED WITH CHANNELS

Channels often produce a velocity anomaly. If the channel cuts down into consolidated material, there is a good chance that the channel fill will have lower velocity than the adjacent rock. Such a channel would cause a velocity push-down. Channels or canyons in the sea bed have the same effect. Figure 3.38 shows a deep sea-floor canyon system with more than 200 ms (about 110 m) of relief that produces undulations in the underlying reflectors (e.g., reflections *A* and *B*). The magnitude of the undulations corresponds to the traveltime differences between water in the canyon and in the laterally adjacent sediments. Depth converted, the reflectors *A* and *B* would be planar. In some channels, however, the channel fill can have a higher velocity than the surrounding sediments and produce a velocity pull-up. Figure 3.39 shows part of a seismic section from the southwestern African continental margin (Jaunich, 1983). A shallow, velocity anomaly, probably a shallow submarine canyon with a compacted sandstone fill, is causing severe disturbances in the shallower horizons below shotpoint 2100. Deeper horizons show a pull-up of 200–300 ms.

VELOCITY ANOMALIES ASSOCIATED WITH GAS SANDS

If thick enough, lower velocity in the gas-filled sand will produce a velocity push-down. The effects of gas are shown very clearly in figure 2.8, a seismic section across a gas-filled reservoir. Not only are the reflectors beneath the gas pushed down but the flat spot at the gas/water contact is tilted. The tilt is entirely a velocity distortion, caused by thickening of the gas-filled zone.

VELOCITY ANOMALIES CAUSED BY VARYING WATER DEPTH

Although not an effect of rock velocity, a change in water depth can produce distortion of the seismic time section. In cases where water depth increases rapidly, the effect can be great enough to produce an entirely false impression of dip in time and, in extreme cases, a complete reversal of the true dip direction. This effect is illustrated by the seismic sections on the North Atlantic slope near the Wilmington Canyon southeast of New Jersey (Morgan and Dowdall, 1983) in figure 3.40. Reflections to the west of the reefoid mass in figure 3.40a dip to the east and there is no structural closure. Figure 3.40b shows the line after depth conversion. The push-down effect of eastward-increasing water depth has been removed to reveal structural closure associated with the reefoid mass.

A

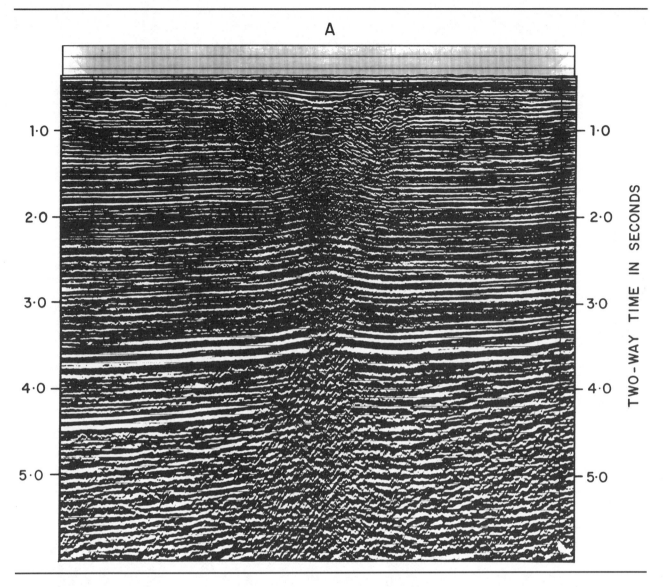

FIGURE 3.39 *Seismic section from the SW African continental margin showing velocity pull-up beneath an in-filled submarine canyon. A shallow velocity anomaly, probably a near, sea bed submarine canyon with a compacted sandstone fill, is causing severe disturbances in the shallower reflections below A. Deeper reflections show a pull-up of 200–300 ms. Reprinted by permission of the AAPG from Jaunich, 1983.*

SIDESWIPE

Sideswipe is a very common feature in structured areas and can produce extremely perplexing reflector patterns. Sideswipe is used to describe reflections that appear on a section from features that lie out of the plane of section. Although the seismic section is presented as a vertical time slice, the section contains data from an expanding wavefront which has ever-increasing breadth with depth. A seismic line shot parallel to a fault may record data from both the upthrown and downthrown sides of the fault, producing a confusing reflector pattern (fig. 3.41). Sideswipe can develop in a similar manner on lines shot along the strike of a steeply dipping surface. The section

samples data from a broad area of the slope and produces a confusing reflector pattern. Sideswipe can often be the reason for structurally incongruous reflectors appearing on an otherwise normal section. Generally, it is impossible to resolve such complexities on a single line and the data must be carefully tied through a grid of data. Regional surveys are frequently too widely spaced to solve the problem. In areas of complex structuring, it is necessary to select carefully the optimum shooting direction to minimize off-line effects.

66

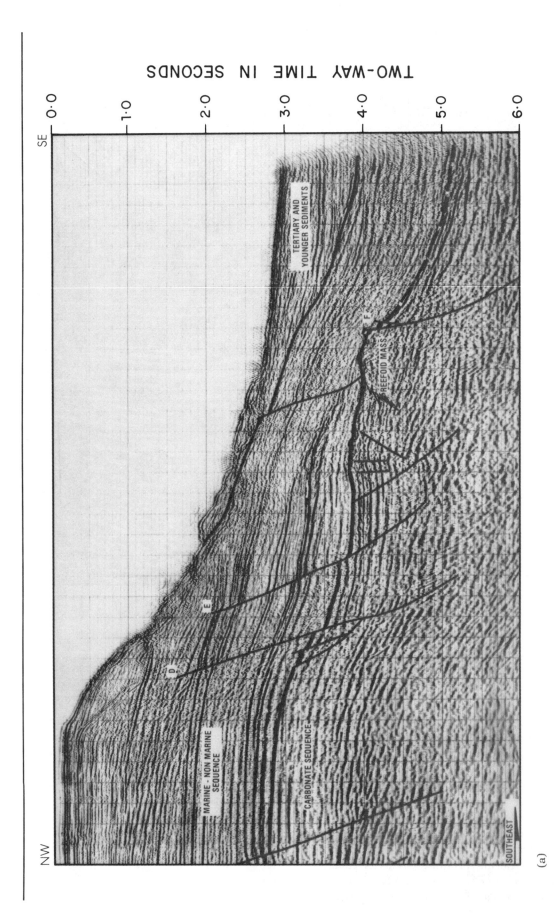

(a)

67

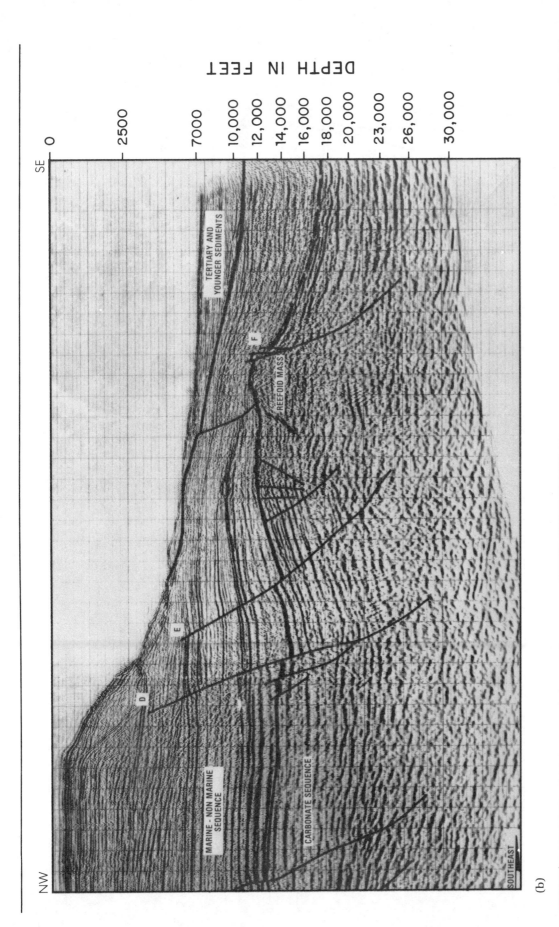

FIGURE 3.40 *Seismic sections showing velocity distortions caused by varying water depth. (a) Time section: Note the seaward dip of reflections to the NW of the reefoid mass. (b) Depth section: The push-down effect of increasing water depth has been removed, revealing landward dips and potential closure on reflections to the NW of the reefoid mass. Reprinted by permission of the AAPG from Morgan and Dowdall, 1983.*

68

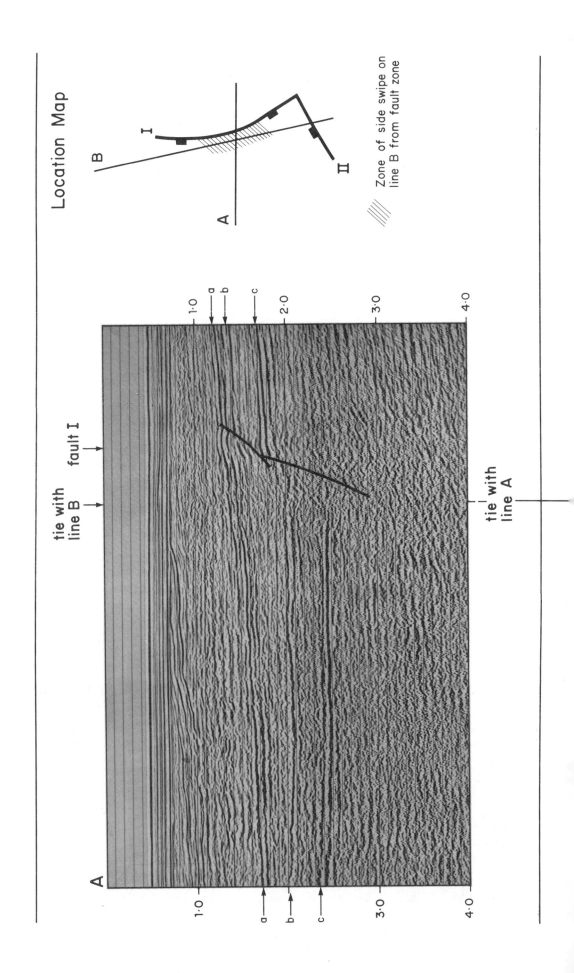

Location Map

B

I

A

II

Zone of side swipe on
line B from fault zone

1·0
a
b
c
2·0
3·0
4·0

tie with
line B

fault I

tie with
line A

A

1·0
a
b
c
3·0
4·0

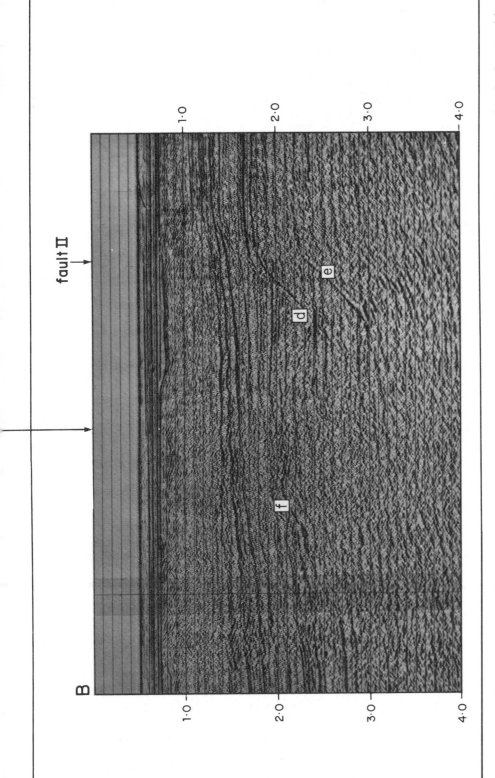

FIGURE 3.41 *Example of sideswipe—reflections from out of the plane section. Reflections from the fault zone in line A appear in line B. (d) Reflected refraction. (e) Water-bottom multiple of reflected refraction d. (f) Sideswipe reflection from footwall block of fault I. Courtesy Saga Petroleum.*

69

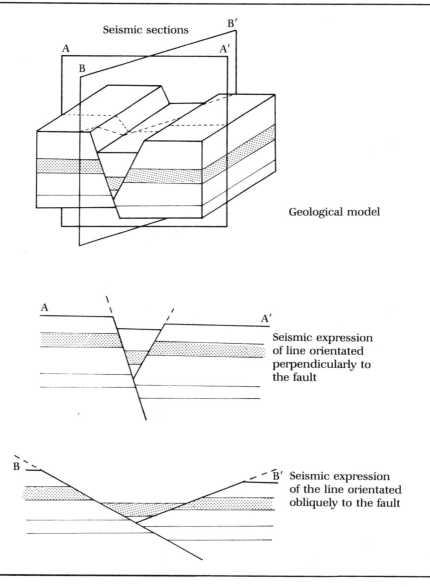

FIGURE 3.42 *Cross-section showing how line orientation can affect the seismic expression.*

Seismic sections

B'

A   A'

B

Geological model

A   A'
Seismic expression of line orientated perpendicularly to the fault

B   B'
Seismic expression of the line orientated obliquely to the fault

POOR LINE ORIENTATION

A variation on the sideswipe theme—sometimes line orientation is unfavorably placed to give a clear subsurface time picture. For example, a line passing obliquely through a fault can generate a complex reflector pattern, as can a line along a sinuous fault trace, where the upthrown and downthrown sides of the fault alternate along the line of section (fig. 3.42).

We can conclude that before a geological model is proposed we must be certain that the feature under consideration is not an artefact. The possibility that the vertical repetition of a structural anomaly down a seismic section might be caused by overlying velocity contrasts should always be considered carefully. Care is especially important in new areas where subsurface stratigraphic control is lacking.

Chapter 4

Geology and Seismic Sections

At first sight the connection between geology and seismic sections might seem obvious and relatively uncomplicated. Many modern seismic sections (and some of the older ones also) bear a striking resemblance to geological cross-sections. But how far can we really go with such a comparison? Is it possible to translate all that we see in a seismic section into geology? The seismic system sees with a biased eye. It can only detect lithological boundaries if the acoustic impedance changes across the boundary; and the change must be above the threshold limit of the seismic system. So, at best, the seismic system detects only a limited proportion of boundaries; and, when these boundaries are closely spaced, interference affects the seismic response, complicating or making impossible our perception of the geology. That the subsurface is viewed, not in depth but in terms of two-way time, is a further handicap. The distortions that this last factor alone introduces, because of both vertical and lateral velocity changes, make a simple and direct link between geology and seismic sections more problematic.

The information gap between what we observe in the seismic section, and what the geology most probably is, has to be filled by the interpreter. The knowledge required for this is twofold. Firstly, the interpreter must be able to identify and eliminate all events relating to noise. Secondly, the interpreter must employ considerable geological skill, including knowledge of sedimentology, stratigraphy, structural geology, etc., to convert the seismic image into a plausible geological reality. Geological knowledge enables the interpreter to conceive geological models and opinions that can be used predictively and as a guide to the interpretation. Although, at a local scale, geology is unique, many processes driven by the same underlying cause produce an overall similar end product. For example, a prograding delta will be unique at a local scale but will share many of the large-scale attributes of other prograding deltas. Recognition of such features in a seismic section relies on attributes of the single reflection and on the overall configuration of the reflections forming characteristic and recognizable geometries. In this context, reflections are important, not only for their individual characteristics, but also for their geometry and relationship to other reflections. Understanding the link between geology and seismic sections is thus a twofold problem. First, we must establish the significance of the individual reflection and second, establish the significance of the relationship of reflections to each other.

THE INDIVIDUAL REFLECTION

Individual reflections have several measurable and descriptive properties that can be related to geology. The attributes most easily linked to, and diagnostic of, lithology are reflection amplitude, polarity, continuity, and spacing or frequency. Caution should always be used when analyzing reflection characteristics, since both processing and noise can create potential pitfalls.

REFLECTION AMPLITUDE

Amplitude is the height of a seismic reflection peak (or trough) and is dependent on the reflection coefficient, but this direct relationship may be lost during processing. Frequently, amplitudes on seismic sections are balanced during processing to produce what is thought to be more easily interpretable sections. Usually, however, this makes it difficult and in many instances no longer possible to determine the relative strengths of reflection coefficients. However, where amplitudes can be differentiated, the qualifying terms of high, medium, and low are used (fig. 4.1). Vertical changes in amplitude can be used to help locate unconformities, whereas lateral changes can be used to help distinguish seismic facies. Great caution must be exercised, however, as interference patterns from tuning, multiples, etc., are responsible for many amplitude changes observed in seismic sections.

REFLECTION POLARITY

Reflection polarity can often be determined from onlap relationships on processed minimum-phase sections, or from the maximum amplitude from zero-phase sections (sees figs. 7.10 and 7.13). Polarity in combination with amplitude may provide a good guide to the likely lithologies causing a reflection. For example, in a shallow young sequence, such as the Tertiary of the U.S. Gulf Coast, a porous sand overlain by clay should produce a medium- to high-amplitude reflection with a negative reflection coefficient; a clay overlying a limestone almost always produces a high-amplitude reflection with a positive reflection coefficient, etc.

REFLECTION CONTINUITY

Reflection continuity describes the lateral persistence of a reflection. A discontinuous reflection is one where an alignment is obvious but the continuous parts of the reflection are separated by gaps. The gaps may be as small as two or three traces. A continuous reflection maintains its character for an appreciable distance (say

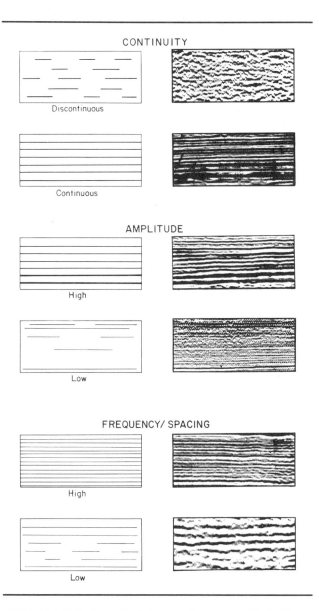

FIGURE 4.1 *Reflection attributes: continuity, amplitude, frequency/spacing.*

several kilometers or miles). Continuity is graded from very continuous to very discontinuous (fig. 4.1). Continuity can be interpreted in geological terms as lateral changes in acoustic impedance and hence in lithology. Discontinuous reflectors are, thus, characteristic of environments where rapid lateral facies change is the rule (e.g., fluvial, alluvial environments). Continuous reflectors are characteristic of depositional environments where uniform conditions are laterally extensive (e.g., deepwater environments).

Potential pitfalls also arise from disruption of reflections by noise, such as, multiples, migration arcs, diffractions, sideswipe. Usually these coherent type of disruptions can be recognized by drawing a line (real or imaginary) connecting discontinuities. If the line is

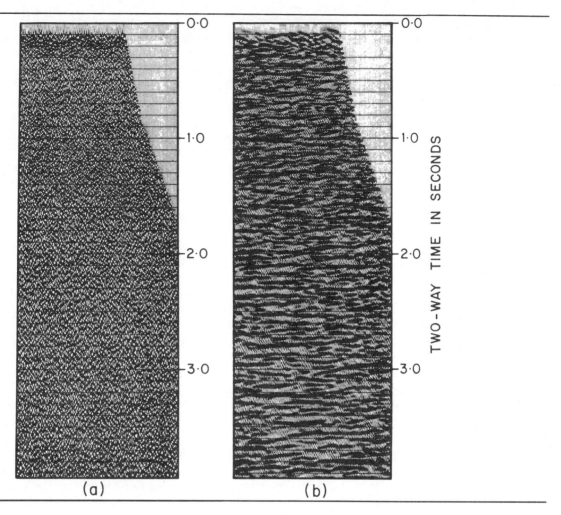

FIGURE 4.2 *Random reflections with continuity enhancement. (a) A stacked section from a common shotpoint gather of synthetically made seismic traces using a random-number generator. The data has zero signal-to-noise ratio and all reflection alignments are apparent and not real. (b) Section (a) after further processing to enhance continuity. The process effectively forces alignments into the data. The apparent improvement is entirely false, and this type of processing is a potential enemy of the interpreter. Reprinted by permission of the AAPG from Howard and Danbom, 1983.*

straight or hyperbolic, the discontinuity is probably not real. A more serious pitfall can arise when continuity is deliberately enhanced during processing (fig. 4.2). For seismic stratigraphic work, processing that has forced continuity into a section is a great disadvantage; unfortunately, it is done all too frequently.

REFLECTION SPACING OR FREQUENCY

Reflection spacing or frequency describes the number of reflections per unit time (fig. 4.1). It is affected by both interference effects and the frequency of the seismic signal. The former effects can be interpreted in terms of bed (reflector spacing), and imparts character to the seismic section. Figure 7.17, in chapter 7, shows a characteristic

reflector spacing that gives an interval a character that can be correlated easily across faults. Vertical changes in reflector spacing can be used as a guide to locating boundaries between depositional sequences, but should not be used (if possible) as the sole criterion. Lateral changes in spacing can be used to infer facies change. However, lateral change in spacing or character is very susceptible to noise and structuring. Multiples can often produce false increases in reflection spacing. The gradual loss of higher frequencies with depth in a seismic section has a marked effect on reflector spacing. The dominant frequency over an interval can be estimated by measuring the reflection spacing (fig. 2.15).

INTERVAL VELOCITY

If reflectors are spaced more than about 100 ms apart, it is possible to calculate interval velocity and so, perhaps, infer lithology. Methods for determining interval velocity from seismic data are described in chapter 6. Using interval velocity to identify lithology may not be simple, since, as figure 4.3 shows, there is considerable overlap in the typical ranges of velocity, density, and acoustic impedance of different lithologies.

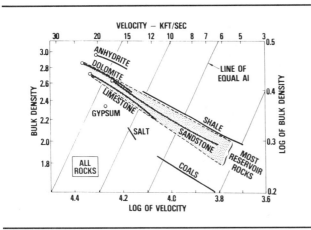

FIGURE 4.3 *Acoustic-impedance graph. Reprinted by permission of the SEG from Gardner et al., 1974.*

LITHOLOGICAL CHANGE AND REFLECTIONS

Excepting reflectors from fluid contacts, practically all other primary reflections originate from acoustic-impedance boundaries caused by lithological change. The significance of lithological change is thus a key to understanding the relationship between geology and seismic sections. In a bedded sequence, lithological change usually occurs at bed boundaries. Bedding planes arise through a multitude of causes; a change in depositional conditions, lithification, variation in sediment supply, seasonal variations, etc. Bedding planes invariably signify a break in deposition. Bedding planes define the external shape of beds. Beds come in a great variety of sizes and shapes, reflecting, to a large extent, the lithology forming the beds, depositional process, and depositional environment. Lithologies can be divided into two main groups:

1. Sediments deposited mechanically—that is, transported by, and settled out from, a fluid
2. Sediments precipitated chemically (e.g., salt or evaporites) or formed biologically (e.g., reefs)

Based on the dominant transport and depositional process, sediments deposited mechanically can be subdivided into two overlapping groups: (a) sediments consisting of grains transported by bedload movements, and (b) sediments consisting of grains, transported by suspension load, that have settled out from suspension. As a gross generalization, these two groups correspond roughly to sand-sized and clay-sized grains. Many beds will contain a mixture of grains deposited by both processes. Obviously, the mechanics of the deposition process will depend on many factors—grain size, grain density, grain shape, grain-size distribution, current velocity, nature of the fluid flow, etc. On a small scale the subdivision is somewhat unrealistic, since most deposits contain grains deposited by both processes (e.g., a bed grading from sand at its base through to clay at its top). Additionally, there is a broad overlap in size of grains that fall into either category. For groups of beds making up a stratigraphic unit, however, the concept becomes useful, especially on the scale of seismic resolution (i.e., for beds or units more than a few meters thick). On this scale, bed-load transport will have been the dominant transport mechanism for sands or clastic deposits, and suspension load the dominant transport mechanism for clays and other fine-grained deposits. The differences in transport mechanisms lead to fundamental differences in the overall shape of beds formed by sand-sized and clay-sized particles. These differences are especially marked where there has been little or no reworking of the deposits—in deep water, for example.

All other parameters being equal, once the current velocity falls below the particular threshold value for the movement of sand-sized grains, transport ceases and deposition occurs. Sand-sized grains being transported partly by suspension load will settle out rapidly once the current velocity falls. Clay-sized particles, although quite difficult to get into suspension because of cohesive forces between grains, once in suspension, are not so susceptible as sand-sized grains to variations in current velocity. They not only require much lower current velocities than sand-sized grains to remain in suspension, but they also are deposited at a much lower rate once the current velocity falls. Modest currents, that can neither induce traction of sand-sized grains nor pick up clay-sized grains into suspension, may, however, be sufficient to ensure that clay-sized grains already in suspension remain in suspension. This effectively reduces or can even temporarily prevent deposition. The depositional rate of clay-sized grains is very sensitive to current velocity.

The transport and depositional behavior of the two groups may be summarized as follows:

1. *Sand-sized grains*, depending on their shape, density, etc., require a minimum current velocity to induce movement and transportation. A current velocity rising above this threshold will transport grains but deposit them immediately as it falls below this threshold.

2. *Clay-sized grains*, depending on their shape, density, etc., require relatively high velocities (compared to their size) to overcome intergrain cohesive forces and get the grains, into suspension. Once in suspension, however, much lower current velocities, although unable to pick up grains, are able to keep the grains in a suspended state. Deposition from suspension occurs at relatively low rates (compared to sand-sized grains). Since variation in current velocity directly effects the depositional rate, currents too weak to pick up and erode but great enough to prevent deposition can interrupt the depositional process.

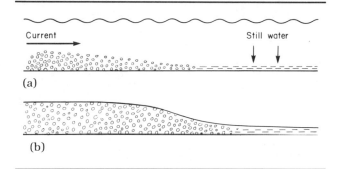

(a)

(b)

FIGURE 4.4 *Fundamental shape relationships between deposits of sand-sized and clay-sized grains. (a) A current transporting sand-sized grains flows into a deep water body from the left and slows down. A tapering bed is deposited. Further in the basin clay-sized grains are deposited out from the suspension load. (b) The resulting sedimentary unit.*

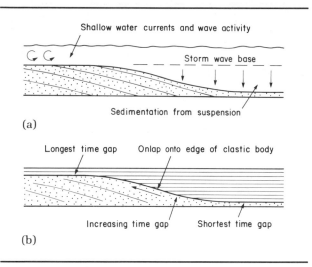

(a)

(b)

FIGURE 4.5 *Sketches showing how the shape of a clastic body can influence subsequent sedimentation.*

Figure 4.4 illustrates some of the consequences of the contrasting behavior of sand-sized versus clay-sized grains. The figure shows a basin containing a large body of deep water into which a current flow bearing a traction load of sand-sized grains is introduced. The current slows on entering the larger water body, transportation ceases, and the sand-sized grains are deposited to form a sand bed with a thickness profile tapered in the downcurrent direction. Over the same time interval that the sands were being deposited, the cumulative thickness of clay-sized grains being deposited from suspension load in the basin center would be many orders of magnitude less. In fact, the current velocity, too slow to transport sand-sized grains, could be sufficient, in the immediate area beyond the edge of the sand deposit, to keep clay-sized particles in suspension, further reducing the short-term depositional rate. The end result is to produce the thickness and shape relationship illustrated in figure 4.4. A density flow (turbidity flow) of sand-sized particles into the basin would have the same effects and produce the same shaped deposit. This tapered shape is seen commonly in seismic sections and appears to be a characteristic of deposits formed of sand-sized and larger grains.

On a small scale, these differences have little practical effect and are irrelevant to our considerations. For example, small-scale ripples at the top of a sand bed would be uniformly buried and draped, if the deposition of clay-sized grains followed the formation of the ripples. As the thickness and size of a clastic unit increases, however, its potential feedback on the deposition of succeeding beds increases. If the episode of clastic sedimentation ceases and the area returns to sedimentation from suspension load, we would intuitively expect the newly formed basin floor topography to be buried and draped by the succeeding sediments to produce an offlapping sequence (fig. 4.5). This, however, seems not to be the general case, at least on a scale where the features are sufficiently large to

be observed in the seismic section. Instead, onlap is usually the predominant infill mechanism. It should be made clear at this point that we are discussing onlap onto a rapidly deposited feature, for example, a fan, part of a delta front abandoned by avulsion of the main delta, etc. These types of deposits are invariably onlapped (fig. 4.5). Several mechanisms are possibly at work to bring this about; but variations of current activity caused by the deposit's morphology or its location are the most obvious influence—more active currents in the shallower water above the feature would inhibit deposition, while quieter conditions in the deeper water, adjacent to the feature, would favor deposition from suspension load. The shape of a clastic unit, by influencing the form of the depositional surface, the water depth, and the current flow, may control the site and rate of subsequent deposition. For clastic units thicker than a few meters, for example, there will be a tendency, all other factors being equal, for subsequent fine-grained deposition to occur in the relatively deeper water near the edge of, or beyond, the clastic body (fig. 4.5). Such a situation results in the clastic body being onlapped by the fine-grained sediments. This type of onlap situation is quite distinct from the more widespread onlap of basin margins, which is a result of basic subsidence processes (Watts, 1982).

The thickness and shape can, in this circumstance, be used to imply a time relationship. Clastics will tend to be onlapped by clays, and the time gap between the sands and clays at the top of the clastic unit will be greater than that in the basinal area (fig. 4.6). These characteristic shape relationships can be seen on all scales, from the small outcrop to units 1000 m thick or more.

Figure 4.7 shows potential shape and time relationships when several episodes of clastic deposition have occurred, and the inferred time relationships. Well *A*,

76

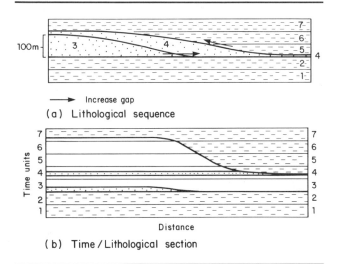

Increase gap

(a) Lithological sequence

(b) Time / Lithological section

FIGURE 4.6 *Inferred time relationships between sand- and clay-sized grain deposits in a deep-water depositional environment. (a) Thickness relationships. (b) Time relationships.*

near the basin margin, encounters a sandy sequence. Well *B*, in a basinal position, encounters a shale sequence. Age dating indicates a similar age range for the deposits in wells *A* and *B*. It is impossible for similar thicknesses of sand-sized grain deposits and fine-grained deposits to be exactly equivalent in age. There must be gaps within the sandy sequence. Many variations on this theme are possible. If we accept these arguments, it is clear that for a given time interval or depositional episode, clastics will tend to form a much thicker deposit than will fine-grained sediments deposited from suspension load. It is not possible to correlate like thicknesses of similar-age clastics and clays without inferring both considerable gaps in the clastic sequence and an onlap relationship between the clastics and clays. We can conclude that clastic sequences tend to be full of gaps, record much less geological history than clay sequences, and that the

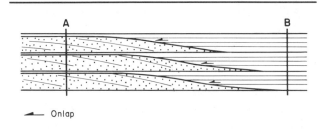

Onlap

FIGURE 4.7 *An example of lateral relationships between sands and clays in a deep-water setting. Well A drilled a sandy sequence, Well B a clay sequence of similar thickness and overall age. It is impossible for sands and clays of similar thickness to be equivalent in age. There must be gaps in the sand sequence. Onlap relationships can be used to locate the gaps and assess their magnitude.*

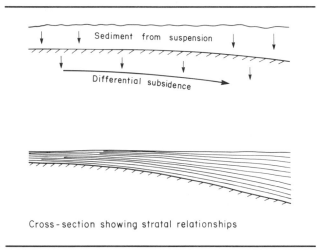

Sediment from suspension

Differential subsidence

Cross-section showing stratal relationships

FIGURE 4.8 *Laterally thickening fine-grained sequences. Rates of sedimentation from suspension load and subsidence are often of a similar magnitude, and differential subsidence can produce laterally thickening fine-grained depositional units.*

thicker the clastic unit resulting from a particular depositional episode, the greater the probable time gap at its top. There are lessons here for the ways in which we correlate wells. The dependence of the depositional process on varying current velocity dictates that sands must be accumulated episodically. The time gap between successive depositional episodes will depend on the process causing the current velocity (tides, storms, earthquakes, etc.). Whatever the process, it is clear that sands cannot be deposited in the continual manner that is theoretically possible (if unlikely) for clay-sized grains. Clay-sized grains, on the other hand, do have the potential to be deposited continually from suspension load in areas of the basin where current activity is low, although only modest currents may be required to retain all clay-sized grains in suspension.

The rate of deposition of sand-sized grains is many orders of magnitude greater than the rate of subsidence of the depositional surface. Clastic deposits, therefore, actually become part of, and modify, the depositional surface. Gradual thickness changes in a clastic sequence—not due to a primary deposition shape effect—imply a gap or unconformity at the sequence's top and most likely at its base. Clay deposits, on the other hand, have depositional rates (ranging from a few meters to a few tens of meters per million years) comparable to subsidence rates, or rates of downwarp and tilting, and, generally, do not have so great an effect on the shape of the depositional surface. Clay sequences, unlike clastic sequences, can thicken laterally due to differential subsidence without involving major bounding or major internal unconformities (fig. 4.8). Chemical and biological deposits also share this property. We can deduce from these very simplified considerations that lateral change from sand-to clay-sized grain deposits has not only lithological but also very significant time implications, and that sandier sequences contain greater gaps than do fine-grained sequences. The idea is not new or original and has received growing attention in recent years.

Ager (1983) sees the stratigraphic record as "a lot of holes tied together with sediment." Dott (1982) and Ager (1983) discuss the importance of the episodic nature of sedimentation and the resultant gaps in the stratigraphic record. Sadler (1981) discussed the problem of gaps in the sedimentary record and the assumption of continuity of deposition from a different view point. He compiled nearly 25,000 rates of sediment accumulation from a wide variety of environments. The calculated rates spanned more than 11 orders of magnitude. He showed that the longer the time span studied, the lower the calculated apparent sediment accumulation rate, and concluded that this was primarily the consequence of unsteady, discontinuous sedimentation—that is, the sedimentary record is full of gaps. Sadler demonstrates that the completeness of many sequences is probably no more than a few percent.

Where is all this lost time—where are the gaps? The vast majority are to be found at bedding planes. The gaps range from the irrelevant (for our purposes) to the highly significant (e.g., the gap developed at the top of a major clastic sequence recognizable in the seismic section of fig. 4.5). In clastic deposits the bedding planes are almost always gaps. If internal structures, such as cross-stratification, are present, both the upper and lower bounding bedding planes will be gaps—the gaps varying in magnitude along the bedding plane (fig. 4.5). If the internal structure is absent, the base of a clastic deposit (e.g., a single turbidite) may approximate to a time line. The unit's top, however, will almost always be a gap. If the clastic unit is followed by fine-grained deposits, an onlap relationship may be inferred.

In fine-grained deposits bedding planes are generally subparallel and extremely laterally extensive compared to bed thickness. Deposition is almost entirely from suspension load, and bedding planes and lithological change result from lithification, variations in sediment accumulation rate, etc. In these cases bedding planes, approximate to, or parallel, time lines. Gaps, even if geologically significant, will also tend to parallel time lines. From the relationship of thickness to lithology we can also conclude that time lines will be more closely spaced in fine-grained sequences than in sand-sized grain deposits.

The time significance of bedding planes, therefore, is variable. It can range from the situation where they parallel time lines, with the gap at the bedding plane ranging from the irrelevant to the very significant, to the situation where the bedding plane changes in age laterally—an unconformity. The time significance of a bedding plane may also change depending whether it is viewed from

above or below. The bedding plane separating a cross-stratified sand bed below and parallel bedded clays above will have a different time significance depending on whether it is viewed from the sand below or the clay above. From above, the bedding plane will appear to parallel a time line marking the onset of clay deposition. Viewed from below, the bedding plane varies in age, becoming younger in the direction of cross-stratification dip. It all depends on which side of a bedding plane (or reflection) you look at, as to whether or not what you see represents a gap or a time line.

This may all seem far removed from seismic reflections. However, we are now in a position to judge the relationship of seismic reflections to bedding planes and thereby assess the possible time significance of individual reflections. Seismic reflections can only arise at a bedding plane if there is also an acoustic-impedance change. Further, there are the problems of lateral and vertical resolution. To investigate the seismic response of bedding planes in different situations we will examine the most favorable case; that is, shallow depth, 1000 m or 1 s two-way time, high-frequency seismic waves (e.g., a frequency of about 50 hertz), and low velocity (e.g., 2000 m/s). These parameters represent about the best that is likely to be encountered in a working exploration situation. An increase in depth, or velocity, or a decrease in frequency will all have a detrimental effect on vertical and horizontal resolution. For these values of frequency and interval velocity, a bed must be at least 20 m thick (half the 40-m wavelength) for no interference to occur between reflections from the bed's top and base. From 20 m down to 10 m (one-quarter wavelength, the tuning thickness), reflections from the top and base of the unit will interfere. Maximum constructive interference occurs at 10 m, the tuning thickness, for a unit where the reflection coefficients at the top and base are different in sign. At tuning thickness the seismic reflection appears to be a simple wavelet at its maximum amplitude (fig. 2.14). For thickness less than 10 m the seismic response is a simple wavelet of constant wavelength but with decreasing amplitude for progressively thinner beds. For isolated beds around 1 m thick there will be a negligible seismic response. The Fresnel-zone radius for these parameters is about 141 m for an unmigrated seismic section.

In basinal clay or shale sequences, deposition is predominantly from suspension load. Conditions of slow but variable, and not necessarily continuous, sediment accumulation typify such sequences. Often deposition of clay-sized grains is interrupted by "rare event" deposits (e.g., turbidite flows induced by storms, earthquakes, etc.). Bed thickness in this type of sequence generally ranges from a few millimeters to a few tens of centimeters with the exceptional bed being more than a meter thick. In view of the thin-bedded nature of this type of sequence, seismic reflections from this depositional setting are almost always an interference response from several acoustic-impedance boundaries. The reflections will, however, follow the attitude of the bedding planes. Since bedding planes in this type of environment typically parallel time lines, the seismic reflections will not be precise time lines, but will certainly parallel them.

Carbonates and evaporites are a special case of fine-grained deposits, which show the same relationship to seismic reflections and time as clay-sized grain deposits. The exceptions to this, however, would be sand-sized grains of carbonate transported and deposited under the influence of current action and biologically formed carbonate deposits (e.g., coral reefs). Carbonates have relatively low accumulation rates and produce deposits where time lines and bedding planes are usually parallel. In this environment, however, bed thickness typically ranges from a few millimeters to tens of meters or more. Thicknesses greater than the half-wavelength criterion for no interference would not be unusual. In such cases, seismic reflections would follow exactly the bedding planes at the top and base of a bed and so follow time lines or gaps (depending on one's view point of what constitutes a significant time unit).

There are many possible exceptions to this admittedly simplistic view. An example given by Ager (1983, p. 62) of supratidal deposits of the Trucial Coast on the southwest side of the Persian Gulf illustrates how not all clay-sized grain deposits are deposited synchronously across an area. All along the coast here, an algal mat is developed in the intertidal zone. This is formed mainly of blue-green algae and makes an efficient sediment trap. Similar deposits have been recognized in ancient sediments. But if one walks inland across the salt marsh and digs a hole, the same algal mat can be found, buried beneath wind-blown sand, with layers of anhydrite and gypsum. In fact, inland for several miles there is a direct continuation of the algal mat that is forming on the present-day beach. Carbon-14 dating from a layer more than 6 km inland has proved the algal mat to be around 4000 years old (Evans and Bush, 1969). In other words, 4000 years of diachronism in 6 km! At this rate, in half a million years—almost negligible in geological terms—the algal mat could extend some 800 km. Seismic reflections from bedding planes at the top or base of such units would parallel the lithogical boundaries but be unconformities.

In clastic environments the potential for complex relationships between seismic reflections, lithology, and time are even more likely. There is potential for reflections to follow both time lines and gaps. For example, in a turbidite basin the reflections from the base of a thick turbidite body could follow a time line.

In other depositional environments, especially in shallow water above storm wave base, reworking is a major factor. In these environments individual units tend not to be as extensive laterally as are typical deposits from deep-

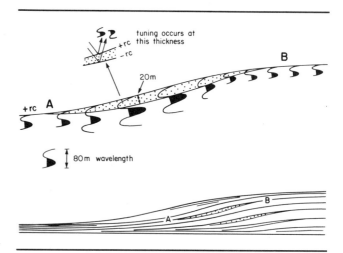

FIGURE 4.9 *Seismic response of clastic units in a shallow-water prograding sequence. Within the range of typical seismic frequencies and interval velocities, most individual shallow-water clastic units must be thinner than the half-wavelength limit for no interference between reflections from the unit's top and base.*

water environments. In a most favorable exploration situation, with a seismic waveform frequency of 50 Hz and an interval velocity of 2000 m/s, no interference occurs for beds more than 20 m thick and tuning thickness for beds about 10 m thick. The thickness of individual clastic bodies is usually less than 20 m and is frequently less than 10 m. Significantly, pinch-out of such clastic units occurs typically in the thickness range between ¼ wavelength and ¹⁄₃₀ wavelength (the minimum thickness typically needed to register a seismic response), where all the thickness detail is contained within the amplitude of an invariant waveform (fig. 4.9). From this we can predict that lateral facies thickness change in a shallow-water clastic environment will be usually expressed by changes in reflection amplitude and continuity. The invariant waveform will preclude an appreciation of the pinch-out shape for units thinner than the tuning thickness. This makes it unlikely that lateral facies change will actually produce a discrete reflection. Individual units are generally too thin to produce a detectable shape in the seismic and, even if thick enough, Fresnel-zone effects will further mask lateral change on unmigrated sections.

To sum up, we can conclude that:

1. Seismic reflections tend to be generated from upper and lower surfaces of units and tend to follow a mixture of gaps and time lines. If internal structure is present (e.g., large scale clinoforms), reflections from both the top and base will both follow unconformities.
2. Reflections follow lithological boundaries but not facies boundaries. Lateral facies change usually results

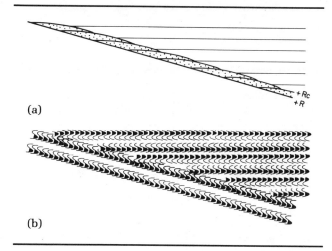

(a)

(b)

FIGURE 4.10 *Coincidental alignment of transgressive sand bodies to produce a seismic response from the lateral facies boundary.* (a) *Geological model.* (b) *Seismic expression.*

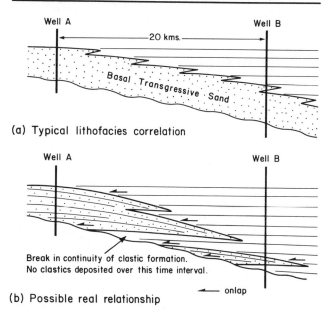

(a) Typical lithofacies correlation

Break in continuity of clastic formation.
No clastics deposited over this time interval.

◄— onlap

(b) Possible real relationship

FIGURE 4.11 *Lithostratigraphic correlation of a basal transgressive sand.* (a) *A typical example of the kind of correlation of sands encountered in wells A and B. Lateral continuity is implied in the diagram.* (b) *One of many possible actual lateral relationships. The basal sand consists of numerous bodies, not all in lateral continuity, onlapped by basal shales.*

in a change of amplitude, waveform or spacing, and continuity.

3. Where thick clastic units form a submarine fan type of deposit in deep-water depositional settings, reflections from upper surfaces and internal structures follow gaps. Reflections from the base of turbiditic clastic intervals may approximate time lines.

4. In shallow-water clastic environments, most individual units are so thin that they fall between the quarter-wavelength tuning thickness and the limit typically required to produce a reflection (about 1/30 wavelength). Such reflections will vary only in amplitude as thickness changes.

5. In argillaceous sequences, reflections result primarily from interference and approximately parallel time lines.

It is possible, in special circumstances, that random alignment could produce a coherent reflection following the lateral facies change (fig. 4.10). Even in this case, however, diachronous time relationships between the sands and clays would be inferred.

SEISMIC STRATIGRAPHY

If we accept the points discussed above we must conclude that seismic reflections primarily depict time relationships and that lithological information is primarily conveyed by the reflection attributes. Perhaps the most important conclusion to be drawn from the above discussion is that seismic reflections provide a means of deducing time relationships between deposits of differing lithologies.

Establishing time relationships, chronostratigraphy, has long been the goal of geologists attempting to correlate rock units. However, the difficulty and often near impossibility of actually establishing chronostratigraphic

relationships using well logs or outcrop data has resulted in an alternative approach to correlation using the concept of diachronous rock-stratigraphic units, lithostratigraphy, centered on formations. This is still the chief stratigraphic tool employed in the oil industry; and is a gradualistic, as opposed to a gappist, view of stratigraphy. The formation is a body of rock identifiable by lithic characteristics and stratigraphic position. It is mappable at the Earth's surface or traceable in the subsurface (North American Commission on Stratigraphic Nomenclature, 1983), and is viewed as the stratigraphic expression of a migrating depositional environment. The preeminence of rock-stratigraphic units is enshrined in the codes of the North American Commission on Stratigraphic Nomenclature (1983) and the International Subcommission on Stratigraphic Classification (Hedberg, 1976). The usefulness and applicability of rock-stratigraphic units is, however, increasingly coming into question (Dott, 1983; Anderson et al., 1984). The fundamental incompatibility of (a) a stratigraphy based on the theory of gradual geographic migration of rock facies in time and (b) the reality of a very incomplete and punctuated rock sequence casts doubt on the relevance and use of diachronous formation boundaries to stratigraphy, or as an exploration tool.

The following simple examples illustrate what nonsense stratigraphy based on correlating similar lithologies

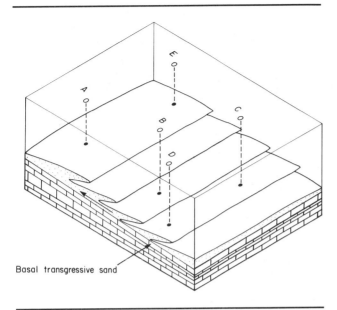

Basal transgressive sand

FIGURE 4.12 *Block diagram showing a series of onlapping basal sands. Only wells drilling sands of the same age should be correlated; for example, A and E, but not A and D.*

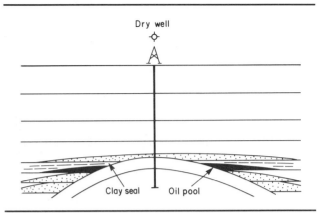

Dry well

Clay seal   Oil pool

FIGURE 4.13 *High structure onlapped by a basal transgressive sand. A dry well has been drilled on the structure's crest, but will only have been a valid test for the entire structure if the onlapping sands are in lateral continuity.*

(lithostratigraphy) can be when applied to typical exploration problems. Figure 4.11 shows a basal transgressive sand above an unconformity. The sand forms a lithostratigraphic unit—it is identifiable as having been deposited under similar conditions, although its age is known to vary; that is, it is a diachronous stratigraphic unit. Unfortunately, the type of lithostratigraphic relationship shown in figure 4.11 is also often taken to imply continuity in both time and space. That is, it is tacitly assumed that the depositional environments gradually migrated across the unconformity surface, continuously depositing a sheet of sand with their passage. While it is unquestionably useful to identify depositional environments and ascertain their influence on reservoir properties, it is quite another matter to infer continuity of deposition and continuity of the sand body. The continuous deposition of sand-sized grains is obviously impossible; and we will often be at risk if we assume continuity within the sand body, as is illustrated in figure 4.11. It is also clear that well logs should only be correlated for sands of a similar age. It would be incorrect, for example, to correlate wells A and D in figure 4.12. Log correlations involve recognizing the same units, not merely similar ones. Only the sands in wells A and E, or D and C, should, in fact, be correlated. There is always the danger that by correlating across time lines we may falsely substitute correlatability with continuity. A second example (fig. 4.13) shows a dry well drilled on top of a structure that is onlapped by a basal transgressive sand. The prospect, however, should not necessarily be written off. If the various sands are not

continuous, closure may still exist on the structure's flank. These examples highlight the importance of time relationships and the superiority of chronostratigraphy (time-stratigraphic relationships) over lithostratigraphy.

Seismic reflection profiles have the potential to bridge the gap between litho- and chronostratigraphy. Vail et al. (1977) argue the case for the chronostratigraphic (time-stratigraphic) nature of reflections using examples from log correlations and seismic sections. In favorable cir-

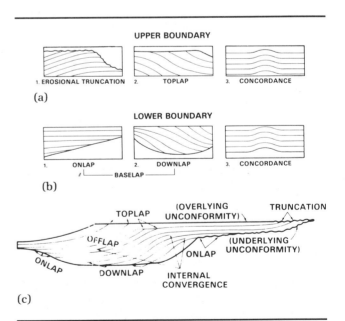

(a)

(b)

(c)

FIGURE 4.14 *Reflection relationships. (a) Relationships at the top of a sequence. (b) Relationships at the base of a sequence. (c) Reflection relationships within an idealized seismic sequence. Reprinted by permission of the AAPG from Mitchum, Vail, and Thompson, 1977, figs. 1, 2, pp. 118, 158.*

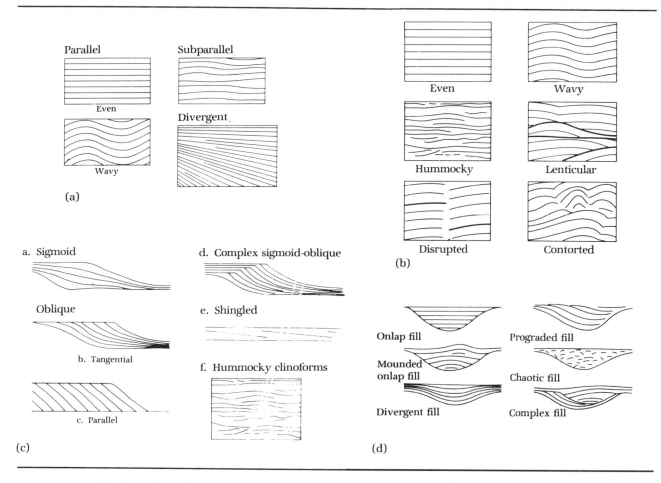

(a)

(b)

(c)

(d)

FIGURE 4.15 *Examples of diagnostic reflection configurations.*
(a) *Parallel, subparallel, and divergent seismic configurations.*
(b) *Modifying seismic reflection configurations.* (c) *Seismic reflection patterns interpreted as prograding clinoforms.*
(d) *Fill seismic facies units. Reprinted by permission of the AAPG from Mitchum, Vail, and Sangree, 1977, figs. 4, 6, 11, 15, pp. 123, 125, 130, 133.*

cumstances, reflection relationships can be used to deduce chronology, whereas reflector configuration and attributes can be used to infer lithology and depositional setting. The previous discussion has focused on bedding planes and beds. But it has long been recognized that the rock record is divisible into depositional sequences, comprising many individual beds, within which the strata are genetically related. Depositional sequences are bounded at their top and base by unconformities and/or their correlative conformities (fig. 4.14). The term *unconformity* is used here in the sense of Mitchum, Vail, and Thompson (1977), who defined it as "a surface of erosion or nondeposition that separates younger strata from older rocks and represents a significant hiatus (at least a correlatable part of a geochronologic unit not represented by strata)." Unconformities are recognized by discordant reflection relationships, and, in seismic stratigraphic jargon, are termed *sequence boundaries*. Sequence boundaries include:

1. Disconformity: an unconformity separating parallel strata where there has been significant erosion. Generally, paleontological control is required for the recognition of disconformities and they are difficult to recognize seismically.

2. Paraunconformity: an unconformity between parallel strata where there has been little erosion. Paraunconformities are also difficult to identify seismically.

3. Angular unconformity: an unconformity where tilting and erosion of strata below the unconformity has been followed by deposition.

4. Other discordant relationships: for example, the progradation of inclined strata across underlying flat-lying beds.

Depositional sequences, lying between sequence boundaries, represent a geologic episode during which the depositional environment(s) and process(es) were essentially constant (e.g., a prograding delta system and its coeval basinal muds). At the level of seismic resolution, seismic sequences approach the duration of standard stratigraphic stages (Bathonian, Oxfordian, etc.). However, seismic sequences are not directly analogous to the

82

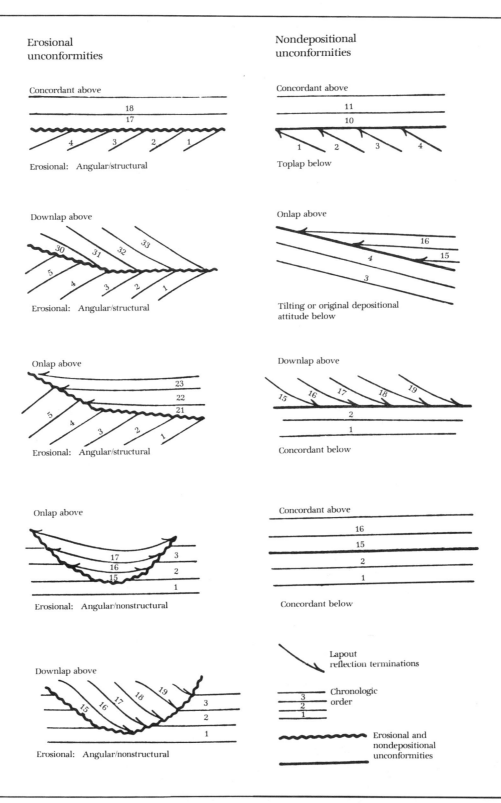

FIGURE 4.16 *Seismic reflection configurations that define unconformities. Reprinted by permission of the AAPG from Brown and Fisher, 1980, fig. 46, p. 82.*

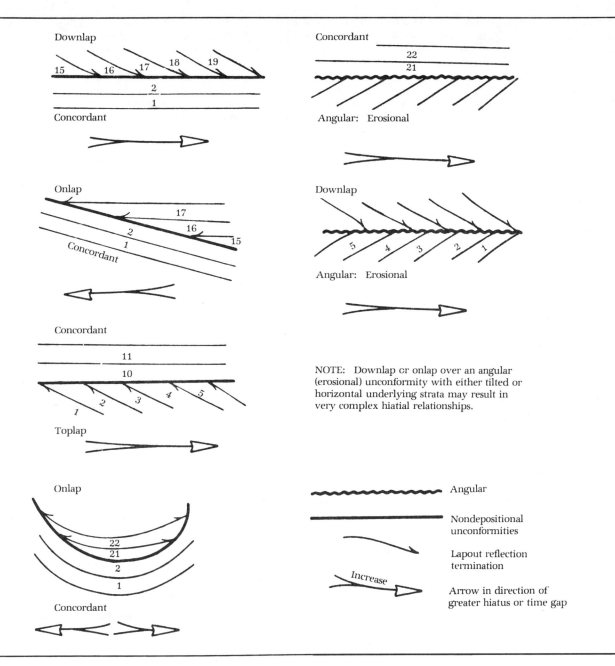

FIGURE 4.17 *Inferring the relative magnitude of a hiatus using seismic-reflection configurations. Reprinted by permission of the AAPG from Brown and Fisher, 1980, fig. 47, p. 83.*

stratigraphic formations, which are based on lithostratigraphy and are commonly time diachronous.

Seismic interpretation using these concepts has become popularly known as seismic stratigraphy and has provided a whole new approach to relating seismic reflections to geology. Brown and Fisher (1980) provide a good discussion and introduction to the topic. Numerous papers in AAPG Memoir 26 (Payton 1977) provide further information. To help standardize this approach and provide a basis for more detailed analysis, a set of terms has been widely adopted to describe reflector relationships. Figures 4.14 and 4.15 display the suite of reflection terminations that define unconformable boundaries to depositional sequences and the internal sequence structure. Fig-

ures 4.16 and 4.17 display possible combinations of reflector relationships and how they can be used to estimate the magnitude of unconformities.

The following description of reflector types is largely taken from Mitchum, Vail, and Thompson (1977) and Mitchum, Vail, and Sangree (1977). Discordance is the main criterion used in determining a sequence boundary. The type of discordance is the best indicator of whether an unconformity results from erosion or nondeposition.

TABLE 4.1 *Terminology proposed by Exxon explorationists to describe reflection terminations, reflection configurations, and geometry of seismic facies*

Reflection terminations (at sequence boundaries)	Reflection configurations (within sequences)	External forms (of sequences and seismic facies units)
Lapout	Principal stratal configuration	Sheet
Baselap	Parallel	Sheet drape
Onlap	Subparallel	Wedge
Downlap	Divergent	Bank
Toplap	Prograding clinoforms	Lens
Truncation	Sigmoid	Mound
Erosional	Oblique	Fill
Structural	Complex sigmoid-oblique	
Concordance	Shingled	
(no termination)	Hummocky clinoform	
	Chaotic	
	Reflection-free	
	Modifying terms	
	Even Hummocky	
	Wavy Lenticular	
	Regular Disrupted	
	Irregular Contorted	
	Uniform Variable	

NOTE: Reprinted by permission of the AAPG from Mitchum, R. M., Vail, P. R., and Thompson, S., 1977, The depositional sequence as a basic unit for stratigraphic analysis, *in* Payton, C. E., Seismic stratigraphy—applications to hydrocarbon exploration: Am. Assoc. Pet. Geol. Mem. 26.

Two main types of termination are recognized. Lapout is the lateral termination of a stratum at its original deposition limit. Truncation is the termination of a stratum resulting from postdepositional erosion. These two types can be subdivided into more specific categories, which are described below. Terminations are determined with greater confidence where several strata within a sequence show a pattern of discordance along a given surface. Table 4.1 summarizes the terminology used to describe reflection terminations, configurations, and geometry.

BASELAP: ONLAP AND DOWNLAP

Baselap is a general term for lapout at the lower boundary of a depositional sequence (see figures 4.14, and 4.18 through 4.23). Two types are recognized. Onlap is baselap in which an initially subhorizontal stratum laps out against an initially inclined surface, or in which an initially inclined stratum laps out against a surface of greater initial inclination. Downlap is baselap in which an initially inclined stratum terminates downdip against an initially subhorizontal or inclined surface. Usually, onlap and downlap can be readily distinguished; but later structural complications may necessitate reconstruction of the depositional surface to determine the type of baselap.

Onlap and downlap are indications of nondepositional breaks (hiatuses). Successive terminations of strata at their depositional limits along the initial depositional sur-

face produce an increasing depositional hiatus in the direction of downlap or onlap (see fig. 4.17).

TOPLAP

Toplap is lapout at the upper boundary of a depositional sequence (see figs. 4.14, 19, 23, and 25). It is a form of offlap. Initially inclined strata such as foreset beds and clinoforms may show this relationship. The updip terminations of reflections may taper and approach the upper boundary asymptotically. On seismic sections, the resolution may be such that the toplap lapout interval is too thin to be resolved and the reflections appear to truncate against the upper surface at a low angle. Toplap is evidence of a nondepositional hiatus. Occasionally the reflector relationships can be very complex. Figure 4.25 shows an example of a sequence(s) displaying offlap. Successive offlapping reflectors onlap preceding offlaps. This is a form of toplap and the upper sequence boundary follows the offlap terminations.

TRUNCATION AND EROSION

Erosional truncation is the lateral termination of a stratum by erosion (see figs. 4.17, 19, 24, 25, and 26). It occurs at the upper boundary of a depositional sequence. Truncation is evidence of an erosional hiatus. Sometimes toplap can resemble truncation (due to limited vertical resolution) and distinction between the two may be difficult; but in the latter case reflections tend to retain

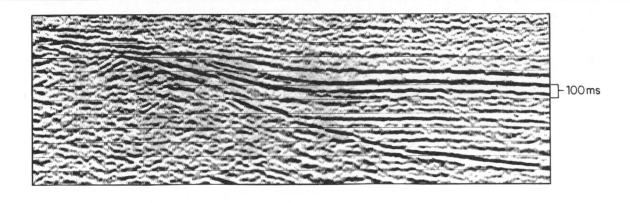

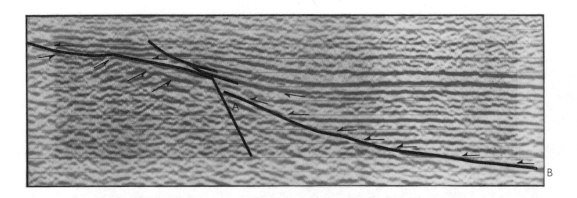

FIGURE 4.18 *Seismic section showing onlap onto a inclined surface. The code shown in figure 7.4 has been used to mark the reflector terminations. Note the possible small-scale, detached, listric, normal fault with associated reverse drag within the onlapping sequence. Courtesy Norsk Hydro.*

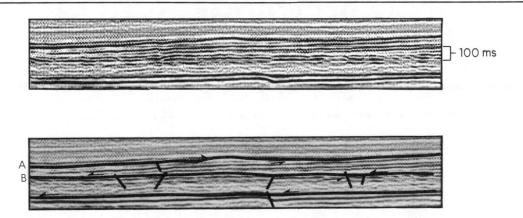

FIGURE 4.19 *Seismic section showing two sequence boundaries, A and B, with an intervening depositional sequence exhibiting downlap onto B and truncation or toplap against A. Courtesy Merlin Profilers Ltd.*

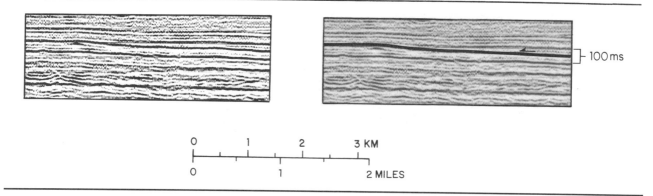

FIGURE 4.20 *Seismic section showing subtle low-angle onlap. Courtesy Merlin Profilers Ltd.*

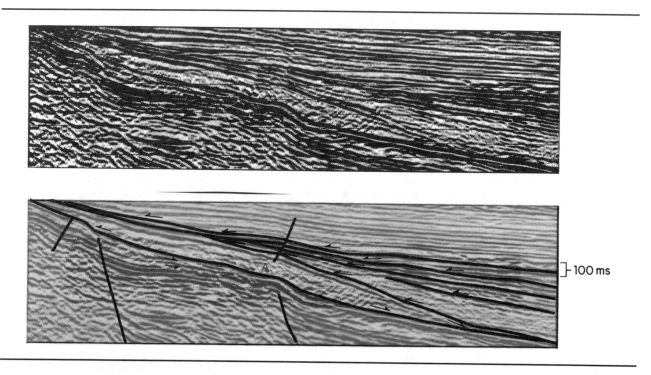

FIGURE 4.21 *Seismic section showing a downlapping sequence A, onlapped by a sequence exhibiting complex internal reflection configuration. Courtesy Merlin Profilers Ltd.*

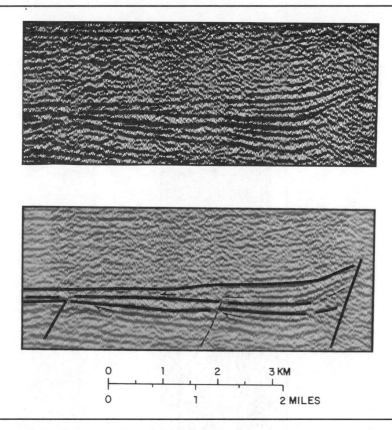

FIGURE 4.22 *Seismic section showing a prograding wedge, developed along a fault scarp, downlapping onto an underlying sequence boundary. Courtesy Norsk Hydro.*

88

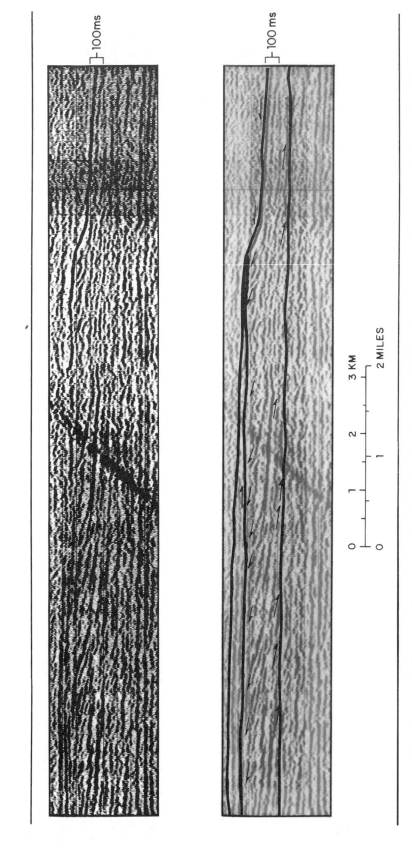

FIGURE 4.23 *Seismic example of a prograding sequence showing toplap, baselap, sigmoidal clinoform pattern, and onlap onto the foreset edge of the sequence. Courtesy Saga Petroleum*

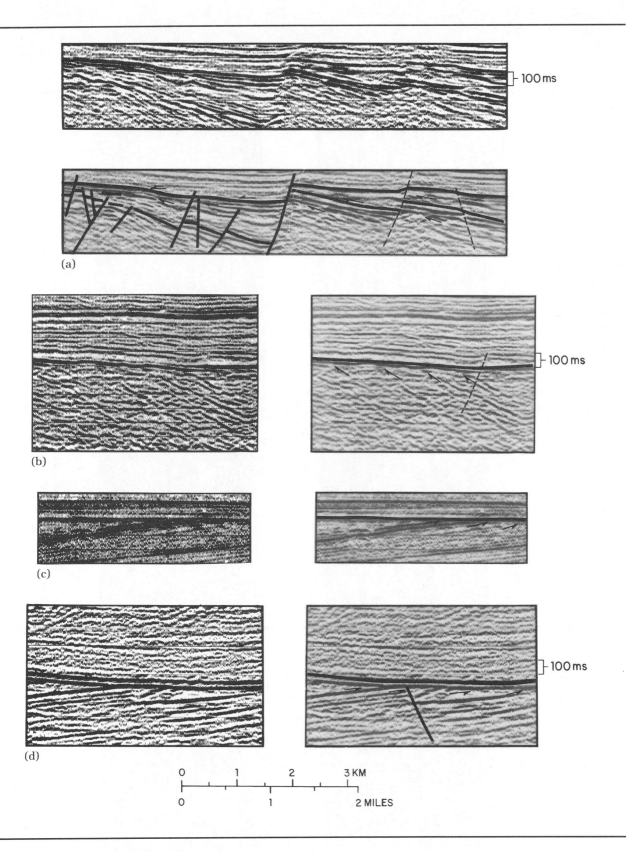

FIGURE 4.24 *Seismic examples of erosional truncation.* a, b, *and* d, *courtesy Merlin Profilers Ltd.;* c, *courtesy Norsk Hydro.*

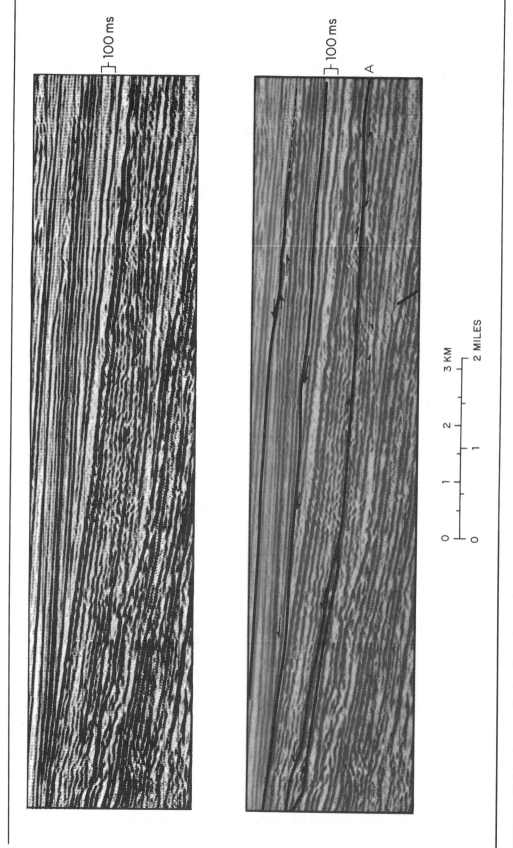

FIGURE 4.25 *Seismic example showing onlap and truncation associated with an inclined sequence boundary A. Courtesy Merlin Profilers Ltd.*

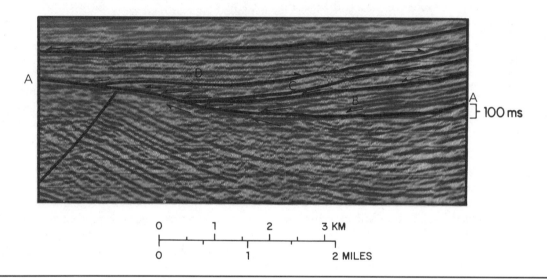

FIGURE 4.26 *Seismic example showing a subcrop sequence truncated beneath an unconformity A, which is downlapped by sequences B and C. Sequence C is onlapped from the left by sequence D. Courtesy Merlin Profilers Ltd.*

parallelism as they terminate abruptly against the upper boundary rather than taper to it.

Both apparent truncation and hiatus of a stratum can also occur by structural disruption. The truncation can be produced by faulting, slumping, salt intrusion, igneous intrusion, etc. Distinction between structural and erosional truncation may be difficult but should be attempted. Although structural truncation may produce discordant reflections and appear to be a sequence boundary, such a disruption has minor, if any, regional chronostratigraphic significance with respect to unconformities and hiatuses.

SEISMIC FACIES ANALYSIS

By combining the analysis of stratal relationships with the attributes of the individual reflection, it is often possible to build up a quite detailed picture of the subsurface geology. The attitude, continuity, pinchout, lapout, or truncation of reflections permit the interpreter to use the seismic section to infer superposition, depositional topography, erosion, nondeposition, and other stratigraphic aspects. Seismic facies parameters and their geological interpretation are listed in table 4.2.

Fitted into this wider framework the attributes of a single reflection, or a small package of reflections, can be grouped into characteristic seismic facies, which can often be directly translated into the most likely lithologies and depositional environment. For some lithologies the external form of the resulting deposit can be diagnostic; see, for example, the salt diapirs in figure 3.33. In most instances, however, the translation of seismic sections to geological cross-sections involves two distinct phases.

First, it is necessary to establish a first-order time-seismic stratigraphic framework by identifying the principal seismic sequences that are correlated throughout the

TABLE 4.2 *Seismic reflection parameters used in seismic stratigraphy, and their geological significance*

Seismic facies parameters	Geologic interpretation
Reflection configuration	Bedding patterns Depositional processes Erosion and paleotopography Fluid contacts
Reflection continuity	Bedding continuity Depositional processes
Reflection amplitude	Velocity-density contrast Bed spacing Fluid content
Reflection frequency	Bed thickness Fluid content
Interval velocity	Estimation of lithology Estimation of porosity Fluid content
External form and areal association of seismic facies units	Gross depositional environment Sediment source Geologic setting

NOTE: Reprinted by permission of the AAPG from Mitchum, R. M., Vail, P. R., and Thompson, S., 1977, The depositional sequence as a basic unit for stratigraphic analysis, *in* Payton, C. E., Seismic stratigraphy—applications to hydrocarbon exploration: Am. Assoc. Pet. Geol. Mem. 26.

seismic grid. This can be illustrated by individual seismic sections and/or by structural and isopach maps.

Second, lesser reflection units and individual reflections within each sequence are analyzed to provide a detailed picture of possible lithology and, by implication from this, lithofacies. Seismic facies are characterized by responses that display distinctive reflection continuity, configuration, amplitude, frequency, external geometry, and possibly interval velocity. Detailed analysis of individual reflections permits a greater sophistication in the interpretation of facies through evaluation of waveform, amplitude, etc.

REFLECTION CONFIGURATION

Reflection configuration is the shape of a reflection or surface. Some depositional environments produce characteristic reflection configurations. For example, a prograding delta produces a characteristic reflection package consisting of subparallel topset reflections, inclined foreset or clinoforms, and subparallel bottomset reflections in the basinal area. Lithology can be inferred from the location and the individual reflection attributes. For example, sigmoidal prograding configurations are more likely to be shale prone than are oblique prograding configurations; slumps tend to occur in shale-prone and so on.

The philosophy of, and assumption implicit in, the preceding discussion is that seismic interpretation is not merely a mechanical following of reflectors through a grid, but can go far beyond this prosaic ambition. Seismic

sections interpreted with imagination and intelligence can reveal details of depositional environment, lithology, rock properties, etc. Tables 4.3, 4.4, 4.5, and 4.6, from Brown and Fisher (1980), describe how this approach can be implemented utilizing the relationship between seismic facies, depositional environment, and lithofacies for parallel and divergent, progradational, mounded and draped, and onlap and fill reflector configurations. The approach not only extracts more information from the seismic but can also be used in a predictive manner as an interpretational aid.

An example of a seismic interpretation incorporating these ideas is shown in figure 4.27. The section, from the southern North Sea basin, a minimum-phase reverse-polarity display, shows very clearly elements of the local stratigraphy and the faulting style. Using the two-way times measured beneath shotpoint 2150 as a reference, the following can be observed:

Tertiary: A zone of high-frequency, low-amplitude reflections with poor continuity characterized the upper 435 ms of the section. Interpretation of this shallow interval is made difficult by muting effects of the processing. For instance, the water-bottom reflection is very attenuated. Great care should be taken in using reflection character in an interpretive manner in the shallow section. The effects are partly geological, however, since the sequence consists of Tertiary marine clays with interbedded thin sands and occasional carbonates. A sequence boundary, recognized by truncation of underlying reflections, is present at about 270 ms at shotpoint 2350. The sequence boundary, at around 300 ms beneath shotpoint 2150, is extremely difficult to detect.

Cretaceous: Upper Cretaceous chalk is present from 435 to 520 ms. The top chalk is a sequence boundary—low angle onlap can be seen to the right of shotpoint 2150. The layout of the onlapping reflections can be used in this minimum-phase data to position precisely the top chalk pick at the onset of the black peak (see fig. 7.12). This is exactly where we would expect the pick to be located, as the top chalk reflection coefficient is strongly positive and so should appear as a peak, with a trough follow-cycle, in minimum-phase data displayed with reverse polarity. The width of the top chalk reflection, around 25 ms, can be used to demonstrate a frequency of about 40 Hz for the seismic response at around 500 ms (see fig. 2.15). The character and continuity of the top chalk reflection is extremely stable, a characteristic of reflections from laterally extensive carbonates or chalks. The base chalk, characterized by a negative reflection coefficient (we anticipate a trough followed by a peak) is also a sequence boundary characterized by truncation of the underlying reflections. Notice how the truncated reflections terminate against the follow-

TABLE 4.3 *Summary of seismic facies characterized by parallel and divergent reflection configurations*

Properties of seismic facies	Depositional environments/Settings			
	Shelf/Platform	Delta platform: **DELTA FRONT/DELTA PLAIN**	Alluvial plain/ Distal fan delta	Basinal plain
Reflection configuration	Parallel/slightly divergent; highly divergent near rare growth faults	Parallel/slightly divergent on shelf; highly divergent near growth faults in deep-water deltas	Parallel, generally grades basinward into delta plain or into shelf/platform facies	Parallel/slightly divergent; may grade laterally into divergent fills or mounds
Lithofacies and composition	Alternating neritic limestone and shale; rare sandstone; undaform deposits	Shallow marine delta front sandstone/shale grading upward into subaerial delta plain shale, coal, sandstone channels; prodelta facies excluded except where toplap is absent; undaform deposits	Meanderbelt and channel-fill sandstone and floodbasin mudstone; marine reworked fan delta sandstones/profan shale; undaform deposits	Alternating hemipelagic clays and siltstone; calcareous and terrigenous composition; fondoform deposits
Geometry and structure	Sheetlike to wedge-shaped or tabular; very stable setting; uniform subsidence	Sheetlike to wedge-shaped or tabular on shelf-prismatic to lenticular basinward of subjacent shelf edge with growth faults and roll-over anticlines; relatively stable, uniform subsidence on shelf; rapid subsidence and faulting in deep-water delta	Sheetlike to wedge-shaped (individually elongate ribbons or lobes), commonly tilted and eroded	Sheetlike to wedge-shaped; may be slightly wavy or draped over subjacent mounds; generally stable to uniform subsidence; may grade laterally into active structural areas
Lateral relationships	May grade landward into coastal facies and basinward into shelf-margin carbonate facies; local carbonate mounds	May grade landward into alluvial systems and basinward into prodelta/slope clinoforms (on shelf) or growth-faulted prodelta/slope facies (deep-water setting)	Grade landward into reflection-free, high sandstone facies; alluvial facies grade basinward into upper delta plain; fan delta facies grade basinward into shelf/platform or into slope clinoforms	Commonly grades shelfward into mounded turbidites, or slope clinoforms; may grade laterally into deep-water mounds or fills
Nature of upper/lower boundaries	Concordant, coastal onlap and/or baselap over upper surface; upper surface may be eroded by submarine canyons; basal surface concordant, low-angle baselap or (rare) toplapped by subjacent clinoforms	Normally concordant at top but may be rarely onlapped or baselapped; upper surface may be eroded by submarine canyons; basal surface generally toplapped by prodelta/slope clinoforms (on shelf); rarely concordant with prodelta on shelf but common in deep-water, roll-over anticlines	Upper surface may be onlapped by coastal facies; top may be angular unconformity; base in generally concordant; fan deltas rarely overlie clinoforms (toplap)	Generally concordant at top and base; may onlap eroded slope clinoforms or eroded mounds; upper surface rarely eroded
Amplitude	High	High in delta front and coal/lignite or marine transgressive facies within delta plain; low/moderate in most delta plain and in prodelta where in continuity with delta front	Variable—low/high	Low to moderate
Continuity	High	High in delta front, coal/lignite and marine transgressive facies; low/moderate in remainder of delta plain and prodelta where in lateral continuity with delta front	Discontinuous; continuity decreases landward	High
Frequency (cycle breadth)	Broad or moderate; little variability	Variable; broader in delta front; coal/lignite and marine transgressive facies moderate; narrower in other delta plain and prodelta where in continuity with delta front	Variable; generally narrower cycles than shelf/platform	Generally narrower than shelf/platform; commonly very uniform breadth throughout

SOURCE: Adapted from Vail, P. R., Todd, R. G., and Sangree, J. B., 1977, Chronostratigraphic significance of seismic reflections, *in* C. E. Payton, Seismic stratigraphy—applications to hydrocarbon exploration: Am. Assoc. Pet. Geol. Mem. 26, 160–168.

TABLE 4.4 *Summary of seismic facies characterized by progradational reflection configurations*

Properties of seismic facies	Slope: ASSOCIATED WITH PROGRADING SHELF/PLATFORM	Prodelta/Slope: ASSOCIATED WITH PROGRADING SHELF DELTA OR SHELF-MARGIN DELTA; OR Slope: ASSOCIATED WITH PROGRADING NERITIC SHELF SUPPLIED PERIODICALLY BY SHELF DELTA/FAN DELTA
		Depositional environments/Settings
Reflection configuration	Sigmoid clinoforms. Progradational in dip profile; parallel to disrupted and mounded in strike profile	Oblique clinoforms. Progradational in dip profile; hummocky, progradational to mounded in strike profile; mounds more common in deep-water slope than in prodelta/slope on shelf
Lithofacies and composition	Hemipelagic slope facies in upper/mid-clinoform; submarine fans common in lower clinoform; generally calcareous clay, silt and some sand (base of clinoform); clinoform deposited in deep water beyond shelf edge	*On shelf:* prodelta (upper) and shallow slope facies (mid-clinoform and lower clinoform); deposited on submerged shelf; composition generally terrigenous clay, silt and sand; sand concentrated in submarine fans at base of clinoform. *Beyond shelf edge:* (1) prodelta and deep-water slope associated with shelf-margin delta; may be growth-faulted; clay, silt and sand (in basal submarine fans); and (2) deep-water slope associated with prograding neritic shelf supplied periodically by shelf deltas/fan deltas; clay, silt and sand (in basal submarine fans)
Geometry and structure	Lens-shaped slope system; poorly defined individual submarine fans and point sources; strike profile may intersect facies to define parallel to slightly mounded configurations; rarely affected by growth faults; represents low rate of sedimentation under relatively uniform sea level rise and/or subsidence rate	Complex fan geometry with apices at shelf-edge point sources; each submarine fan resembles a bisected cone; total slope system lens- to wedge-shaped; strike profiles intersect fans or cones to display complex mounds; seismic facies deposited rapidly relative to subsidence and/or sea level rise; highly unstable slopes associated with deep-water deltas (growth faults, roll-over anticlines)
Lateral relationships	Grades updip through shelf/platform edge facies into parallel/divergent shelf/platform (undaform) reflections; may grade downdip into basinal plain (fondoform) or mound/drape seismic facies; grades along strike to similar facies; may change landward to oblique facies	Terminates updip against base of delta platform or shelf/platform (undaform) facies and may grade downdip into basinal plain (fondoform), or mound/drape facies; may change basinward into sigmoid facies; grade along strike into mounded facies and locally submarine canyon-fill facies
Nature of upper/lower boundaries	Generally concordant at top and downlap (baselap) terminations at base; upper surface of outer or distal sigmoids may be eroded by submarine erosion and submarine canyons; eroded surface commonly onlapped by continental rise facies	Toplap termination at top and downlap (baselap) termination at base; may contain local or minor submarine erosion/onlap sequences; outer or distal oblique clinoforms commonly eroded by submarine erosion and submarine canyon cutting; eroded surface generally onlapped by continental rise facies
Amplitude	Moderate to high; uniform	Moderate to high in upper clinoform; moderate to low in lower clinoform; highly variable
Continuity	Generally continuous	Generally continuous in upper clinoform; discontinuous in mid-clinoform and lower clinoform; may exhibit better continuity near base
Frequency (cycle breadth)	Broadest in mid-clinoform where beds thickest; uniform along strike	Broadest at top and generally decreases downdip as beds thin; variable along strike

SOURCE: Adapted from Vail, P. R., Todd, R. G., and Sangree, J. B., 1977, Chronostratigraphic significance of seismic reflections, *in* C. E. Payton, Seismic stratigraphy—applications to hydrocarbon exploration: Am. Assoc. Pet. Geol. Mem. 26, 160–168.

TABLE 4.5 *Summary of seismic facies characterized by mounded and draped reflection configuration*

Properties of seismic facies	Depositional environments/Settings		
	Reefs and banks: **SHELF/PLATFORM MARGIN, BACK SHELF PATCH REEFS AND PINNACLE/BARRIER REEFS**	Submarine canyon and lower slope: **PROXIMAL TURBIDITIES, SLUMPED CLASTICS**	Hemipelagic clastics: **PROXIMAL BASIN AND LOWER SLOPE**
Reflection configuration	Mounded, chaotic, or reflector-free; pull-up or pull-down common	Mounded; complex and variable	Parallel; mirrors underlying surface
Lithofacies and composition	Shallow-water carbonate biogenic buildups; may or may not exhibit reef-forming framework	Sand and shale submarine fans; complex gravity-failure fans or mounds; turbidity flow; other grain flows, submarine landslides/debris flows; clinoform/fondoform deposits	Terrigenous and calcareous clays (commonly alternating); pelagic oozes; deposition from suspension plumes and nepheloid clouds; fondoform deposits
Geometry and structure	Elongate lens-shaped (shelf/platform edge and barrier reefs); elongate to subcircular lens-shaped (patch and pinnacle reefs/banks); form on stable structural elements	Irregular fan-shaped to mounded geometry; common but not restricted to unstable basins	Sheet to blanket geometry exhibiting drape over underlying surface; common in deep, subsiding basins
Lateral relationships	Shelf/platform edge facies grade updip into parallel/divergent shelf/platform facies; grade downdip into talus and sigmoid clinoform facies; patch reef/bank facies grade updip and downdip into parallel/divergent shelf/platform facies; pinnacle and barrier facies grade downdip into talus clinoforms and to basinal plain (fondoform) facies	May grade shelfward into progradational clinoforms (normally oblique), canyon onlap fill, or pinch out against eroded slope; may grade basinward and laterally into basinal plain (fondoform); onlap fills or drapes	Commonly grades laterally or basinward into basinal plain (fondoform) facies; may grade shelfward into submarine canyon onlap fill; may onlap eroded slope
Nature of upper/lower boundaries	Upper surface concordant or may be onlapped by flank reflections; basal surface concordant, baselapping, or may overlie clinoform toplap; pull-up or pull-down of basal surface common	Upper surface commonly erosional and onlapped, baselapped, or concordant (with drape); basal surface irregularly baselapping; may appear concordant (low resolution), or may onlap (mounded onlap fill)	Upper surface commonly concordant, but may be onlapped or baselapped; basal surface generally concordant but may onlap eroded mound or slope
Amplitude	High along boundaries; may be moderate to low internally; commonly reflector-free	Variable; generally low; some higher internal amplitudes may be thin hemipelagic drapes	Low to moderate; some high-amplitude reflections (well defined on high-frequency, shallow data)
Continuity	High along boundaries; internally discontinuous to reflector-free	Discontinuous to chaotic	High
Frequency (cycle breadth)	Broad; cycle may diverge into massively bedded buildup	Highly variable; commonly narrow	Narrow, uniform

SOURCE: Adapted from Vail, P. R., Todd, R. G., and Sangree, J. B., 1977, Chronostratigraphic significance of seismic reflections, *in* C. E. Payton, Seismic stratigraphy—applications to hydrocarbon exploration: Am. Assoc. Pet. Geol. Mem. 26, 160–168.

TABLE 4.6 *Summary of seismic facies characterized by onlap and fill reflection configurations*

Properties of seismic facies	Depositional environments/Settings			
	Coastal (paralic) onlap facies	Continental rise: **SLOPE-FRONT FILL AND ONLAP CLASTICS**	Submarine canyon-fill deposits	Other deep-water fill deposits: **MOUNDED, CHAOTIC, STRUCTURALLY ACTIVE BASINS**
Reflection configuration	Parallel; coastal onlap	Parallel/divergent; platform or shelfward onlap	Parallel/divergent; landward and lateral onlap	Parallel/divergent; chaotic, mounded onlap
Lithofacies and composition	Delta/alluvial plain and medial fan delta sands and shales; supratidal clastic/carbonate facies; rarely beach/shoreface clastic facies	Sand and shale deposited in submarine fans by turbidity flows; hemipelagic terrigenous/calcareous clays; distal pelagic oozes	Sand and shale deposited by turbidity flow in submarine fans near base; hemipelagic and neritic shale/calcareous clays in middle and upper sequence, respectively; locally may contain coarse proximal turbidites	Sand and shale deposited by turbidity flow in submarine fans; hemipelagic terrigenous/calcareous clays; pelagic oozes; locally proximal turbidites
Geometry and structure	Sheetlike or tabular; uniform subsidence during deposition; periodic tilting and erosion; deposited near basinal hinge-line during subsidence and/or sea level rise	Wedge-shaped lens; may be fan-shaped or lobate in plan view; slow subsidence	Elongate; lens-shaped in transverse section; may bifurcate updip; pinches out updip; slow subsidence	Variable lens-shaped; commonly irregular; reflects bathymetric configuration of structural depression; slow to rapid subsidence
Lateral relationships	Pinches out landward; grades basinward into lower delta plain, distal fan-delta, or shelf/platform facies; may grade laterally into marine embayment facies	Pinches out updip; grades basinward into basinal plain or hemipelagic drape facies; continuous laterally for tens of kilometers	Pinches out updip and laterally; grades downdip into continental rise mounded turbidites, or large submarine fans	Pinches out in every direction
Nature of upper/lower boundaries	Upper surface commonly tilted, eroded, and onlapped by similar deposits; base of facies onlaps unconformity, commonly angular	Upper surface commonly baselapped by prograding clinoforms; basal surface onlaps updip against eroded slope (and commonly outer shelf); may show baselap basinward against mounds or bathymetric highs	Upper surface may be concordant with overlying shelf or platform reflections or commonly baselapped by prograding prodelta and slope facies; basal surface onlaps updip and laterally; baselap onto basin floor rarely observed	Upper surface may be concordant with hemipelagic drape or baselapped by prograding clinoforms; basal surface onlaps in all directions
Amplitude	Variable; locally high but normally low to moderate	Variable; hemipelagic facies moderate to high; clastics low to moderate	Variable; generally low to moderate	Variable; generally low to moderate
Continuity	Low in clastics; higher in carbonate facies; decreases landward	Moderate to high; continuous reflections in response to hemipelagic facies	Variable; generally low to moderate	Variable; poor in chaotic or mounded fill; high in low-density turbidites and hemipelagics
Frequency (cycle breadth)	Variable; generally moderate to narrow	Narrow; uniform	Variable but generally narrow	Variable; commonly narrow; may increase breadth toward axis of fill

SOURCE: Adapted from Vail, P. R., Todd, R. G., and Sangree, J. B., 1977, Chronostratigraphic significance of seismic reflections, *in* C. E. Payton, Seismic stratigraphy—applications to hydrocarbon exploration: Am. Assoc. Pet. Geol. Mem. 26, 160–168.

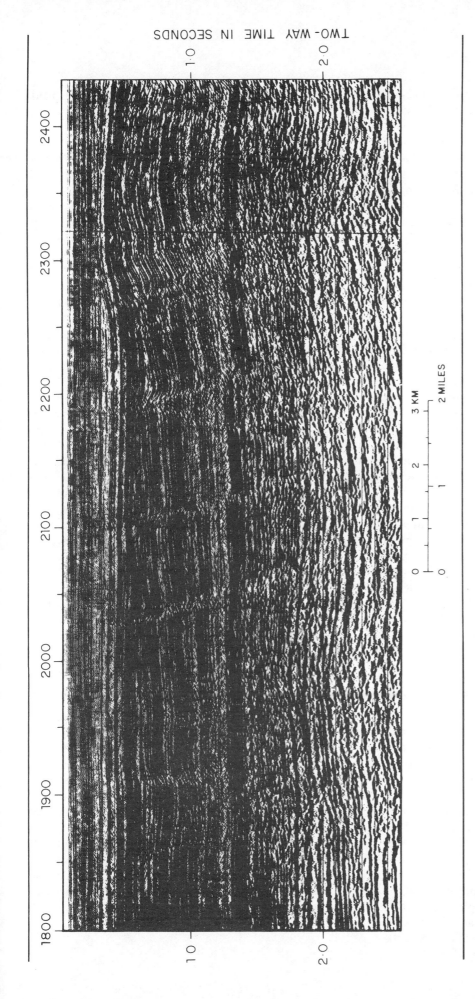

FIGURE 4.27 *Seismic facies interpretation in the southern North Sea. Courtesy Merlin Profilers Ltd.*

cycle peak of the base chalk reflection. Truncation terminations are a poor criterion to use for locating the correct position of a sequence boundary and pick. Apart from the characteristic reflection coefficients, there is little else that can be observed in the seismic section that is immediately indicative of a chalk or carbonate. The interval is just about thick enough, however, for its interval velocity to be assessed from a seismic velocity analysis display (this is considered in chap. 7).

A Lower Cretaceous sequence is present from 520 to 570 ms. The thin interval is identified using the sequence boundaries developed at its top and base. Both sequence boundaries are characterized by truncation below, from which the negative reflection (at least at shotpoint 2150) can be deduced. The thinness of the interval mitigates against the development of characteristic reflections, as does the probable lithology—predominantly clays with some sands. The negative reflection coefficients at top and base of the sequence indicate a lower interval velocity than that of the chalk above and the Triassic sediments below.

Triassic: The Triassic interval is beautifully depicted by the seismic section. In this part of the basin the Triassic is characterized by three intervals during which evaporites and associated carbonates were deposited, the Rot, Muschelkalk, and Keuper. These lithofacies produce packages of high-amplitude, high-continuity reflections which can be picked easily between 640 and 740 ms, 830 and 920 ms, and 1060 and 1050 ms, respectively. The excellent quality of the seismic data enables detailed relationships of the lateral facies to be mapped. The intervening intervals, consisting of claystones, silts, and sandstones produce a less striking seismic response, and it is difficult to recognize individual lithotypes in these intervals without the help of well data.

Permian: The Permian, present from 1285 to 1470 ms, consists of two sequences. An upper sequence (the Zechstein Group) of carbonates deposited marginally to a major evaporite basin and a lower sequence (the Rotliegend Group) of water-laid sandstones and silts. The Zechstein carbonates are easily recognized by their associated high-amplitude reflections. These maintain their character over large areas and facilitates mapping of change in lateral seismic facies. When tied to well control, the seismic facies maps can be used to make accurate predictions concerning the lithofacies of the Zechstein carbonates. The underlying Rotliegend sediments have a less characteristic seismic expression at this locality. The interval is seismically quiet, its base being picked using the low-angle truncation of the underlying Carboniferous (e.g., at 1460 ms, shotpoint 2250). However, toward the basin's margin the Rotliegend water-laid sediments pass laterally into a se-

quence of eolian dune sands. The eolian dune sands have a very distinctive seismic expression.

Carboniferous: In figure 4.27 the Carboniferous can be subdivided into two main sequences; an upper sequence of high- to moderate-continuity reflections (faulting spoils the continuity) that truncate beneath the basal Permian unconformity; a lower sequence of subparallel, low-frequency reflections (e.g., 1860 ms at shotpoint 2100), onlapped by reflections in the overlying interval. The upper sequence consists of Upper Carboniferous Coal Measures which onlap the underlying Lower Carboniferous Limestone. The positive nature of the top Lower Carboniferous Limestone reflection coefficient can be determined from the onlap relationships. The strong top-limestone reflection has a duration of around 40 ms (from the onset of the lead half-cycle peak to end of the follow half-cycle trough) and can be used to demonstrate that the seismic section has a frequency of about 25 Hz at this depth.

Figure 4.28, part of a seismic section through part of a complex shallow-water prograding sequence, shows examples of clinoforms, onlap, downlap, toplap, and truncation. Apart from the characteristic overall shape and internal structure, other important diagnostic characteristics seen here are the changes in amplitude and continuity. Amplitude and continuity are lowest in the basinal area, although reflector spacing is closest there. This seismic facies is typical of fine-grained, parallel-bedded sediments. Amplitude and continuity increase gradually up the clinoforms with some of the highest amplitudes in the upper part of the clinoform zone. Reflection spacing is also at a maximum here. This is the zone where shallow-water sands and silts and more basinal clays have a maximum interfingering. These reflections pass up into the subparallel high-amplitude, good-continuity reflections of the topset sequence, which, in this particular case, probably consists of interbedded sands, clays, and lignites. In detail, the prograding sequence is very complex. The ultimate goal of any interpretation, within the limitations and constraints imposed by resolution, data quality, etc., is to identify individual lithologies. The examples in figures 4.27 and 4.28 show how difficult this can be in practice. Other examples of seismic sections can be found in Brown and Fisher (1980), Payton (1977), *Am. Assoc. Pet. Geol. Memoirs* 29, 30, 32, 34, journals such as *Bull. Am. Assoc. Pet. Geol., Geophysics, Marine and Petroleum Geology,* and occasionally in other journals. It is generally much simpler to identify a seismic facies, typical of a depositional environment and consisting of several possible lithological combinations, rather than to identify individual lithologies.

99

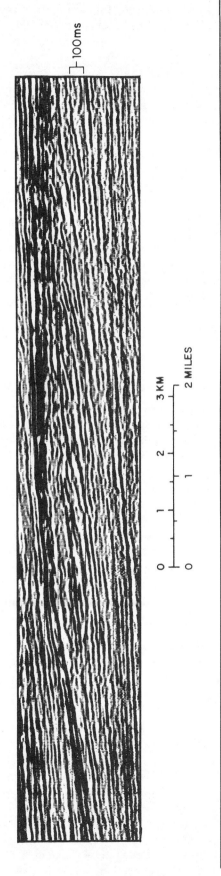

FIGURE 4.28 *Seismic section across a shallow-water prograding sequence. Courtesy Merlin Profilers Ltd.*

RECOGNIZING LITHOLOGY

It is beyond the scope of this book to attempt to provide a comprehensive atlas of seismic expressions of lithology and depositional environments. However, there are occasions when lithology or rock type can be identified with some degree of certainty. The following pages discuss some of the criteria identifying lithology using seismic sections and show some examples of seismic records from fine-grained sediments, clastics, carbonates, salt, basement, and igneous rocks.

CLAYS AND SILTS

Clays and silts include sediments settled from suspension, whatever the depositional environment. Such sediments tend to be thin bedded and produce closely spaced reflections (relative to other reflection spacings for a particular seismic section) (fig. 4.29). If the depositional area is extensive, the reflections generally show moderate to good continuity. Amplitude tends to be moderate to poor, but is very dependent on bed spacing (interference effects) and lithology. Divergent reflection patterns are diagnostic of fine-grained sediments, as they indicate deposition under conditions where subsidence and sedimentation rates are of similar magnitude.

Not uncommonly, acoustic-impedance contrasts are so low that the interval appears reflection free (fig. 4.29a). Alternatively, destructive interference by beds of a thickness 1/30 wavelength or less, can also produce reflection-free intervals. Chaotic reflection patterns can result from deep-sea current activity or slumping, and from flowage due to loading, elevated pore pressure, or slope instability (fig. 4.29).

CLASTICS

Clastics are the group of lithologies that every interpreter would like to be able to identify with certainty, but they appear in a great variety of thicknesses, shape, and lateral extent. They are deposited in all environments. Sangree and Widmier (1977) discuss seismic criteria from the interpretation of clastic facies and Anstey (1980b) devotes a short book to the topic.

Interval velocity is not a good indicator (fig. 4.3). The depositional setting is usually the best guide; and here we rely heavily on configuration, internal structure, and facies association. Assuming that the deposits are thick enough to be resolved, deeper-water clastic facies can be characterized by mounded configurations and/or sheet-like forms. Because of their high accumulation rates, clastics have the ability to modify the topography of the basin floor and thus influence the deposition of succeeding sediments. Figures 4.30b and 4.30c show examples of what are interpreted to be mounded clastic facies.

In shallow-water depositional settings, individual clastic units tend to be thin, often below the thinnest required for seismic resolution, and their presence has to be

inferred from depositional setting and amplitude variations (see, e.g., fig. 4.28). As a generalization, Sangree and Widmier (1977) suggest that oblique progradational sequences are more sand prone than sequences with sigmoidal internal structure. Figure 4.31 shows a part of the edge of a thick (>400 m) shallow-water clastic complex that has a sheet-like form and gently inclined clinoforms. The complex has a tapered edge that is onlapped by basinal shales. In a shallow-water environment, internal structure may be the product not only of depositional processes but also of erosional or reworking processes. Figure 4.30d shows part of the same clastic complex; and, although the interval is about 400 m thick, internal reflections are entirely lacking and seismic character here is totally nondiagnostic.

More typical, however, is the case in figure 4.31a, a seismic section across part of the giant Oseberg field, offshore Norway, where the clastic target interval lacks any diagnostic features. The reservoir interval, middle Jurassic Brent Gp. sandy sequence, although more than 100 m thick, has a sheet-like external form, and is too thin to produce seismic features diagnostic of its clastic nature.

CARBONATES

Normally, reflections from the top boundary of a carbonate unit have a large positive reflection coefficient because carbonates usually have high velocity and density compared to other common sedimentary rocks. Only in cases where the carbonates are very porous or fractured are reflection coefficients of upper boundaries likely to be negative. The usually high interval velocity introduces a potential resolution problem. Not only do thick sequences appear thin in time on seismic sections due to high velocities but the minimum thickness required for adequate vertical resolution can be quite high. Interval velocities between 4500 and 6000 m/s are not uncommon for older carbonate units. A carbonate 100 m thick, with an interval velocity of 5500 m/s, would be represented by only 36 ms two-way time. Alternatively, for a seismic frequency of 25 Hz and interval velocity of 5500 m/s, the half-wavelength thickness for no interference between reflections from top and base is 110 m and the quarter-wavelength tuning thickness is 55 m.

From a seismic viewpoint, carbonates can be conveniently divided into three groups:

1. Sheet-like deposits: These are often extremely extensive laterally and consist of fine-grained carbonate particles or calcareous microfossils deposited from suspension (e.g., micritic limestones, chalk, calcareous claystones, etc.). These deposits show characteristics similar to those of other fine-grained deposits but can usually be recognized by their high amplitudes, good continuity, and—if thick enough—by high interval velocities, which are rarely less than 3500 m/s. Mistaking

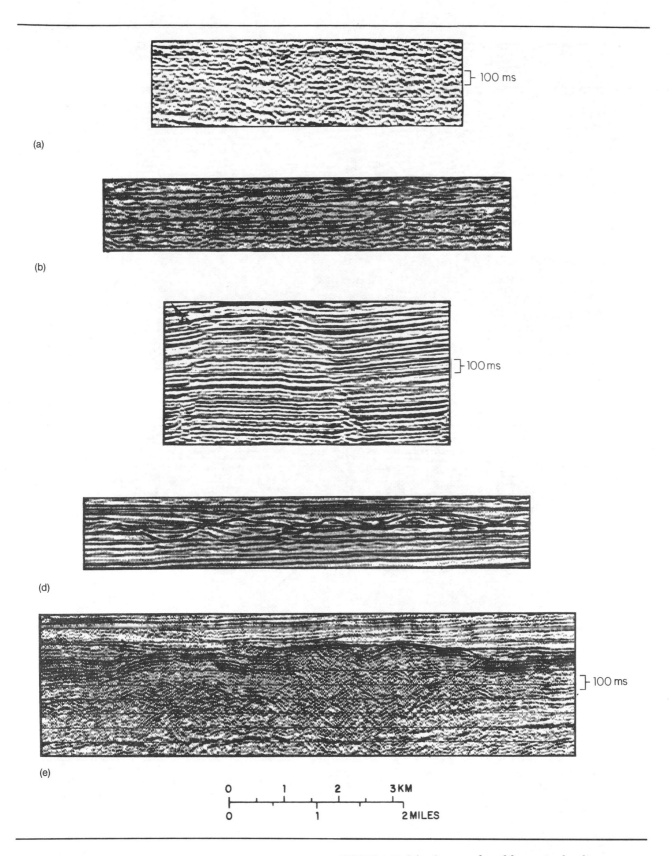

FIGURE 4.29 *Seismic examples of fine-grained sediments.* a *and* e, *courtesy Norsk Hydro;* b, c, *and* d, *courtesy Merlin Profilers Ltd.*

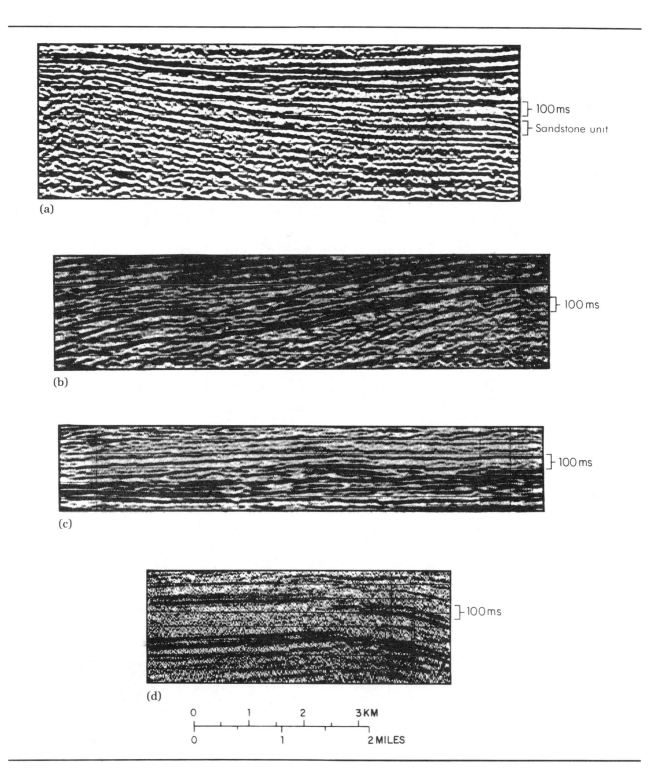

FIGURE 4.30 *Seismic examples of clastic facies.* a *and* d, *courtesy Norsk Hydro;* b *and* c, *courtesy Merlin Profilers Ltd.*

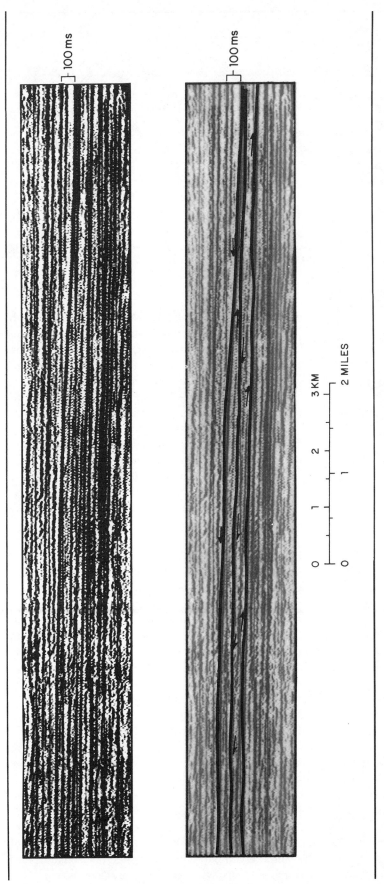

100 ms

100 ms

0   1   2   3 KM

0   1   2 MILES

FIGURE 4.31 *Seismic section across a major shallow-marine clastic complex. The tapered profile is typical of clastic deposits. Courtesy Norsk Hydro.*

Direct

Boundary configuration   Internal patterns

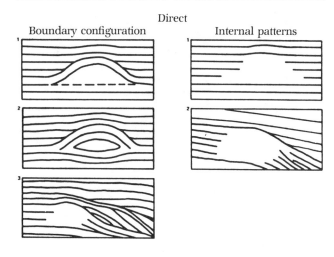

Indirect

Effects   Basin architecture

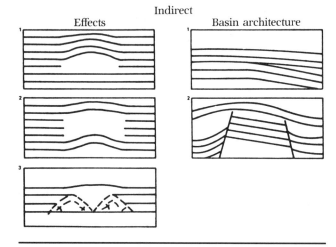

FIGURE 4.32 *Carbonates: Examples of diagnostic reflection configurations. Reprinted by permission of the AAPG from Bubb and Hatlelid, 1977, fig. 3, p. 188.*

volcanic ash or tuff beds for carbonates is a potential interpretation pitfall. Tuff beds have high interval velocities and are laterally extensive, producing a seismic response similar to that of bedded carbonates.

2. Bioclastic deposits: Consisting of sand-sized carbonate grains transported and deposited by high-energy currents, these will have the same form and depositional setting as other noncarbonate clastics. Bioclastics may possibly be identified by their expected higher interval velocity and higher reflection amplitudes. Other considerations, such as the paleogeography and other recognizable associated lithologies may aid an identification. In many cases, however, it may be impossible to differentiate between bioclastics and noncarbonate clastics.

3. Buildups, reefs, biotherms, banks, mounds, etc.: This type of deposit has a large biological element comprising the skeletal remains of living organisms. These

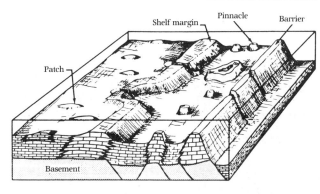

FIGURE 4.33 *Types of carbonate buildups most easily recognizable using seismic data. Reprinted by permission of the AAPG from Bubb and Hatlelid, 1977, fig. 1, p. 186.*

deposits are usually characterized by shape and high interval velocity. Figure 4.32 shows reflection configuration criteria for recognizing carbonate buildup on seismic profiles. Bubb and Hatlelid (1977) subdivided carbonate buildups into four major types (fig. 4.33):

  i. Barrier buildups—tending to be linear with relatively deep water on both sides during deposition.
 ii. Pinnacle buildups—roughly equidimensional features surrounded by deep water during deposition.
iii. Shelf margin buildups—linear features with deep water on one side and shallow water on the other.
 iv. Patch buildups—usually formed in shallow water, either in close proximity to shelf margins, or over broad, shallow seas.

Figure 4.34 shows a carbonate shelf buildup from the Aptian/Albian of Rodessa-Mooringsport Fm. of central Louisiana. The back shelf margin to the north consists of an interbedded sequence of limestone and shales, with a seismic response of parallel high-frequency, low-amplitude reflections. The shelf margin buildup consisting of high-energy porous deposits, has poorly developed interval reflections. The basinal area to the south, consisting of fine-grained calcareous deposits, is characterized by downlap and lateral amplitude variations. Figure 4.35 shows a seismic profile through an Upper Jurassic patch buildup or reef in the Smackover of the U.S. Gulf Coast. The reef, 30–40 m thick, with a lateral extent of several square kilometers, is associated with a dim spot on the Smackover reflection.

A grid of good seismic data, often with special processing and always with meticulous interpretation, is required to define the shape and depositional environment of carbonate buildups. The (often) relative small size of the buildups compared to vertical and horizontal resolution limits is always a potential problem (see, for example, figs. 4.36 and 4.37). Indirect methods, using for example, velocity pull-up or push-down effects beneath a buildup, or differential compaction of overlying layers, can sometimes be used to overcome the problem (see figs. 8.22 and 8.23).

The loss of reflection amplitude often associated with reefs is not always a good indication of lower acoustic impedance and high porosity. Nath (1975) describes how defocusing, by dispersion of the seismic signal from the coastal areas of Silurian pinnacle reefs in Michigan, causes dim spots on the unmigrated seismic sections, due to the convex shape of the surface. The apparent fall in reflection coefficient, in these cases, is entirely geometric and not necessarily related to increased porosity.

SALT

Salt (see fig. 4.38) and associated evaporites are quite common in many sedimentary sequences. Salt has a low density (2.2 gm/cm^3), lower than that of most other commonly occurring sediments. When deposited in sufficiently thick layers, it becomes inherently unstable if it is buried; and a density inversion between the overburden and salt is achieved. In such circumstances, salt flowage is initiated and passes through three widely recognized stages of pillowing, diapirism, and postdiapirism. Bishop (1978) discusses the complex interaction between depositional history of the surrounding sediments and growth of the salt structure. Controversy surrounds the question of whether the dominant processes in development of a salt diapir involve intrusion or extrusion of the salt.

Regardless of the mechanism responsible for salt movement, flow of salt into a growing structure creates a withdrawal basin that is a structural low and an isopach thick. Figure 4.39, a schematic diagram from Seni and Jackson (1983), showing the three main growth stages of salt diapirs observed in the East Texas basin, has more general applicability. The model in figure 4.39 can be used as a basis to interpret seismic-reflector configurations. Diagnostic configurations for the various stages are:

Pillow stage: Syndepositional thinning of sediments over the pillow crests and flanks, developed in response to the pillow's growth, is the most diagnostic feature of this stage. Only minor thickening usually develops into the primary rim syncline.

Diapir stage: Withdrawal of the salt into the growing diapir leads to a collapse of the flanking sequence that thinned toward the original pillow. A secondary rim syncline, its axis immediately adjacent to the diapir's edge, develops above the collapsed area. The secondary rim syncline is usually more extensive than the primary rim syncline and also accumulates a thicker sequence. The thickened sequence in the primary rim syncline is usually outside of the collapsed zone and, in interdomal locations, undergoes passive structural reversal

from synclines to anticlines, the "turtle structures" of Trusheim (1960).

Postdiapir stage: During this stage, diapirs stay at or near the sediment surface (assuming there is sufficient salt for continued movement) despite continued subsidence. A small, often subtle, tertiary rim syncline flanks the diapir.

Not all diapirs, however, pass through all three stages.

The reflector configuration produced by shale diapirs can be the same as that produced by salt diapirs. If reflectors are present beneath the diapir, the two lithologies can usually be distinguished by velocity effects. Salt should produce a pull-up while shale diapirs should produce a push-down on deeper reflectors (see figs. 3.34 and 3.35). In the absence of deeper reflectors, it may be difficult to distinguish the two lithologies. Lohmann (1979) discusses seismic criteria for the recognition of salt diapirs. Frequently, collapse features are associated with postdiapiric dissolution of salt (fig. 4.40). Jenyon (1984) discusses the formation of collapse features above salt structures and seismic criteria for their recognition. Potentially, dissolution can occur in deeply buried salt structures by salt-undersaturated water deep in the subsurface being brought into contact with the salt. Increasing brine density causes gravitational flow and removal of salt (Anderson and Kirkland, 1980). Alternatively, in the shallow section, meteoric waters can come into contact with a shallow diapir or salt layer and cause dissolution. Shale diapirs would not normally be expected to exhibit collapse features. Care must be taken, however, to distinguish true collapse features due to dissolution—from crestal faulting that typically occurs in competent units due to extension—above any type of anticlinal feature.

Interpretation problems can arise in mapping salt-diapir flanks, a common location of potential traps. Reflections from the steep dips or even overhanging walls, typical of salt-diapir flanks, are difficult to record or display correctly on normal seismic profiles. May and Covey (1983) describe how inverse modeling by many methods can be used to reconstruct steeply dipping structures.

Salt, because of its low density, has a much lower acoustic impedance than would be expected from its high velocity. In young basins, such as the U.S. Gulf Coast where salt diapirs intrude relatively uncompacted clays and sands, the acoustic impedance of salt is usually large enough to ensure a moderate positive reflection coefficient. In basins where salt pushes up or intrudes more compacted sediments, the acoustic-impedance contrast between overlying lithologies and salt may be too small to produce good top-salt reflection. This can be a serious problem if potential prospects are located above salt diapirs (fig. 4.41). It is very embarrassing to drill such a prospect and then to find the reservoir interval absent and top salt much higher than expected. In such a situa-

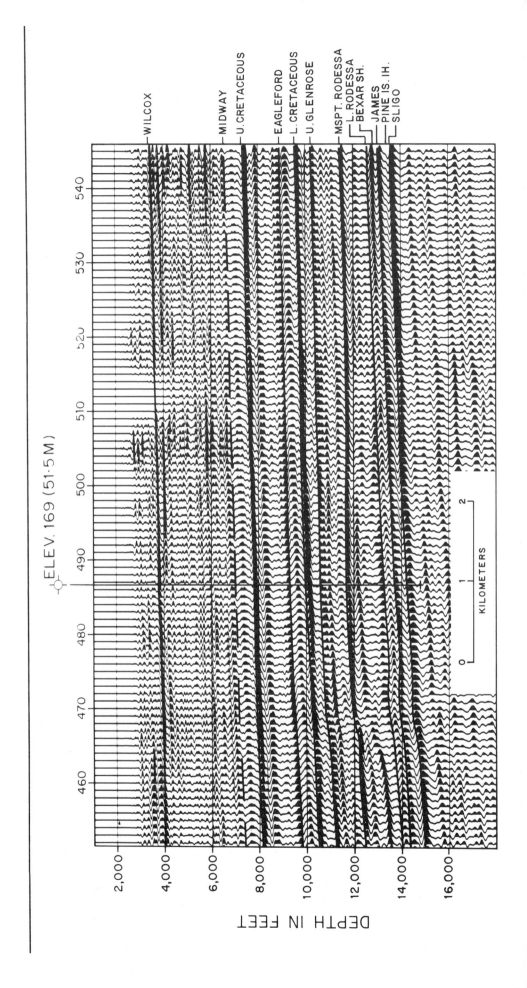

107

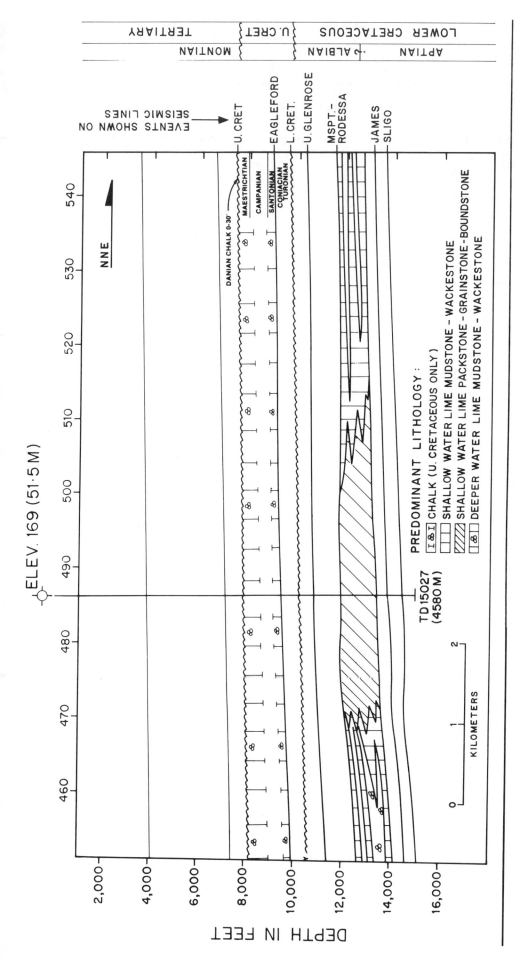

FIGURE 4.34 *Seismic and geological cross-sections across the Cretaceous carbonate shelf, Central Louisiana. Reprinted by permission of the AAPG from Phelps and Roripaugh, 1983.*

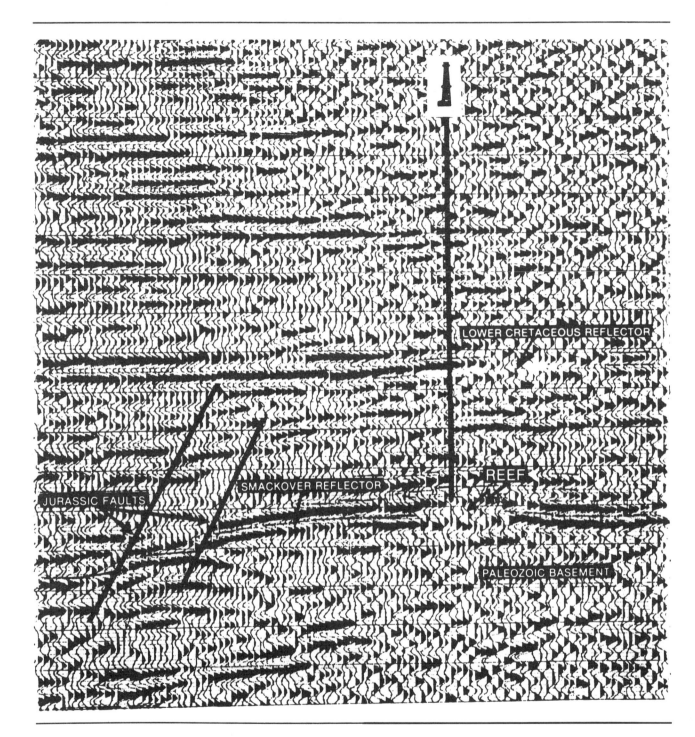

FIGURE 4.35 *Seismic section across porous Upper Jurassic Smackover reef section, U.S. Gulf Coast. The reef is indicated by a dim spot on the Smackover reflection. Reprinted by permission of the AAPG from Baria et al., 1982, fig. 29, p. 1479.*

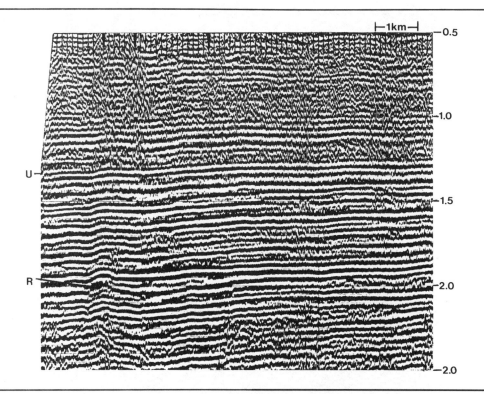

FIGURE 4.36 *Phase section over a reef in Western Canada, R = reef. Note the differential compaction over the reef and velocity pull-up below. The differential compact effects can still be seen to affect unconformity U. Courtesy Seiscom Delta.*

110

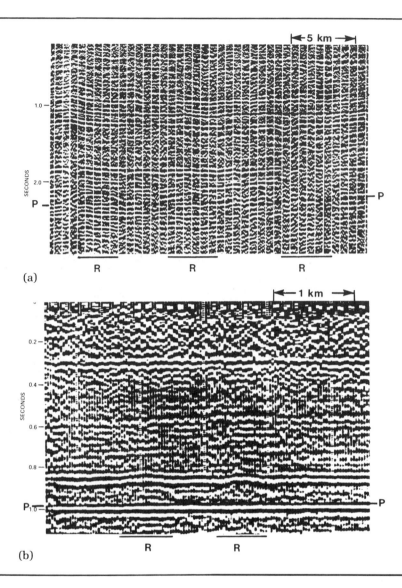

(a)

(b)

FIGURE 4.37 *Patch reefs. The platform on which the reefs grew is labeled* P *and the reefs are labeled* R. (a) *Three African reefs, the one on the right having grown appreciably higher than the two on the left.* (b) *Two small Canadian reefs. Reprinted by permission of the AAPG from Bubb and Hatlelid, 1977, figs. 8, 10, pp. 193, 195.*

111

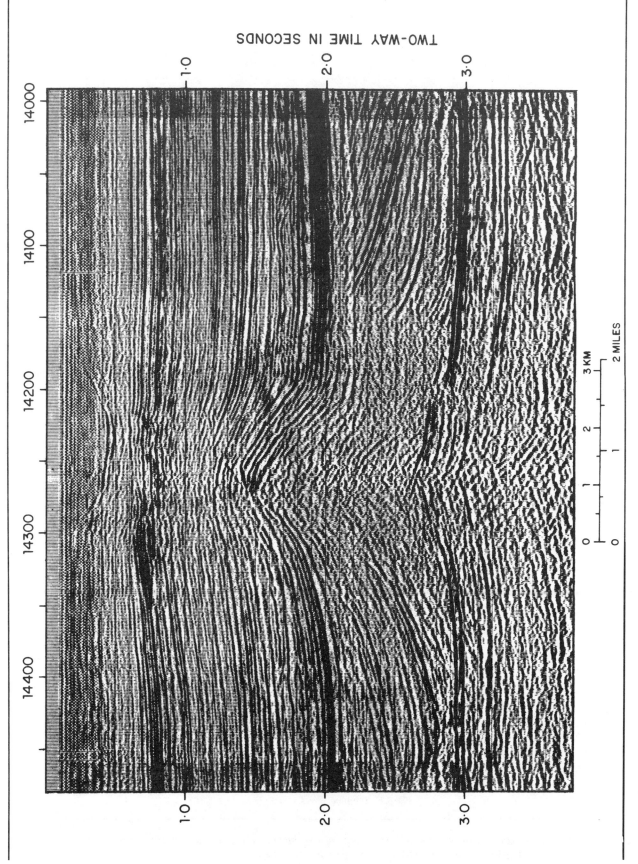

FIGURE 4.38 *Seismic section across a salt diapir. Courtesy Merlin Profilers Ltd.*

GROWTH STAGE	UPLIFTED AREA	WITHDRAWAL BASIN

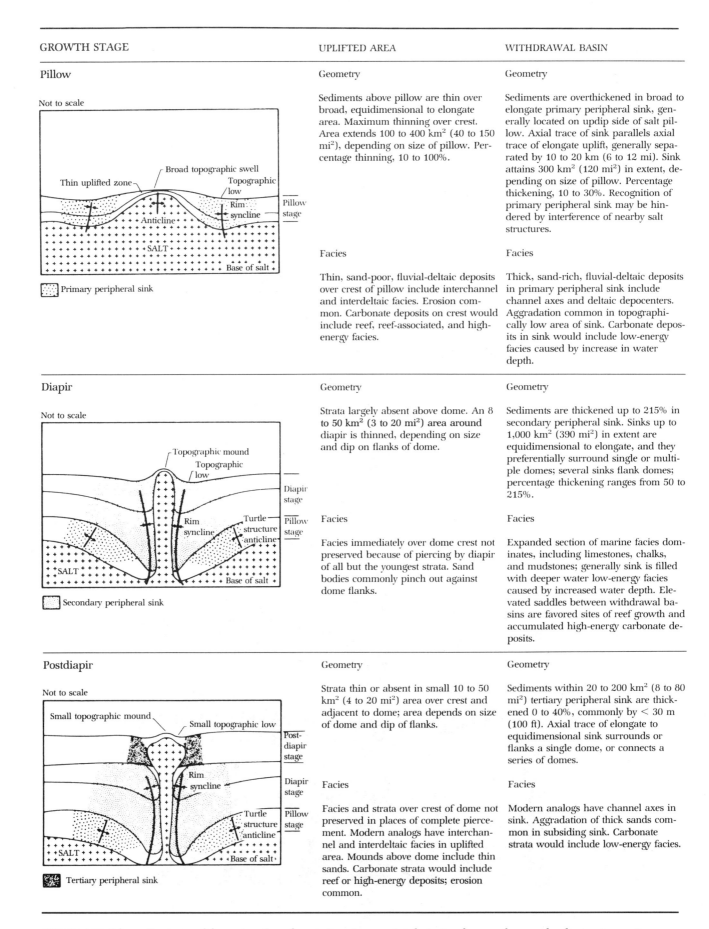

Pillow

Not to scale

Primary peripheral sink

Geometry

Sediments above pillow are thin over broad, equidimensional to elongate area. Maximum thinning over crest. Area extends 100 to 400 km² (40 to 150 mi²), depending on size of pillow. Percentage thinning, 10 to 100%.

Facies

Thin, sand-poor, fluvial-deltaic deposits over crest of pillow include interchannel and interdeltaic facies. Erosion common. Carbonate deposits on crest would include reef, reef-associated, and high-energy facies.

Geometry

Sediments are overthickened in broad to elongate primary peripheral sink, generally located on updip side of salt pillow. Axial trace of sink parallels axial trace of elongate uplift, generally separated by 10 to 20 km (6 to 12 mi). Sink attains 300 km² (120 mi²) in extent, depending on size of pillow. Percentage thickening, 10 to 30%. Recognition of primary peripheral sink may be hindered by interference of nearby salt structures.

Facies

Thick, sand-rich, fluvial-deltaic deposits in primary peripheral sink include channel axes and deltaic depocenters. Aggradation common in topographically low area of sink. Carbonate deposits in sink would include low-energy facies caused by increase in water depth.

Diapir

Not to scale

Secondary peripheral sink

Geometry

Strata largely absent above dome. An 8 to 50 km² (3 to 20 mi²) area around diapir is thinned, depending on size and dip on flanks of dome.

Facies

Facies immediately over dome crest not preserved because of piercing by diapir of all but the youngest strata. Sand bodies commonly pinch out against dome flanks.

Geometry

Sediments are thickened up to 215% in secondary peripheral sink. Sinks up to 1,000 km² (390 mi²) in extent are equidimensional to elongate, and they preferentially surround single or multiple domes; several sinks flank domes; percentage thickening ranges from 50 to 215%.

Facies

Expanded section of marine facies dominates, including limestones, chalks, and mudstones; generally sink is filled with deeper water low-energy facies caused by increased water depth. Elevated saddles between withdrawal basins are favored sites of reef growth and accumulated high-energy carbonate deposits.

Postdiapir

Not to scale

Tertiary peripheral sink

Geometry

Strata thin or absent in small 10 to 50 km² (4 to 20 mi²) area over crest and adjacent to dome; area depends on size of dome and dip of flanks.

Facies

Facies and strata over crest of dome not preserved in places of complete piercement. Modern analogs have interchannel and interdeltaic facies in uplifted area. Mounds above dome include thin sands. Carbonate strata would include reef or high-energy deposits; erosion common.

Geometry

Sediments within 20 to 200 km² (8 to 80 mi²) tertiary peripheral sink are thickened 0 to 40%, commonly by < 30 m (100 ft). Axial trace of elongate to equidimensional sink surrounds or flanks a single dome, or connects a series of domes.

Facies

Modern analogs have channel axes in sink. Aggradation of thick sands common in subsiding sink. Carbonate strata would include low-energy facies.

FIGURE 4.39 *Schematic stages of dome growth and variations in associated strata above and around salt structures. Reprinted by permission of the AAPG from Seni and Jackson, 1983, fig. 4, p. 1223.*

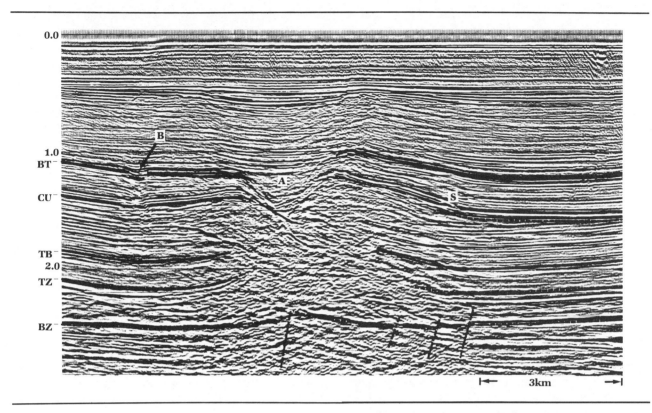

FIGURE 4.40 *Migrated seismic section across a salt diapir and associated collapse feature* (A). *BT–CU, Upper Cretaceous chalk; TZ, top Zechstein salt; BZ, base Zechstein salt. Reprinted from Jenyon, M. K., MARINE AND PETROLEUM GEOLOGY, 1984, fig. 3, p. 30, by permission of the publishers, Butterworth & Co. (Publishers) Ltd. ©.*

tion a possible, though not foolproof, solution to locating the top salt in the seismic section is to use the pull-up on the base-salt reflection, if one is developed (fig. 4.41). For the method to work, it is necessary to know the interval velocity of salt and of the sediments adjacent to the salt and also to assume that the base-salt reflector is planar in depth. In such a situation any structure on the base-salt reflection is assumed to be due to the pull-up effect of the salt. If the difference in velocity between the salt and adjacent rocks is known, the thickness of salt required to produce the pull-up can be calculated from

$$\text{salt thickness} = \frac{t\,\text{pull-up} \times V_L \times V_S}{2(V_S - V_L)},$$

where

t pull-up = observed pull-up,
V_L = velocity in adjacent lithology,
V_S = velocity salt.

BASEMENT

There are two definitions of basement rocks; igneous or metamorphic crystalline rocks; or economic basement, indurated low-porosity, sedimentary rocks that have no reservoir potential. Neither type of "basement" necessarily has a unique reflection character.

Figure 4.42a shows an example of shallow crystalline basement. Beneath the strong top-basement reflection (positive reflection coefficient) the seismic record is reflection free and seemingly dead. Figure 4.42b shows crystalline basement outcropping at the sea floor. The strong internal reflections are multiples. The "ringing" multiples in figure 3.11 are developed in crystalline basement. Crystalline basement usually produces a largely reflection-free seismic response, and so care must be taken that crystalline basement is not confused with other lithologies that can produce a similar response; for example, salt and shale diapirs, basalt flows, igneous intrusions, etc. When deeply buried, crystalline basement becomes more difficult to identify. The top crystalline basement should have a positive reflection coefficient when overlain by practically any sedimentary rock; but weathering of the upper few tens of meters may not only reduce the reflection coefficient but may also produce potential reservoir properties.

The crystalline basement in figures 4.42a and 4.42b is free of internal primary reflections. The presence of internal reflections, however, does not preclude the possibility of crystalline basement. Weathering can produce reflections, as can internal layering or structural zones within the basement (fig. 4.42c). If good internal reflections are developed, crystalline basement may possibly be identified by its high-interval velocity.

Economic basement is more difficult to define, because its definition is subjective. As a generalization, low-porosity indurated rocks will be characterized by weak discontinuous reflections and poor data quality. Weak reflections with poor continuity will be common, because, although the actual acoustic-impedance values would be high, acoustic-impedance contrasts would be small.

Structural closure involving either type of basement can never be immediately downgraded and disregarded. P'an (1982) describes oil and gas fields with basement rock reservoirs from many different basins, for example, the near billion-barrel La Paz field, Venezuela, the fields of the Central Kansas Uplift, etc. Basement reservoirs are characterized by thick reservoir intervals; and, although porosity and permeability are usually highly variable, production rates are typically high and reserves large.

IGNEOUS AND VOLCANIC ROCKS

When overlain by practically all sedimentary lithologies, igneous and volcanic rocks, including intrusive and extrusive rocks, are characterized by high-interval velocities, positive reflection coefficients, and high-amplitude reflections. Very poor data quality is not uncommon. Gravity and magnetics can be invaluable aids to seismic data in identifying igneous and volcanic rocks. On the basis of their geometry, intrusive igneous rocks can be grouped into major bodies—for example, laccoliths and batholiths, dikes (near vertical intrusions); and sills (laterally extensive sheets).

Large intrusive bodies generally produce seismically dead intervals. The intrusive nature of the body may be evident from upturning of the adjacent sediments. Igneous intrusives will not show the secondary rim syncline characteristic of salt or mud diapirs. If, however, only the upper part of a deep salt diapir is visible it could prove difficult to separate the two possibilities seismically. Figure 4.43 shows a seismic profile through the mafic intrusion, known as the Great Stone Dome, 100 km E of New Jersey in the center of the Baltimore Canyon Basin. The igneous stock was intruded into, and deformed, a sequence of shallow-water marine sandstones and shales. The effects of the intrusion, rather than the intrusion itself, are the main features of the seismic section. Uplift and disruption associated with the intrusion are evident up to 16 km away. Differential compaction has caused structuring of the overlying Cretaceous and Tertiary sediments (Crutcher, 1983).

Dikes are more difficult to recognize, as the reflection seismic section is unsuited to imaging near-vertical features. In addition, the lateral extent of dikes is generally not great and may be below the Fresnel-zone size for horizontal resolution in many cases. Linear dikes are perhaps most easily recognized on unmigrated sections, where it may be possible to follow the course of a dike by mapping diffractions from its top through a seismic grid.

Frequently, dikes and sills occur together (fig. 4.44).

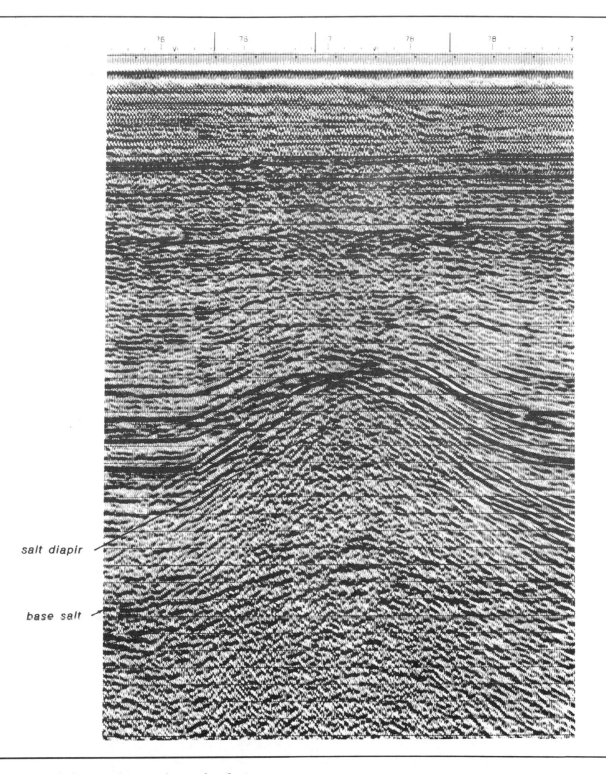

FIGURE 4.41 *Salt diapir without good top salt reflection.*
Courtesy Merlin Profilers Ltd.

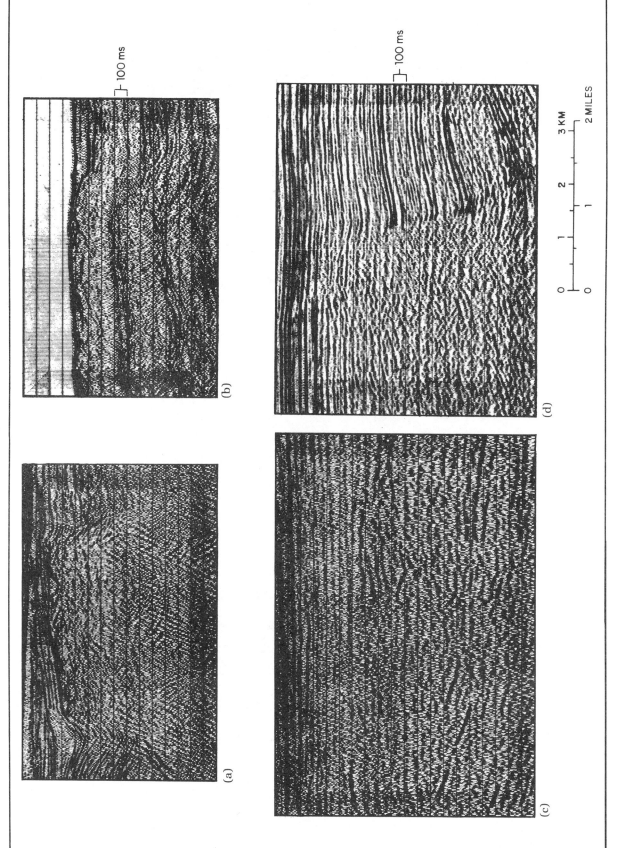

FIGURE 4.42 *Examples of the seismic expression of crystalline basement. a and c, courtesy Statoil; b, courtesy Norsk Hydro; d, courtesy Merlin Profilers Ltd.*

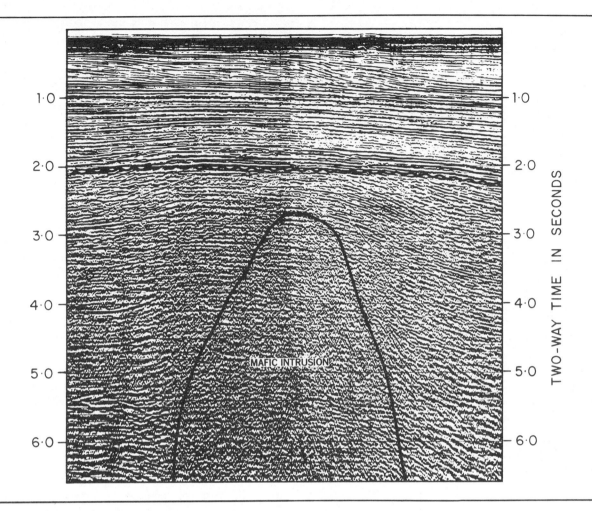

FIGURE 4.43 *Seismic section across the Great Stone Dome mafic intrusion in the Baltimore Canyon Trough off the U.S. east coast. Reprinted by permission of the AAPG from Crutcher, 1983.*

Sills are igneous bodies intruded laterally into rock sequences and are more easily identified, or at least produce a more pronounced effect in the seismic. Sills can be very laterally extensive, covering thousands of square kilometers. More commonly, individual sills are less extensive, with areas of a few tens of square kilometers. Sills can produce a seismic expression very similar to that of carbonates or evaporites. If thick enough, a sill may, perhaps, be identified by high-interval velocities. The best criterion for the recognition of sills is to observe discordant reflector relationships that demonstrate the intrusive nature of the sill (fig. 4.45).

Volcanic rocks are, by definition, extrusive and form three main groups: lavas, tuffs (airborne deposits), and water-deposited volcanic deposits. Lavas can be up to thousands of meters thick and may be difficult to differentiate seismically from intrusive igneous rocks, but they may be expected to show some relationship to a volcanic center or fissure system. Figure 4.46 shows a seismic sec-

tion across the Paleocene Erlend Complex, N of the Shetland Islands in the North Atlantic. The form of the volcano can be seen clearly in the profile, with reflections from the lava flows dipping radially outwards, at up to 20°, from a central volcanic vent. The vent is roughly circular in plan, with a diameter of about 2 km and a depth of 300–400 m. Drilling results show the basalts to have unusually low interval velocities of around 3500 m/s, which Gatliff et al. (1984) interpret to be probably due to the lava pile having been built up by the extrusion of thin flows, each in turn being weathered before burial by the next lava flow. In the absence of a central vent or gravity data, a seismic interpretation of the volcano in figure 4.46 could be difficult. Not only are the interval velocities uncharacteristically low for typical lavas, but the clinoform prograding pattern of the radially outward-dipping lava flows could be mistaken for a prograding sedimentary sequence in situations where it was not possible to demonstrate the overall shape of the feature, for example, with a widely spaced seismic grid.

Tuffs, ignimbrites, and water-laid volcanic clastics will share external forms and internal structures in common with other sedimentary rocks. If thick enough, interval

118

FIGURE 4.44 *Seismic expression of an igneous plug with branching sills. Reprinted by permission of IHRDC Press from Badley and Anstey, 1984.*

velocities may be diagnostic; and such deposits could easily be confused in the seismic section as being carbonates. Figure 4.47 shows a Middle Miocene volcanic mound in the Sea of Japan. Morphologically, the feature is similar in appearance to a reef but consists of basaltic lavas, tuffs, and doleritic intrusions. In this case the volcanic mound is the site of an oil accumulation (Suzuki, 1983), so they are not always bad news.

REFLECTIONS ASSOCIATED WITH HYDROCARBON AND DIAGENETIC EFFECTS

Apart from noise (multiples, diffractions, etc.), attention has been centered on reflections arising from lithological changes. However, an extremely important group of reflectors originates from acoustic-impedance change that is not directly related to lithological change. These are the reflections associated with hydrocarbons and with diagenesis.

GAS

The presence of gas in a reservoir often produces a detectable suite of responses in the seismic record; and it is obviously very important for the interpreter to be able to recognize these gas effects. Discussed below are the main criteria for recognizing the presence of gas on a seismic section.

Acoustic-Impedance Effects. The way in which a reservoir responds to the presence of gas depends on the acoustic impedance of the gas-filled portion of the reservoir, the water-filled reservoir, and the cap rock; and the thickness of the gas-filled interval. If the gas column is thick enough and there is an acoustic-impedance contrast between the gas-/oil- or the gas-/water-filled portions of a reservoir, a

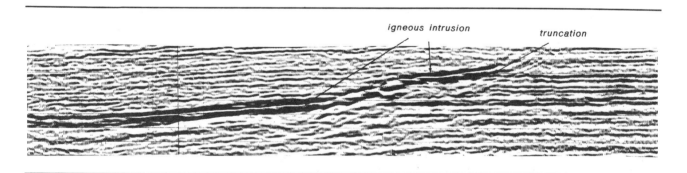

FIGURE 4.45 *Seismic expression of a sill. Note the diagnostic discordant nature of the high-amplitude reflections. Courtesy Merlin Profilers Ltd.*

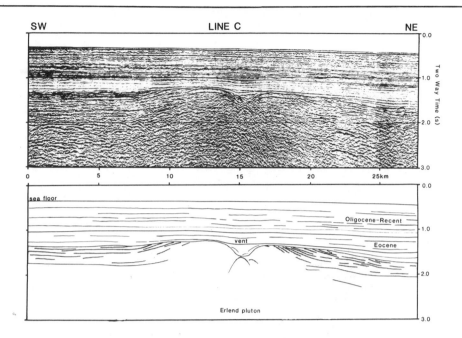

FIGURE 4.46 *Seismic section across the Ereland Paleocene Volçanic Complex, north of the Shetland Islands in the North Atlantic. The form of the volcano can be seen clearly as can reflections from radially outward dipping lava flows. Reprinted by permission of The Geological Society of London from Gatliff et al., 1984, fig. 4 part C.*

reflection commonly called a *flat spot* will result. As a rule of thumb, flat spots are likely to be found in porous sandstones or carbonates down to about 2.5 km. Below this depth the effect of gas on velocity is less marked and the chance of getting a good reflection from a gas contrast is reduced. Flat spots will always have positive reflection coefficients, appearing as a trough on seismic sections displayed with SEG normal polarity or a peak on reverse polarity sections (fig. 4.48). Although gas contacts are usually horizontal in depth, they do not always appear horizontal in time due to the push-down effect of the lower velocity in the gas interval (fig. 2.8).

Flat spots are perhaps the best indication of gas, although other diagnostic acoustic-impedance changes between the cap rock and gas-bearing reservoir affect the amplitude and polarity of the top-reservoir reflection. Amplitude anomalies fall into two groups:

1. Anomalies of very high amplitude, commonly termed *bright spots,* and
2. Anomalies of very low amplitude, commonly termed *dim spots.*

The interpreter should be interested in any local change of reflection strength that does not appear to owe its origin to the geology. Bright spots are usually associated with porous sands. In a typical sand-claystone sequence, the claystone-to-sand reflection is ordinarily positive and of medium strength for water- or oil-saturated sands of poor porosity. The reflection becomes weak or nonexistent with higher porosity. If the sand is very porous and contains gas, the reflection will have a strong negative reflection coefficient—a bright spot (fig. 4.49). While bright spots due to gas are usually associated with porous sands, dim spots due to a reduced reflection coefficient of the top-reservoir reflector are more common with less porous or well-compacted sands and carbonate reservoirs. In these cases the claystone/compacted-sand or claystone/carbonate would usually have a strong positive reflection coefficient. Gas in the reservoir reduces the reflection coefficient, causing the top-reservoir reflector to lose amplitude and dim (fig. 4.50). Amplitude anomalies are sometimes accompanied by corresponding polarity changes. These polarity effects are summarized in figure 4.51. A polarity reversal of the top-reservoir reflector at the gas-oil or gas-water contact is a common feature of bright spots.

Velocity Effects. If the gas column is sufficiently thick, a push-down may be observed on underlying reflectors (fig. 2.8). The differential velocity required to produce a push-down can provide a check on the possible gas column. If the interval velocity is unreasonable, for example, 1000 m/s (3300 ft/s), then something is wrong and the effect cannot be caused by gas alone.

Other Effects. A frequency loss is sometimes observed beneath bright spots. This has been attributed to greater absorption of the seismic wave within gas-bearing as op-

120

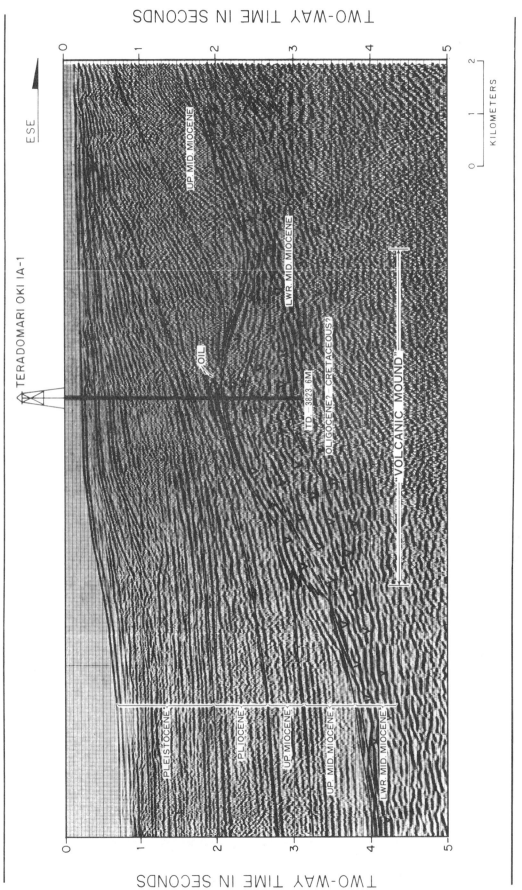

FIGURE 4.47 *Seismic section across a Middle Miocene volcanic mound, Sea of Japan. Reprinted by permission of the AAPG from Suzuki, 1983.*

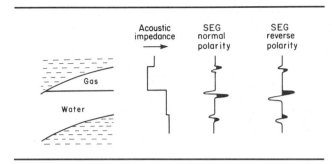

FIGURE 4.48 *The effect of gas on acoustic impedance and seismic response for normal- and reverse-polarity wavelets.*

posed to water-bearing intervals. This absorption selectively depletes the signal of higher frequencies. Both amplitude decrease and increase are sometimes associated with bright spots. Actually, anticipated transmission losses through a gas-saturated reservoir are so low as to be scarcely measurable. Amplitude decrease both above and below a bright spot may be due to automatic gain effects—a processing step to balance amplitude across a seismic section—and merely a response to the extra high amplitude of the bright spot. An amplitude increase beneath a bright spot is most likely due to increased signal levels associated with multiples of the bright spot. However, if a shadow is obvious only below, and not above, a bright spot, it could be caused by transmission losses through multiple gas reservoirs.

Diffractions are developed where there is a significant lateral contrast in acoustic impedance and are often seen at the edges of bright spots. They will not be expected in cases where the thickness of the gas interval decreases gradually. "Gas chimneys" or "gas clouds"—poor data zones above gas-bearing structures—are quite common and can be very characteristic (fig. 4.52). Poor data zones are thought to be caused by scattering of seismic energy by escaped gas penetrating the cap rock above a gas reservoir. Gas leakage into the cap rock can occur through a variety of mechanisms (e.g., leakage along fault planes; fractures; or overpressure exceeding the mechanical strength of the seal rocks. Although gas chimneys provide an easy way of locating possible gas-bearing structures, they also have a negative side. If a gas field is found beneath a gas chimney, pity the poor interpreter who must prepare reservoir maps from the seismic record. Usually, data quality beneath gas chimneys is quite deplorable.

Pitfalls. Care should be taken in using any one of the above effects as the sole criterion to infer the presence of gas. The more effects that can be observed together, the more likely that gas is responsible. Frequently, however, not all of the effects are developed and there are a number of pitfalls:

1. Gas saturation: Unfortunately, it only takes a gas saturation of about 5% to produce a detectable amplitude anomaly in a porous sand (Domenico 1973). The maximum velocity decrease occurs at a gas saturation of about 20%. Sands with such low gas saturations, while generating the amplitude effects, would flow only water if tested by a well.

2. Amplitude anomalies: Not all bright spots are caused by gas. Carbonates, igneous intrusions, thinning beds at tuning thickness, can all produce anomalously high reflection coefficients (fig. 4.53). In the case of carbonates, igneous intrusions and other rocks with high acoustic impedance, the reflection coefficient would be positive (gas should produce a strong negative reflection coefficient) and detectable on a polarity display. However, a tuning-thickness amplitude anomaly, associated with a thinning unit of porous sand could have both high amplitude and a negative reflection coefficient. Coal beds can also generate high-amplitude but negative-polarity reflections. Obviously care should be taken in assessing amplitude anomalies.

3. Flat spots caused by diagenetic effects: These are discussed in the following.

OIL

The presence of oil should have no measurable effect in the seismic record; it should, at best, produce a slight reduction in acoustic impedance. Substituting oil for water has only a relatively small effect on velocity and density. Flat spots are reported at the oil-water contacts of some fields. Meckel and Nath (1977) show a synthetic seismic section across the North Sea Brent Field with a flat spot developed at the oil/water contact. Flat spots associated with oil are not always directly attributable to the effect of oil on the seismic system, but with the inhibiting effect of hydrocarbons on the diagenetic reservoir growth of cementing minerals in the reservoir (Hancock and Taylor, 1978). A number of fields within the North Sea Province show this effect: within the hydrocarbon-bearing intervals the sands are relatively uncemented, but beneath the oil/water contact the sands are well cemented by kaolinite and/or illite (De'Ath and Schuyleman, 1981). The effects of cementation on the acoustic impedance can be large enough to produce a reflection at the oil/water contact. It must be a pleasant surprise to drill a flat spot, expecting gas, and find oil instead.

GAS HYDRATES

Under appropriate conditions water saturated with natural gas can freeze. Instead of crystallizing in the usual hexagonal crystal lattice, the ice crystallizes into a cubic form, which traps gas molecules in voids within the crystal lattice. Gas hydrates are stable only over a limited

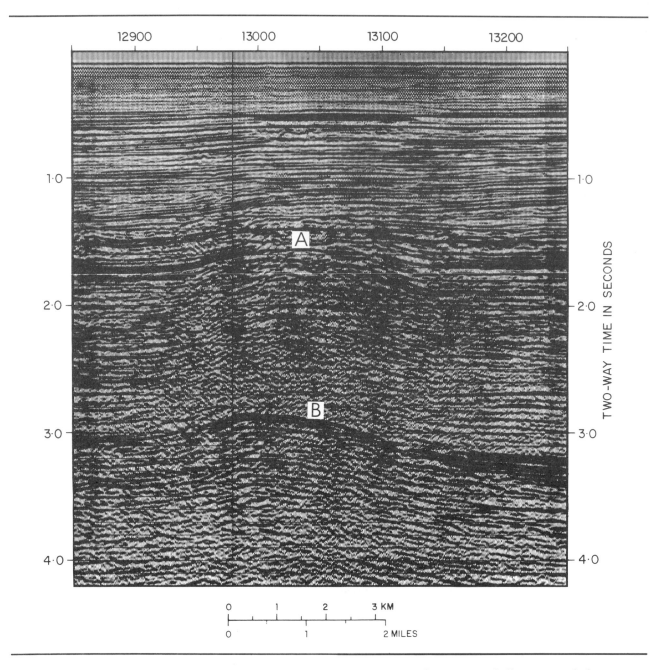

FIGURE 4.49 *Bright spot in a shallow-gas sand above a deeper salt structure. Courtesy Merlin Profilers Ltd.*

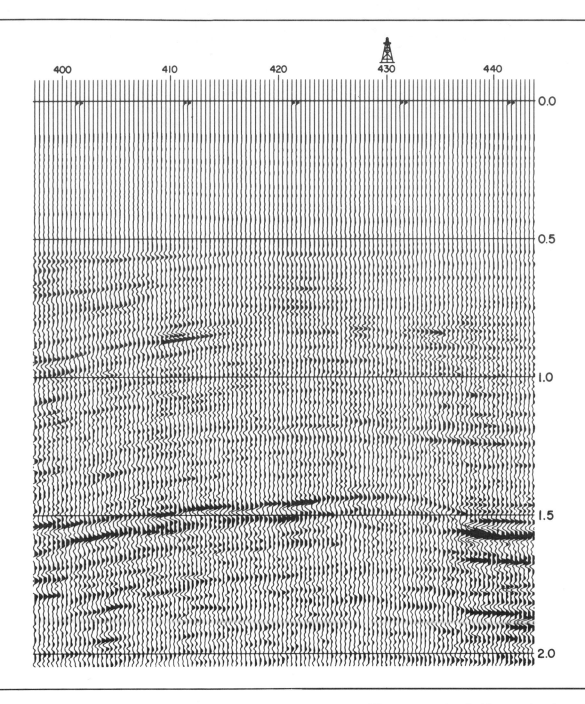

FIGURE 4.50 *Dim spot associated with a gas-bearing porous carbonate overlain by interbedded sands and shales. Reprinted by permission of Teledyne Exploration Company from Barry and Shugart, 1973.*

124

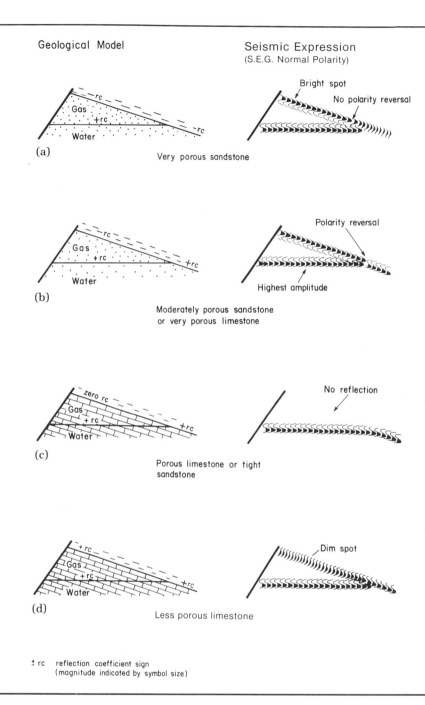

FIGURE 4.51 *Effect of different reservoir properties on the seismic response to the presence of gas. In the example, the reservoir is overlain by relatively low-acoustic-impedance shale. (a) Reservoir of porous sand with lower acoustic impedance than the shale. (b) Moderately porous sand with slightly greater acoustic impedance than the shale. (c) A porous limestone or low-porosity sandstone with greater acoustic impedance than the shale. (d) A less porous limestone with much higher acoustic impedance than the shale.*

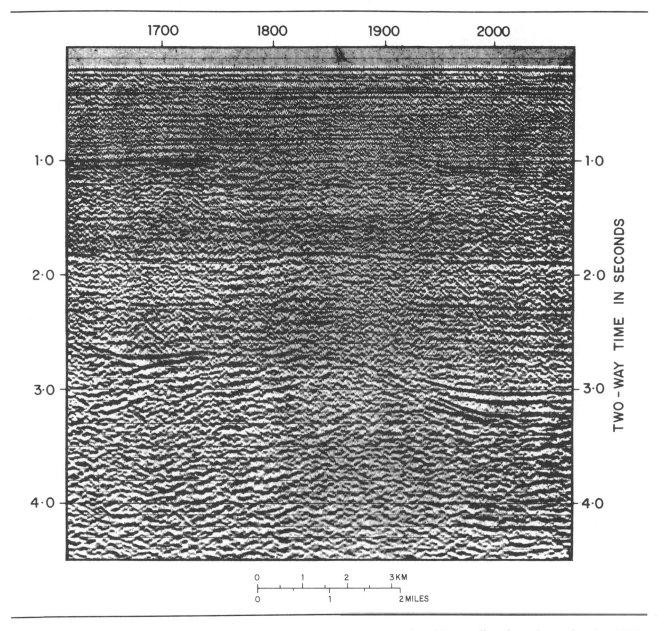

FIGURE 4.52 *Gas-chimney effect above the gas-bearing 34/10 alpha structure, offshore Norway. Courtesy Norsk Hydro.*

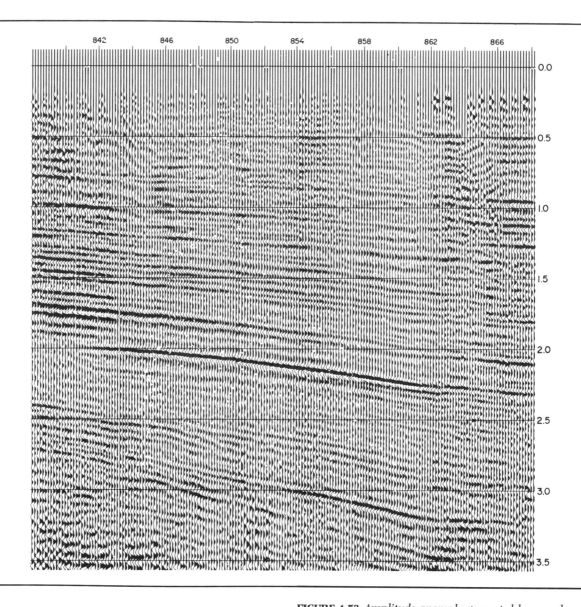

FIGURE 4.53 *Amplitude anomaly generated by a carbonate unit within a comparatively low-velocity sand/shale sequence. The bright spot is not related to hydrocarbons. Reprinted by permission of Teledyne Exploration Company from Barry and Shugart, 1973.*

range of pressure and temperature and their thickness is largely determined by water depth and the geothermal gradient within the gas hydrate-bearing sediment (fig. 4.54). As a general rule the greater the water depth the thicker the potential gas hydrate-bearing interval. Mac-Leod (1982) discusses the factors controlling the occurrence of gas hydrates. Because the reflections from the base gas hydrate tend to follow the sea-floor topography they are sometimes called bottom-simulating reflections or BSRs. Gas hydrates are important for the interpreter because the contrast in acoustic impedance between the gas hydrate and underlying sediments can produce a reflection (fig. 4.55). Gas hydrates increase both velocity and density of the host sediments, and the associated reflection at the base of the hydrate layer has a strong negative reflection coefficient. Interbedded multiples, sideswipe reflections, reflections from slump surfaces, and unconformities can mimic gas-hydrate reflections. Additionally, it is possible to confuse anomalous reflections from the diagenetic boundary with hydrate reflections.

Gas hydrates have yet to be exploited commercially. In fact, their main interest may not be as a source of hydrocarbons but as the seal to gas accumulations trapped below the hydrate layer.

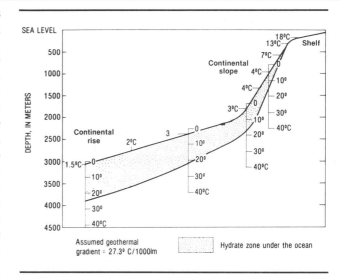

FIGURE 4.54 *Idealized section that shows the zone of gas hydrate stability for outer continental margins. Stippled area is potential region of gas hydrate formation where pressure and temperature conditions are correct for hydrate stability, assuming an adequate methane supply. The following assumptions apply: (1) geothermal gradient of 27.3°C/km; (2) lithostatic and hydrostatic pressure gradients of 0.1 atm/m; and (3) bottom-water temperature range from 1.5 to 18°C depending on water depth. Reprinted by permission of the AAPG from Kvenvolden and Barnard, 1982.*

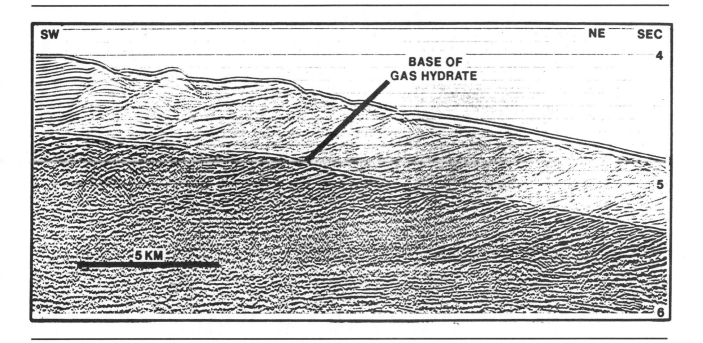

FIGURE 4.55 *Seismic section from the eastern flank of the Blake Outer Ridge. The reflection at the base of the gas hydrate follows the sea-floor bathymetry and crosscuts dipping reflections. The lower amplitude of reflections above the gas hydrate may be the result of reduced acoustic-impedance contrasts in the presence of the gas hydrate. Reprinted by permission of the AAPG from Shipley et al., 1979.*

128

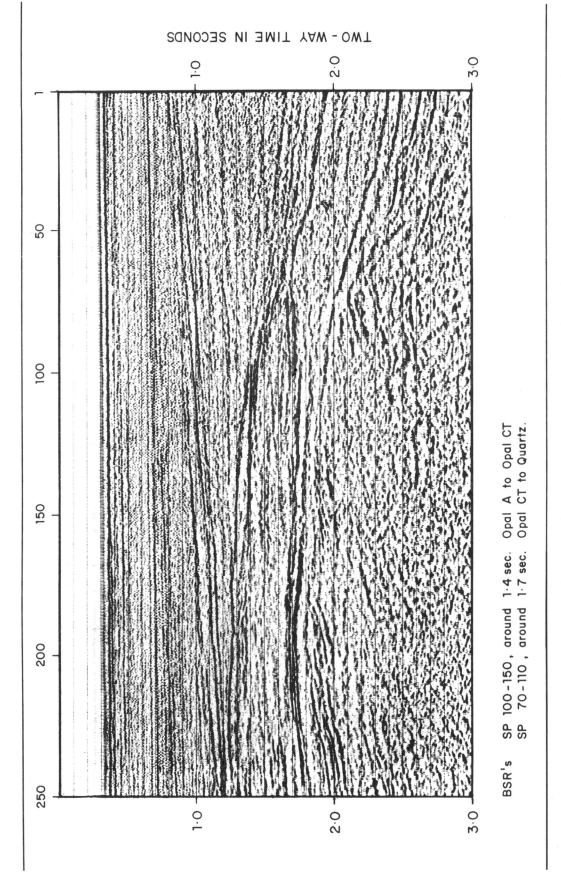

TWO - WAY TIME IN SECONDS

BSR's   SP 100-150, around 1·4 sec.   Opal A to Opal CT
        SP 70-110, around 1·7 sec.   Opal CT to Quartz.

FIGURE 4.56 *Bottom-simulating reflections: Reflections from an opal-A to opal-CT diagenetic front around 1.45 s between shotpoints 100–150 and an opal-CT to quartz diagenetic front around 1.7 s between shotpoints 70–100. Courtesy Norsk Hydro.*

DIAGENETIC EFFECTS

The potential of diagenesis effects to produce reflections has already been described in connection with oil/water contacts. The diagenesis of fine-grained silica-rich sediments, also, may cause an acoustic-impedance boundary. Hein et al. (1978) showed that the dissolution and precipitation of diatom frustules (the silicous cell walls of microscopic single-celled plants) involved a change from opal-A to opal-CT. The change causes a marked porosity reduction, which results in increases in both density and velocity. These increases can produce a detectable acoustic-impedance contrast. Since the change from opal-A to opal-CT is dependent on burial depth, the resulting reflection tends to parallel the sea floor and is another type of BSR. Opal-CT eventually changes to quartz, and the associated diagenesis front may also form a reflection.

The opal-A to opal-CT diagenesis changes are depth dependent, they should, therefore, migrate gradually upward through the sequence with time and burial. Below the migrating front, diagenesis could account for the commonly observed reduced reflection amplitude and coherency often seen below BSRs. Hammond and Gaither (1983) show examples of BSRs from the Bering Sea Shelf. Potential interpretation pitfalls are possible where a BSR intersects other reflectors at an angle, opening the way for its incorrect interpretation as a sequence boundary or even a flat spot (fig. 4.56). In this case it may be extremely difficult to determine that the reflection comes from a BSR. The configuration could show the features associated with a gas accumulation, for example, a flat spot, polarity reversal and edge diffractions, etc.

Chapter 5   Structural Features

Aside from purely stratigraphic traps, nearly all traps involve some element of structuring, even if this only amounts to subtle postdepositional tilting. An appreciation of structure and styles is essential for the interpreter.

The objective of this chapter is to describe, and provide guidelines for the identification of, some of the more common structural features that can be typically observed in the single seismic section—that is, structures on a scale up to a few tens of kilometers across. The correct identification of structures will usually require a grid of seismic profiles. Obviously, it is beyond the scope of this chapter to provide a comprehensive treatment of the topic. However, many other examples can be found in the literature. The AAPG *Studies in Geology Series 15: Seismic Expression of Structural Styles* (Bally, 1984), contains numerous seismic examples, and is highly recommended.

Before describing different structures it is necessary first to review briefly some of the limitations of the seismic method in depicting structures. If unmigrated seismic sections are used for structural analysis, distortions will result from assumptions made by the CMP method; dip will be too low; reflections positioned incorrectly in the downdip direction from their true subsurface positions (fig. 3.20); anticlines will be too broad and synclines too narrow (fig. 3.25), and in severe cases, confusing reflection patterns will result—the bow-tie effect (fig. 3.27), for example. Migration of the data is usually able to resolve many of these problems. In areas of complex structure, however, migration may not be completely successful because of difficulty in evaluating subsurface velocity and severe bending of the seismic raypaths. This latter effect, especially, can invalidate the assumption that CMP stacking produces a good approximation to traces at zero-offset (i.e., the assumption that the reflection point is located vertically beneath the source). In such cases migration will not provide a correct subsurface image and specialized processing techniques, such as migration before stacking (Larner et al., 1983), must be attempted.

Even correctly migrated time profiles are not always

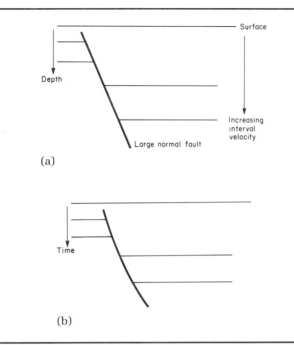

FIGURE 5.1 *The effect of increasing velocity with depth can result in a planar normal fault having a concave-up seismic expression. (a) Geological expression. (b) Seismic expression.*

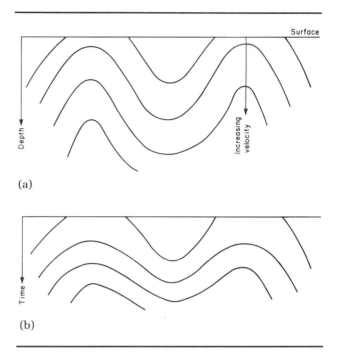

FIGURE 5.2 *Effect of increasing velocity with depth on geometry of large faults. (a) Geological expression. (b) Seismic expression.*

ideal for structural interpretations, due to velocity distortion. Figure 5.1 shows the potential distortion of a fault plane, planar normal in depth, to what appears to be a curved or listric fault in the seismic. This effect is due to increasing velocity with depth. Velocity distortions of folded intervals can be equally severe. Figure 5.2 shows the effect of increasing velocity on a set of large-scale folds. Even on a correctly migrated seismic profile, velocity distortion will lengthen the upper part of the fold limbs with respect to the lower parts, and units will appear thicker in the anticlinal crests than in the synclinal axes. The obvious message in these examples is that great care must be taken to account for velocity distortions when describing structure geometry and style using seismic time sections.

Velocity distortions affect large-scale features, but resolution limitations are equally important for our ability to recognize small-scale structures, especially faults. Figure 5.3 shows a reflector affected by a series of faults with an increasing amount of throw. The throw of the faults is indicated in terms of the dominant seismic wavelength. As is the case for vertical resolution, the quarter-wavelength appears to be a critical limit. Faults with throws a quarter-wavelength or greater are probably not too difficult to pick. Faults with throws smaller than that wavelength produces a diffraction on unmigrated sections might easily be missed. The fault with a throw of only $\frac{1}{16}$

and measurable difference in traveltimes on its up- and downthrown sides. In practice, however, such small faults would be easy to miss in the presence of noise and other reflections, etc.

FOLDS AND FLEXURES

The previous chapter gave examples of the characteristic forms and configurations adopted by sedimentary deposits. Frequently, these original forms are modified and structured by tectonic processes. The most easily observed types of structuring are folds and flexures, which are readily identifiable from the dip changes of reflections. Figures 5.4, 5.9, 5.18, 5.19, and 5.21 show examples of fold and flexure structures. Folds and flexures are found at all scales, from the hand-specimen size, to features tens of kilometers across, and develop under a wide range of conditions—from regional compression, to downbending associated with subsidence, to frictional drag associated with faulting, etc. Fold and flexure structure can be grouped into five main groups:

1. Folds associated with compression on a regional scale due to major crustal processes (e.g., the Appalachian fold-belt)
2. Smaller-scale folds associated with local compression that does not have regional significance (e.g., anti-

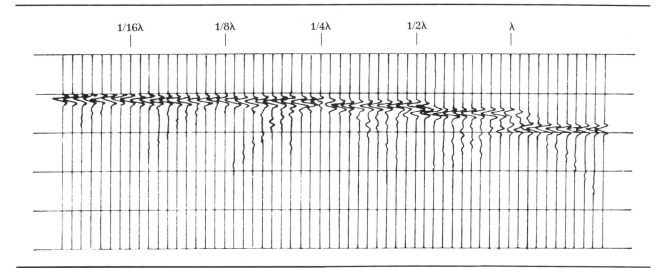

FIGURE 5.3 *Series of faults with increasing amounts of throw. The throw on the faults is indicated in terms of the dominant wavelength. Reprinted by permission of the AAPG from Sheriff, 1982, fig. 51, p. 53.*

clinal features associated with strike-slip faulting; see fig. 5.21)
3. Folding, flexure, and drag directly related to faulting (e.g., rollover anticlines developed by movements on a listric normal fault, as in fig. 5.9; normal and reverse drag associated with frictional forces on fault planes, as in fig. 5.15; etc.)
4. a. Monoclinal folding and flexure of sedimentary layers overlying a reactivated deeper fault or through differential compaction over a deeper feature (fig. 5.15)
   b. Hinge lines associated with basin downwarp
5. Folding or upbending caused by the rise of an underlying intrusive feature (e.g., salt and shale diapirs, igneous intrusions, etc.; see, for example, figs. 4.38, 4.43)

Folds can be described in terms of their amplitude, wavelength, plunge, axial trace, etc. Fold form is dependent on the nature, and layer thickness, of the material(s) being folded. Ductility contrasts between differing materials can produce differing fold styles within the same sequence. Folds developed in multilayered sequences are generally controlled in their distribution and wavelength by the more competent members of the sequence.

FAULTS

Fault-plane reflections are only rarely observable in seismic sections; their location and geometry is usually inferred from reflection terminations, diffractions, dip changes, etc. Basic fault terminology is shown in figure 5.5. On the basis of their geometry and kinematics faults can be divided into three categories:

1. Normal faults
2. Reverse and thrust faults
3. Strike-slip or wrench faults

The following discussion is somewhat biased toward normal faults. This is partly because of their ubiquitous occurrence in practically all types of basin and the relative ease with which they can be recognized in the seismic section as opposed to the difficulty often encountered in recognizing strike-slip or thrust faults.

NORMAL FAULTS

A normal fault is a fault where dip-slip is dominant and on which the hanging wall has moved down relative to the footwall. Unless the fault plane is vertical, normal faulting produces net extension of the faulted strata.

Planar Normal Faults. Planar normal faults (fig. 5.6) are the most common type of fault in most basins with throws varying from a few centimeters to kilometers. Planar normal faults are recognized by the following features:

a. An approximately planar fault plane: the fault-plane dip remains approximately constant with depth.
b. Normal drag against the fault plane: normal drag is not always developed in association with planar faults. Normal drag on the hanging-wall block only may indicate downward movement of hanging-wall block against an essentially static footwall block. This feature is quite common on faults accommodating subsidence within a basin.
c. No dip change of reflectors from the footwall to hanging-wall blocks
d. Antithetic faults (commonly associated with planar normal faults)

134

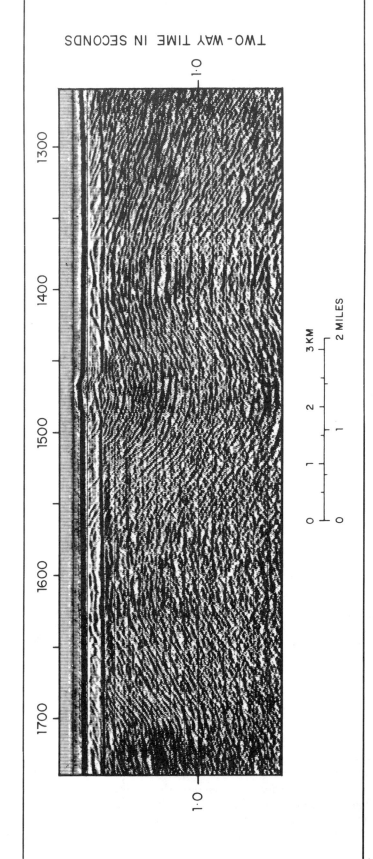

FIGURE 5.4 *Seismic example of large-scale folds with a wavelength of more than 5 km. M is the water-bottom multiple. Courtesy Merlin Profilers Ltd.*

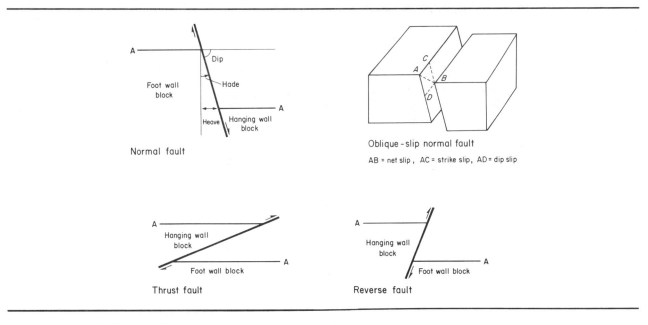

FIGURE 5.5 *Basic fault terminology.*

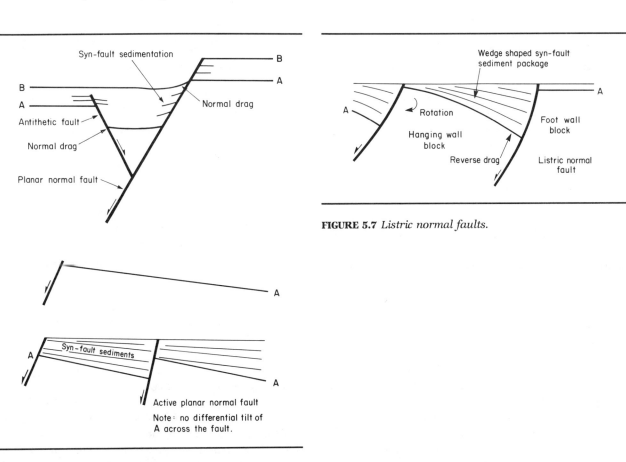

FIGURE 5.7 *Listric normal faults.*

FIGURE 5.6 *Planar normal faults.*

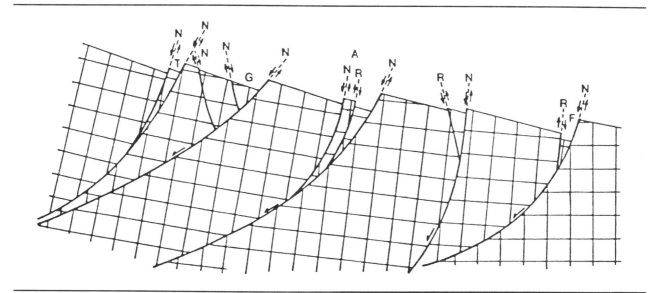

FIGURE 5.8 *Sketch showing progressive rotation across listric normal faults and secondary structures produced by different combinations of syn- and antithetic accommodation faults. Note the crestal terrace (T), graben (G), horst (A), and horst-foot graben (F), as well as the possibility of a number of reverse faults. Reprinted with permission from* Journal of Structural Geology, *Vol. 5, Gibbs, A. D., Seismic sections in areas of extensional tectonics, Copyright 1983, Pergamon Press, Ltd.*

Syn-fault sedimentation, or growth faulting, is commonly associated with planar normal faults. If planar normal faulting involves, or affects, a dipping surface the resulting infilling sediment package will be wedge shaped (fig. 5.6).

Listric Normal Faults. Listric normal faults have a curved fault plane, which enables the hanging-wall block to rotate (fig. 5.7). Listric normal faults are recognized by:

a. Differential tilting of the hanging and footwall blocks
b. Common development of reverse drag of reflectors in the hanging-wall block back into the fault plane
c. Antithetic faults that have developed updip of the reverse drag (Antithetic faults alone are not diagnostic of listric movements because they also develop in association with planar normal faults.)
d. Syn-fault sedimentation (almost always a feature of listric normal faults)

Because syn-fault sedimentation is so commonly associated with listric normal faults, the terms "growth fault" and "listric normal fault" have become synonymous. Strictly, however, the term growth fault can be applied to any fault shown to have had syn-fault sedimentation movements. Many planar normal faults, for example, show evidence of syn-fault sedimentation and are therefore also growth faults. The combination of tilting, reverse drag, and antithetic faulting produces a wedge-shaped sediment package (fig. 5.7).

Listric normal faults can be both basement involved and basement detached. Basement-involved listric nor-

mal faults are believed to be one of the main mechanisms of extension in the upper crust during rifting and are common in rift basins and passive margins. The exact manner in which basement-involved listric normal faults sole out, and the depth at which this occurs, is still open to conjecture. Published studies of deep seismic investigations and extrapolation from observed fault-block geometry indicate that soling out occurs at depths of several kilometers. Complex combinations of syn-faults and antithetic accommodation faults, including the possibility of reverse faults, can occur with sets of listric faults of differing curvatures (fig. 5.8). Figure 5.22 shows an example of listric and planar normal faults associated with a major tilted block in the North Sea rift basin.

Detached listric normal faults occur entirely within the sedimentary cover. They are especially common within thick sedimentary sequences, such as those of the U.S. Gulf Coast and Niger Delta. Their geometry is similar to that of basement-involved listric normal faults, excepting that the faults sole out within the sedimentary sequence (fig. 5.9). Because of the greater fault-plane curvature on these detached faults, reverse drag is also usually well developed, often producing rollover anticlines (fig. 5.9). Detached listric normal faults are adjustment structures developed under the combined influence of gravity and elevated pore pressures (Mandl and Crans, 1981).

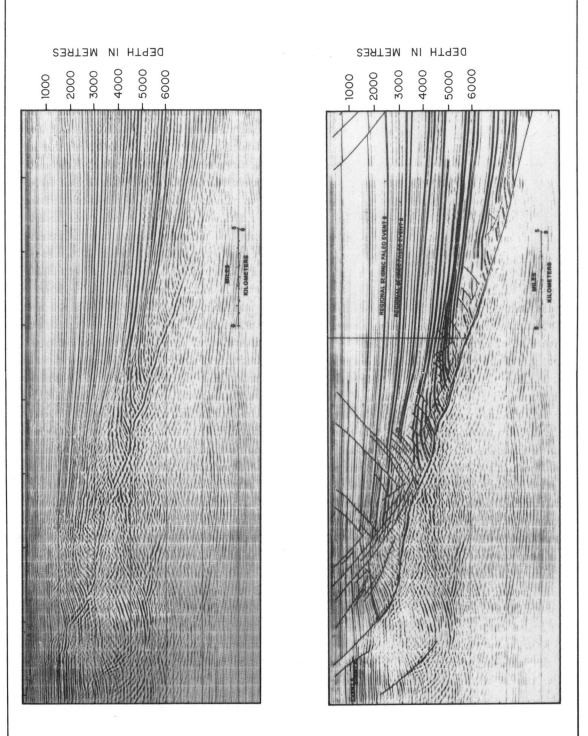

FIGURE 5.9 *Detached listric normal fault (Miocene Brazos Ridge growth-fault system) offshore, Texas. The fault exhibits very large-scale movements with a heave of about 16 km. Reverse drag and antithetic faults are developed within the hanging-wall block sequence. The fault-plane reflection is very variable due to changing acoustic-impedance contrasts across the fault. Reprinted by permission of the AAPG from Christensen, 1983.*

138

Transfer Faults. Gibbs (1984) proposes the term *transfer fault* to describe the cross-faults, characteristic of extensional settings, that allow leakage of movement between extension faults with differing slip rates. Transfer faults link major fault offsets and are often especially conspicuous at basin margins. It is important that such offsets are not automatically assumed to be the product of wrench or strike-slip faults. Transfer faults in extensional terrains are analogous to transform faults associated with sea-floor spreading in ocean basins. The geometry of transfer faults is analogous to lateral ramps in thrust tectonics (see Boyer and Elliott, 1982). A varied suite of minor structures, both extensional and compressional, are often associated with transfer faults. The type of associated structure depends on the orientation of the transfer fault relative to the slip direction of the extensional faults.

Footwall Uplift. Jackson and McKenzie (1983) discussed the role of footwall uplift in a review of the geometrical evolution of normal faults. Footwall uplift, a combined isostatic and elastic rebound response to downfaulting of the hanging-wall block, is estimated to amount to about 10% of the downthrow in a typical case where syn-fault sedimentation occurs (fig. 5.10). The uplift is real and can be of great significance. In cases where faulting occurs in a submarine environment, footwall uplift may produce a bathymetric high leading to reduced sedimentation. If the footwall uplift is sufficient to raise the upthrown block above storm-wave base, an erosional unconformity may result. Figure 5.11 shows a complex fault zone with repeated fault reactivations. Reverse drag on reflectors *e, f,* and *g* indicates a period of listric-normal movements followed by planar-normal movements indicated by normal drag of reflectors *c, b,* and *a.* The syn-fault sedimentation occurred over the interval *d–c,* depositing more than 400 m sedimentation. The corresponding interval on the footwall block is represented by an unconformity extending 3–4 km into the footwall block. The erosion indicated by the unconformity is interpreted to have been the result of footwall uplift during syn-fault sedimentation over the hanging-wall block.

FAULT REACTIVATION
Many faults show evidence of repeated movements. Such movements are often separated by considerable time intervals and may even involve a change in faulting type (e.g., a normal fault reactivated as a reverse fault as in fig. 5.12). If the fault reactivation occurs during sedimentation, the fault will propagate up through the cover sequence, maintaining its dip. However, if the faulting is episodic and a significant sedimentary cover overlies the old fault before it is reactivated, a change in fault geometry can be produced. Figure 5.13 shows a hypothetical situation where a vertical planar normal fault in the basement is reactivated. In this example, faulting in the base-

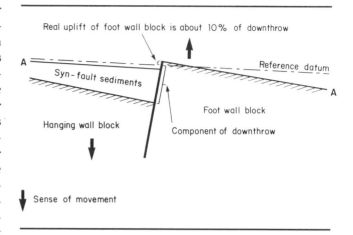

FIGURE 5.10 *Footwall uplift.*

ment produced extensional stress in the overlying section. The maximum extensional stress is oriented vertically. Any fault developing in the cover will develop at an angle to the vertically oriented maximum stress. The initial movement is likely to occur above the hanging-wall block, producing an incipient high-angle reverse fault. As there can be no net extension or contraction in the cover due to the faulting, any reverse movements must be balanced by normal faulting (or vice versa). Sandbox experiments by Horsfield (1977) indicate that, in cases where the reactivated fault has a dipping fault plane, the propagating fault will have a steeper dip in the sedimentary cover than the original fault. Where the hade of the reactivated fault is more than a few tens of degrees, antithetic faulting often develops to help provide the required extension in the cover sequence (fig. 5.14). In figure 5.15, which shows part of a seismic line through a fault zone, there is evidence of several episodes of movement. The older segments of the fault plane are steeply inclined but the geometry of the shallowest faulted interval indicates a low fault-plane dip, with local tilting, reverse drag, and even possible small-scale reverse movements. These differences between observed and experimental results have various possible (or combinations of) causes. For example, in the situation shown in figure 5.15, flexuring of the cover sequence could have led to faulting with a low fault-plane dip, or elevated pore pressures could have contributed to the low fault-plane dip (Mandl and Crans, 1981). Elevated pore pressures are common in shallow sequences with relatively thin overburden. The presence of discontinuities (e.g., bedding planes or lithology contrasts) in combination with high pore pressure can allow the activation of discontinuities inclined at a very low angle to the maximum principal stress axis. Jones and Addis (1984) suggest that differential compaction between clays and sandstones and/or limestones can cause

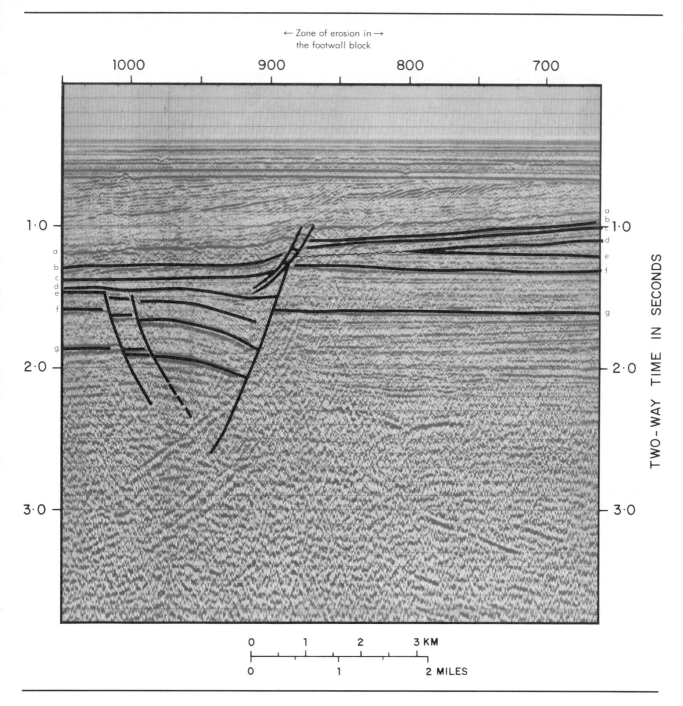

FIGURE 5.11 *Example of footwall uplift on a complex fault zone. Courtesy Norsk Hydro.*

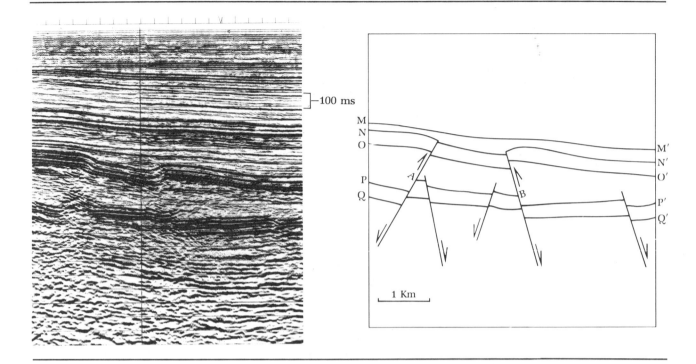

-100 ms

1 Km

FIGURE 5.12 *Seismic section showing two normal faults A and B, that have been reactivated as reverse faults. Reflections P–P′ and Q–Q′ show normal fault geometry across faults A and B. Reactivation of the faults occurred after the deposition of the beds producing reflections N–N′ and O–O′. The reverse movement has been insufficient to cancel the original normal downthrow affecting P–P′ and Q–Q′. Fault movement had ceased by the time of deposition of the beds causing reflection M–M′. It is likely that many thrusts are seeded along former normal faults. Courtesy Merlin Profilers Ltd.*

the fault plane to take on a stepped geometry, preserving steeper dips where it crosses sandstone or limestone layers and becoming more flat-lying in the shale.

REVERSE FAULTS AND THRUSTS

A reverse fault is a dip-slip fault, either high or low angle, on which the hanging wall has moved up relative to the footwall (fig. 5.5). Low-angle reverse faults are commonly termed thrusts and the term reverse fault is used here only for high-angled faults.

Thrusts develop only under a compressional stress system and to develop require high pore pressures beneath the thrust plane. The complex array of structures commonly associated with thrusts, although observed in outcrop, are difficult to see in the seismic section. For example, the details of the faulting in duplex zones that are frequently figured in geological cross-sections are often

best described as schematic, rather than an accurate depiction of the detailed duplex-zone structure. Duplex zones are sometimes inferred from anomalous thickening of a particular lithological unit. In view of the difficulty often encountered in outcrop studies, it is not surprising that seismic sections in low-angled thrust terrains are often extremely difficult to interpret. In these terrains, lateral and vertical velocity changes can make it almost impossible to obtain good seismic data. Despite these problems, seismic investigations in thrust belts have been given great impetus in recent years by the discovery of major oil reserves in the Rocky Mountain overthrust belt, and also by the realization, following results of the deep seismic reflection program COCORP, that sedimentary sequences underlie overthrusted basement rocks in many thrust belts. In many instances, it is difficult to interpret seismic sections from thrust belts and novel techniques must be employed (e.g., forward-modeling techniques) (McCellan and Storrusten, 1983). In particular, comparison of synthetic seismic sections based on geological models with real seismic sections is a common interpretation technique. The modeling continues, on a trial-and-error basis, until a best fit is achieved. The interpreter, while hoping that the best-fit model is the correct interpretation, also realizes that there are perhaps several other possible model solutions that could also give a best fit to the actual seismic data.

Thrust faults occur as both basement-involved and detached faults. Basement-involved thrusts can result in the

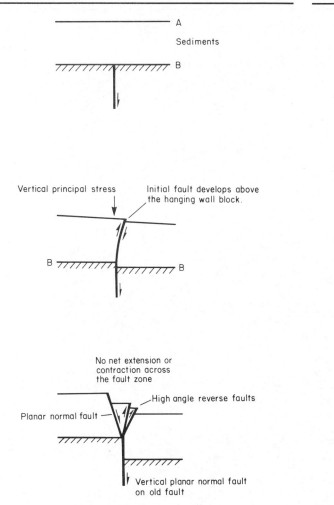

FIGURE 5.13 *Effects of fault reactivation on a normal fault. See text for discussion.*

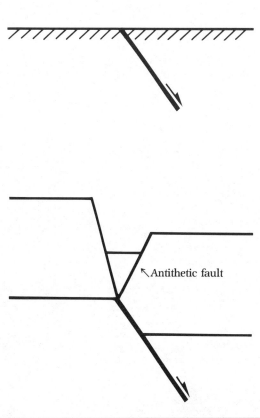

FIGURE 5.14 *Antithetic fault associated with a reactivated normal fault. The antithetic fault nucleates at the top of the earlier fault. The nucleation points of antithetic faults can sometimes be used to date the reactivation on faults with repeated movement episodes.*

overthrusting of considerable thicknesses of basement rocks over sediments. Figure 5.16, a seismic section across the northern margin of the Ngalia Basin, Australia, shows a basement-involved overthrust that has transported basement rocks on to basinal sediments. The overthrust has a vertical displacement of about 5 km and a horizontal displacement of about 71.5 km. A velocity pull-up of reflections from the sediments would be expected beneath the thrust. King and Brewer (1983) conclude that because this is not observed some structural downwarp must occur beneath the thrust.

Figure 5.17 shows a N–S seismic section across the Northern Apennine thrust fold belt beneath the eastern Po Plain, Italy, where the Ferrara-Romagna folded arc attains its maximum width (Pieri, 1983). Individual thrusts and thrust blocks can be seen clearly and analysis

of the seismic sequences on the flanks of the thrust sheets could be used to provide a detailed history of thrust movement.

Figure 5.18, a seismic section across the NE Bighorn basin, Wyoming, shows thrusts and associated folds, typical of oil-bearing structures in the area (Stone, 1983). The faults are basement involved and affect Precambrian basement and Palaeozoic sediments, with reservoir rocks in the Carboniferous Madison Fm. Some velocity pull-up may be present beneath the high-velocity (± 6000 m/s) Precambrian rocks (Stone, 1983).

Whereas the lower-angle thrust faults indicate compression, this is not necessarily the case with higher-angle reverse faults. The majority of reverse faults develop in

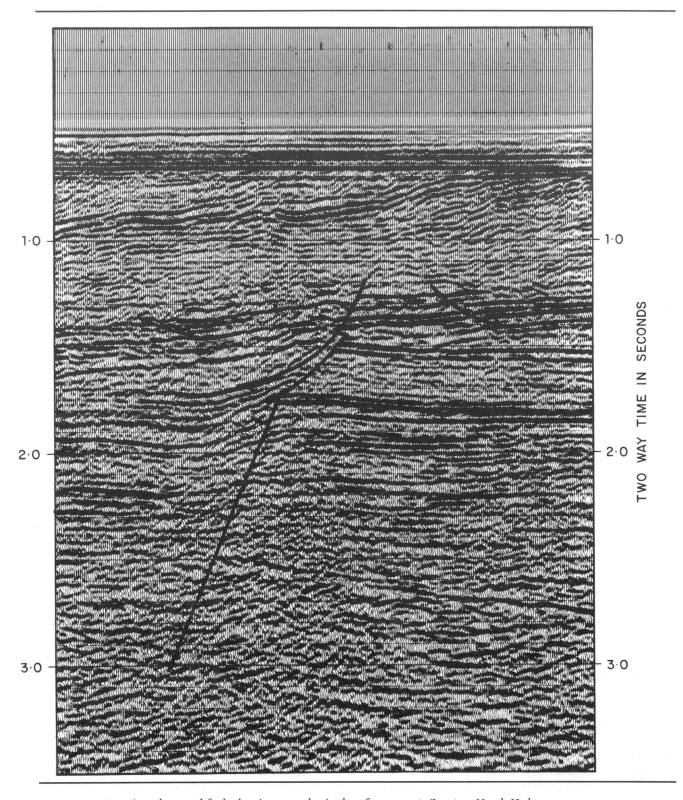

FIGURE 5.15 *Reactivated normal fault showing several episodes of movement. Courtesy Norsk Hydro*

143

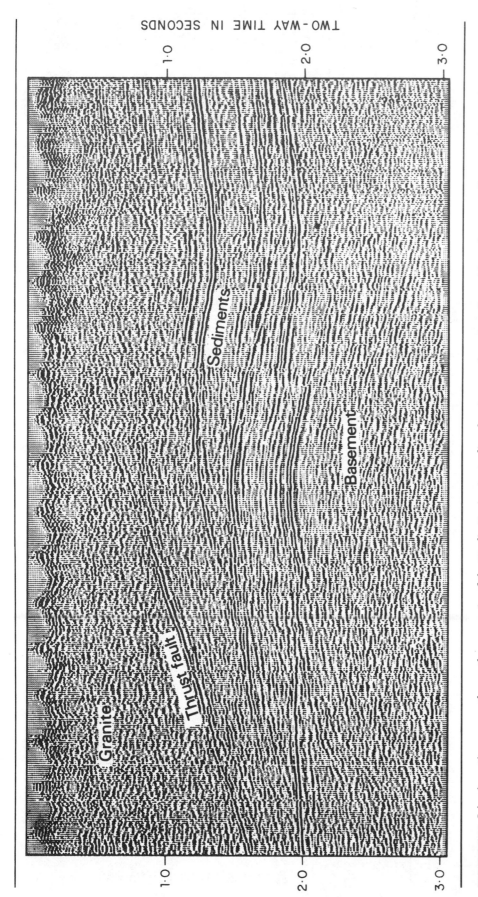

TWO-WAY TIME IN SECONDS

FIGURE 5.16 *Seismic section across the northern margin of the Ngalia Basin, Australia, showing overthrusting of granitic rocks onto sediments. The overthrust fault shows a vertical displacement of about 5 km and a horizontal displacement of about 11.5 km. Reprinted by permission of the author from Mathur, 1976, fig. 6, p. 283; after Wells, Moss, and Sabitay, 1972.*

144

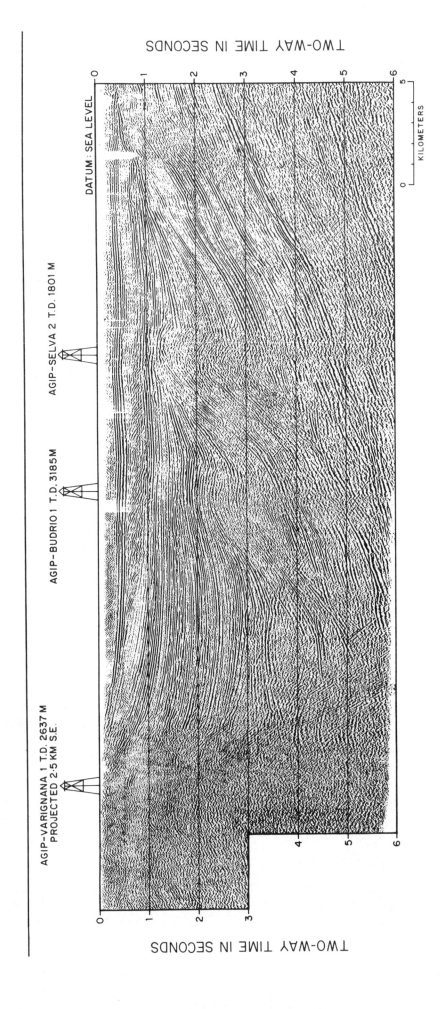

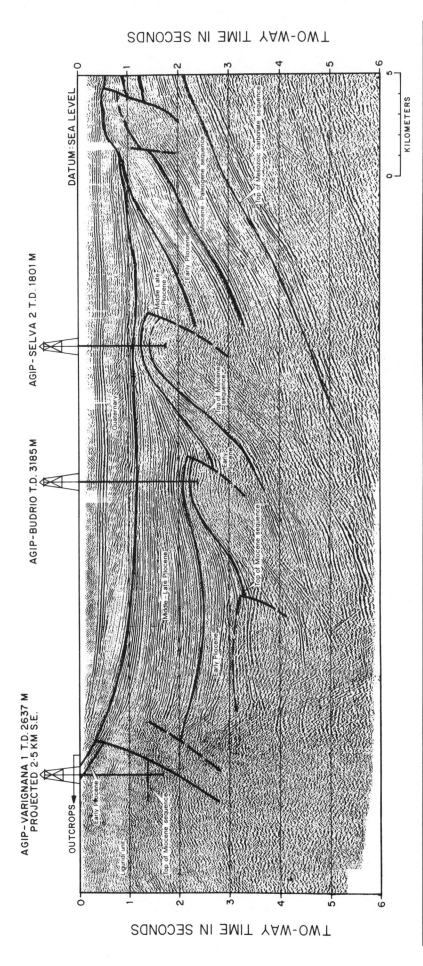

FIGURE 5.17 *Seismic section across the northern Appennines thrust-fold belt beneath the eastern Po Plain, Italy. Reprinted by permission of the AAPG from Pieri, 1983.*

146

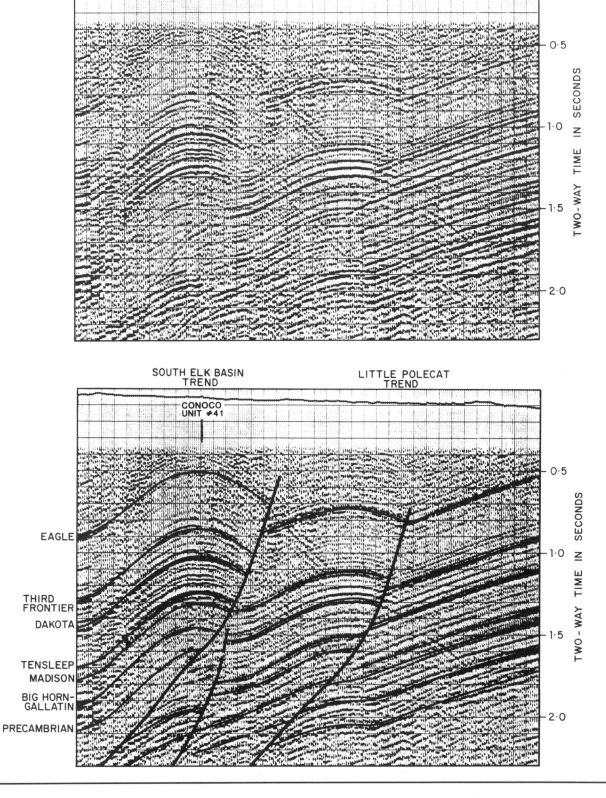

FIGURE 5.18 *Seismic section across thrust structures in the NE Bighorn Basin, Wyoming. Reprinted by permission of the AAPG from Stone, 1983.*

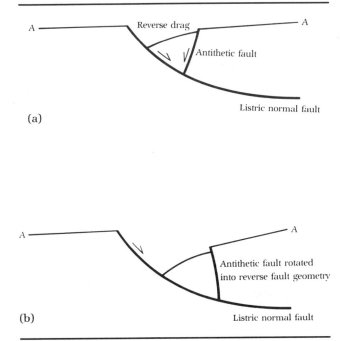

(a)

(b)

FIGURE 5.19 *Rotation of antithetic faulting in association with a listric fault to form reverse fault geometry.* (a) *Antithetic fault forms in association with a listric normal fault.* (b) *Continued movement on the listric normal fault causes the antithetic fault to rotate and assume a reverse fault geometry.*

response to compression, which often reactivates preexisting normal faults (fig. 5.12). Reverse faults also develop in response to reactivation of deeper vertical faults (fig. 5.13), in association with listric normal faulting (fig. 5.8), and by rotation of originally normal faults (fig. 5.19). The latter is an example of the potential pitfall in using present-day geometry for fault classification. The fault in figure 5.19 is clearly a planar normal fault that has subsequently been rotated; but if its hade were referenced to horizontal datum, it would be classified as a reverse fault. Estimates of lateral displacement on thrust-fault systems, ranging to a few hundreds of kilometers, are often based on section balancing techniques that attempt to unravel the thrust system and restore the stratigraphy to its prethrust position (Dahlstrom, 1969).

STRIKE-SLIP OR WRENCH FAULTS

A fault with dominant strike-slip displacement is called a strike-slip fault. Strike-slip faults usually have vertical dips; and when more than a kilometer or so in length they are invariably basement involved. Large-scale strike-slip faults are commonly called wrench or transcurrent faults. The sense of strike-slip displacement is described as sinistral or dextral, or alternatively, left lateral or right lateral. The structures associated with strike-slip faults are more diverse than those associated with any other fault type.

Frequently, folds, and normal, reverse, and thrust faults occur in association with strike faults (fig. 5.20). Strike-slip faults are difficult to identify in the seismic section, especially if the strike-slip movements occur in basement rocks with an overlying sedimentary cover. In such a situation the strike-slip movement may not be directly relayed into the cover sequence, but may be manifest in a variety of structures ranging from en-echelon grabens, to thrusts and folds, their axes inclined at an angle to the direction of strike-slip movement. "Flower structures" are supposedly characteristic of strike-slip movements (Harding and Lowell, 1979); but they also occur above reactivated normal faults. Not surprisingly, good and convincing seismic examples are hard to find and document. Bally (1983) contains several examples of strike-slip fault zones.

Figure 5.21 is a seismic section from the NW shelf of Palawa, Philippines, across a zone of strike-slip fault. The geology is extremely complex. The section in figure 5.21 illustrates, perhaps as well as any, that it is not possible to look at a single seismic section and say immediately, "Ah, that must be a strike-slip fault."

STRUCTURAL ANALYSIS

An important aspect of any structural interpretation is to attempt to understand the causes of the structuring. A correct interpretation of structure and its causes is fundamental to understanding geology. At a basic level, structures can be grouped into three broad categories:

1. Primary structures caused by deep crustal processes—for example, basin margin faults, strike-slip faults (such as the San Andreas fault)—related to the plate movement (By definition, all primary structures are basement involved.)
2. Secondary structures, directly related to, and a direct consequence of, the primary structures—for example, folds developing in the sedimentary cover over deeper fault basement blocks and subsidiary faults related to stresses developed by major basement-involved structures
3. Passive or adjustment structures developed as a consequence of, or as an after effect of, primary structural and secondary structures effects—for example, local crestal faulting of competent beds over the crest of an anticlinal fold; salt diapirism triggered by basin subsidence and other related factors; folding developed in association with strike-slip faulting; detached listric normal faults developed in prograding sequences

The subdivision of structures into such a scheme is an important aid, since it can provide an appreciation of cause and effect and so be used predictively. To illustrate this concept, rift basin development in the Northern North Sea, and the seismic expression of the resulting structures is discussed briefly. The description is taken from Badley

148

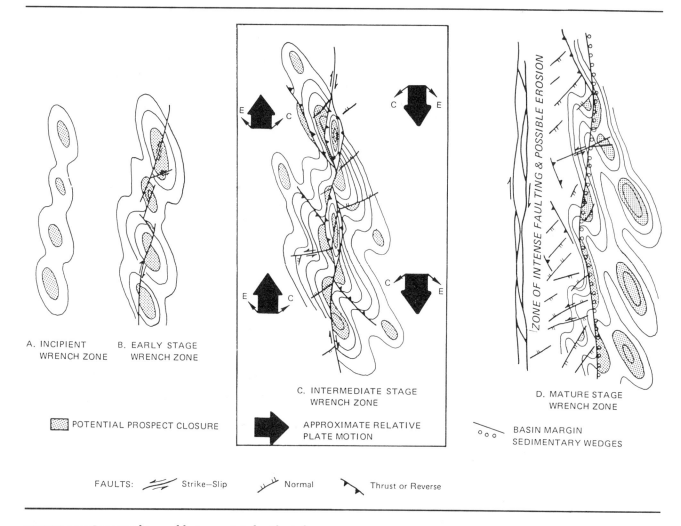

A. INCIPIENT
WRENCH ZONE

B. EARLY STAGE
WRENCH ZONE

C. INTERMEDIATE STAGE
WRENCH ZONE

D. MATURE STAGE
WRENCH ZONE

ZONE OF INTENSE FAULTING & POSSIBLE EROSION

POTENTIAL PROSPECT CLOSURE

APPROXIMATE RELATIVE
PLATE MOTION

BASIN MARGIN
SEDIMENTARY WEDGES

FAULTS: Strike–Slip   Normal   Thrust or Reverse

FIGURE 5.20 *Structural assemblage associated with strike-slip fault. Reprinted by permission of the AAPG from Harding and Lowell, 1979, fig. 5, p. 1024.*

et al. (1984). The approach described below is equally applicable to the interpretation of seismic sections in passive margins, thrust belts, etc.

Rifting initiates a chain of events that can shape subsequent basin evolution for tens of millions of years. Simple rift basins typically show two stages of development:

1. A rifting phase with thinning of the crust and lithosphere by mechanical extension (McKenzie, 1978), leading to subsidence and sedimentation: Basin geometry is largely controlled by the fault pattern resulting from the overall extensional stress regime. Basement-involved listric normal faults, accompanied by tilting, produce the characteristic tilted fault blocks. Rapid sediment thickness variations occur across the tilted blocks, especially across the listric normal faults, producing a complex sedimentation pattern.

2. A postrift phase of thermal subsidence, which decreases with time as the asthenosphere cools: The thermal subsidence is accompanied by flexure of the lithosphere under sediment loading, an effect which also decreases with time as the lithosphere cools and increases its flexural rigidity (Watts, 1982). This produces a relatively simple sedimentation pattern in which units show an overall thickening toward the basin center.

The processes described above affect basement rocks. Our main interest lies in the effect of these processes on the overlying sedimentary cover. To use the above model in a predictive way, and also to interpret correctly some of the features observed in the seismic, we must take the following into account:

1. *Recognition of the rifting phase:* Rifting can be defined as the period during which a basin experiences mechani-

cal extension; syn-rift sequences would include coeval sediments. Because listric normal faults are believed to be the main extension mechanism of the upper crust during rifting, rift phases are considered to have occurred when basement-involved listric faulting involving the normal basin can be demonstrated. Listric normal faults can be recognized using the following criteria.

a. Differential tilting of the prerift reflectors between the hanging and footwall blocks indicates a rotational component to the faulting. Surlyk (1977) used this criterion in East Greenland to recognize listric normal faults.

b. Reverse drag, downbending, or turnover of hanging-wall-block reflections into the fault: The reverse drag often exhibited by the prerift and the older syn-rift reflections on the downthrown side of some major faults is interpreted to be diagnostic of accompanying rotational movements on a curved fault plane. Reverse drag is not developed in association with all faults suspected of being involved in rotational displacements, nor is it generally present along the entire length of a particular fault trace.

c. The wedge shape of the syn-rift reflector package indicates active tilting during sedimentation, as does downlap on to prerift reflectors adjacent to the downthrown side of the fault by syn-rift reflectors. The wedge shape is the poorest of the criteria because wedge-shaped units can also result from the infilling of preexisting topography offset by planar normal faults in the postrift stage.

Other types of fault activity, predominantly planar normal, but possibly also rotational normal and strike-slip, can also occur during the rifting stage. Syn-fault sedimentation is common to all fault types.

2. Recognition of the postrift stage. A sequence boundary is usually developed, with truncation below and baselap above, separating everywhere the syn- and postrift sequences. It is called the postrift unconformity.

The reflector relationships at postrift unconformities are often extremely subtle and low angle, and it is difficult sometimes to recognize locally the truncation and/or baselap. Thermally induced subsidence is the main process operative during the postrift phase. The subsidence is achieved through a combination of processes:

a. Regional downwarp, which generally preserves dip relationships and is nonrotational: affects the whole basin.

b. Flexure, with well-defined hinge lines and involving rotation: operates on a more local scale.

c. Planar normal faulting: accommodates locally both subsidence and flexure-induced stress.

TILTED FAULT BLOCKS

Tilted fault blocks are one of the characteristic products of rifting and have excellent potential for producing traps (e.g., typical North Sea fields such as Piper, Oseberg, Brent, etc.).

The typical seismic expression of a tilted fault block and associated fault scarp is shown in figure 5.22. The most important features of the seismic expression are:

a. The unconformity defining the fault scarp

b. The generally convex nature of the fault scarp, with the individual fault compartments clearly discernible

c. The boundary between the tilted strata within the rotated fault block and the overlying sediments

d. The deeper unconformity within the tilted fault block between the steeper dipping subparallel reflectors of the prerift sediments and the wedge of syn-rift sediments which downlap and onlap on to the tilted surface

The tilted fault block shown in figure 5.22 comes from the Oseberg fault block structure and fault scarp from Norwegian block 30/6. The Oseberg structure (Larsen et al., 1981), is a major Mesozoic tilted fault block structure located in the northern Viking Graben immediately to the E of the Jurassic rift axis. The fault block and its complex history is representative of fault blocks in the northern Viking Graben, although the postrift faulting activity persisted longer in the Oseberg complex fault scarp than was the case for most other fault scarps in the area. The general principles of fault-block development described here are applicable to similar structures in other rift basins. Drilling has provided sufficient stratigraphic control to enable a detailed reconstruction of the evolution of the structure; it has confirmed the presence of postrift Lower Cretaceous strata not only at the foot of the complex fault scarp within the graben axis, but also on the flank of the tilted block, now at a structural level 1400 m higher than the deposits in the graben axis.

Listric faulting, restricted to the rifting stage, is recognized by differential tilting, local reverse drag and antithetic faulting, and a wedge-shaped reflector package into the major faults. Planar normal faults were also active during the rifting stage. Both types of fault exhibit growth or syn-fault sedimentation. The initiation of rifting is dated by baselap on to prerift reflectors, and its cessation is dated by an unconformity beneath the generally onlapping postrift reflections. Faulting on steeply dipping planar normal faults in the complex fault scarp, continued for about 70 Ma (million years) after the cessation of rifting. The last movement on these planar normal faults becomes younger away from the rift axis. Differential subsidence across these faults in the postrift stage, in combi-

150

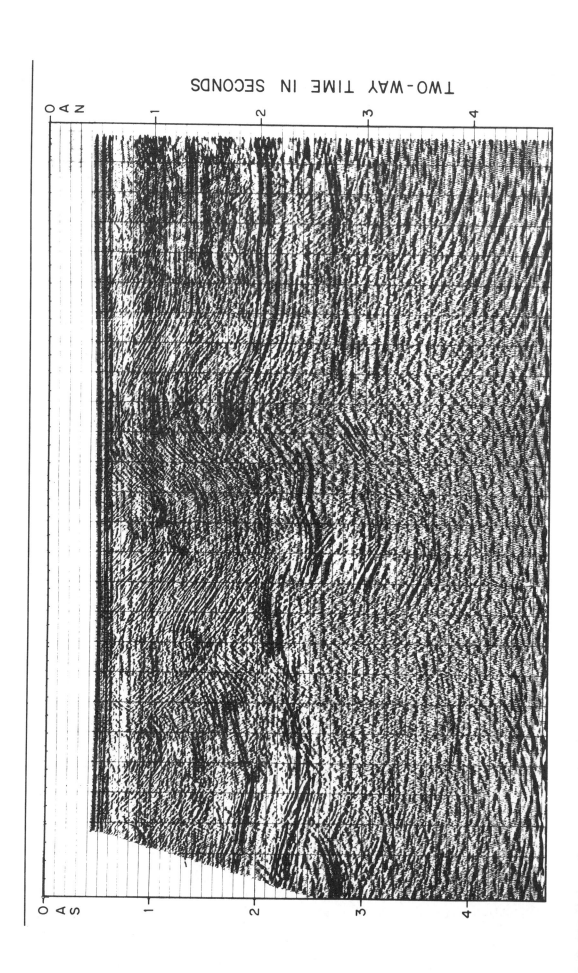

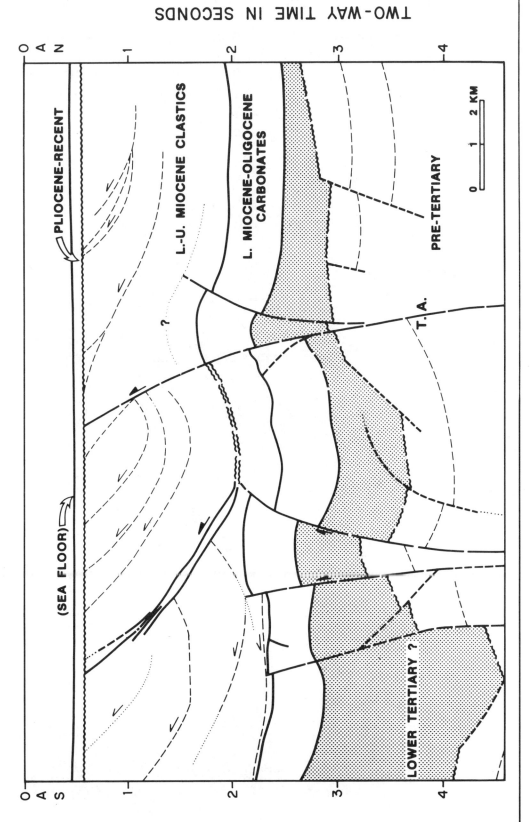

FIGURE 5.21 *Seismic section across a strike-slip fault on the NW Shelf of Palawa, Philippines. Reprinted by permission of the AAPG from Roberts, 1983.*

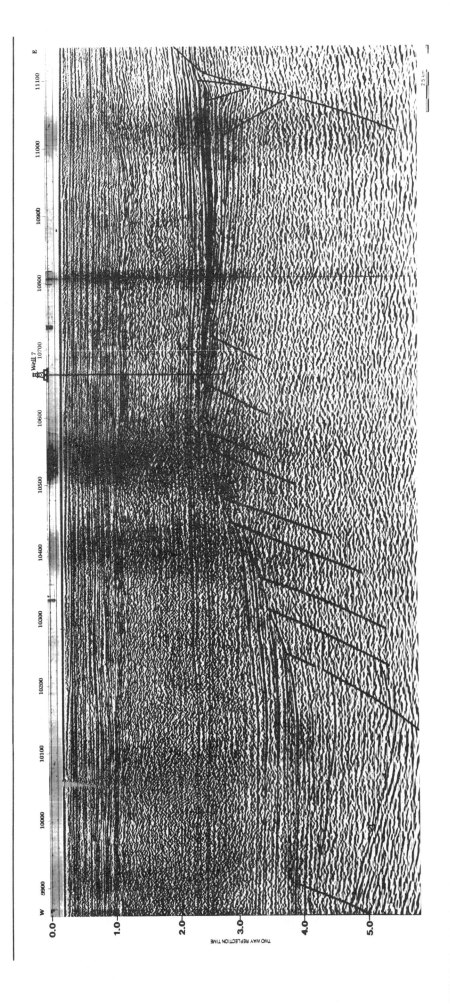

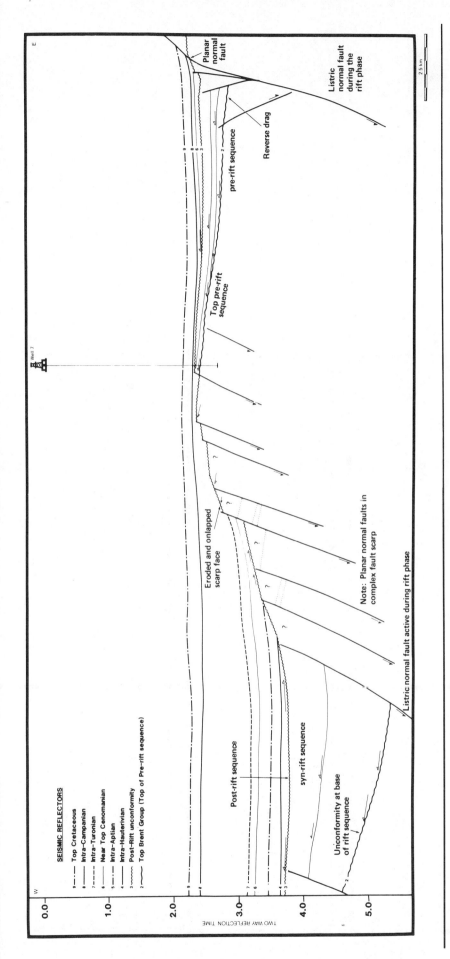

FIGURE 5.22 *Seismic section across the Oseberg tilted fault blocks structure, offshore Norway. Reprinted by permission of The Geological Society of London from Badley, Egeberg, and Nipen, 1984.*

SEISMIC REFLECTORS

9 ---- Top Cretaceous
8 ---- Intra-Campanian
7 ---- Intra-Turonian
6 ---- Near Top Cenomanian
5 ---- Intra-Aptian
4 ---- Intra-Hauterivian
3 ---- Post-Rift unconformity
2 ---- Top Brent Group (Top of Pre-rift sequence)

TWO WAY REFLECTION TIME

Planar normal fault

Listric normal fault during the rift phase

pre-rift sequence

Reverse drag

Top pre-rift sequence

Well 7

Eroded and onlapped scarp face

Note: Planar normal faults in complex fault scarp

Post-rift sequence

syn-rift sequence

Unconformity at base of rift sequence

Listric normal fault active during rift phase

2.5 km

154

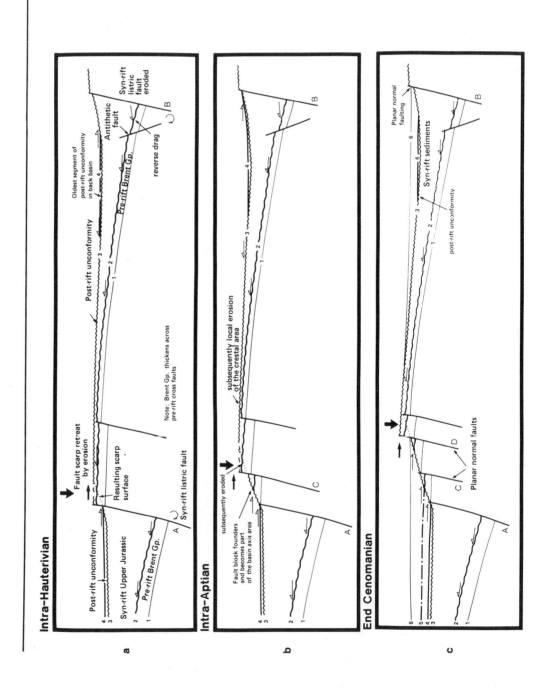

Intra-Hauterivian

Fault scarp retreat by erosion

Post-rift unconformity

Resulting scarp surface

Syn-rift Upper Jurassic

Pre-rift Brent Gp.

Syn-rift listric fault

4
3
2
1

A

a

Intra-Aptian

subsequently eroded

Fault block founders and becomes part of the basin axis area

subsequently local erosion of the crestal area

Post-rift unconformity

Oldest segment of post-rift unconformity in back basin

Syn-rift listric fault eroded

Antithetic fault

Pre-rift Brent Gp.

reverse drag

Note: Brent Gp. thickens across pre-rift cross faults

4
3
2
1

4
3

2
1

A

C

B

b

End Cenomanian

Planar normal faulting

Syn-rift sediments

post-rift unconformity

Planar normal faults

6
5
4
3

2
1

4
3
2
1

A

C

D

B

c

155

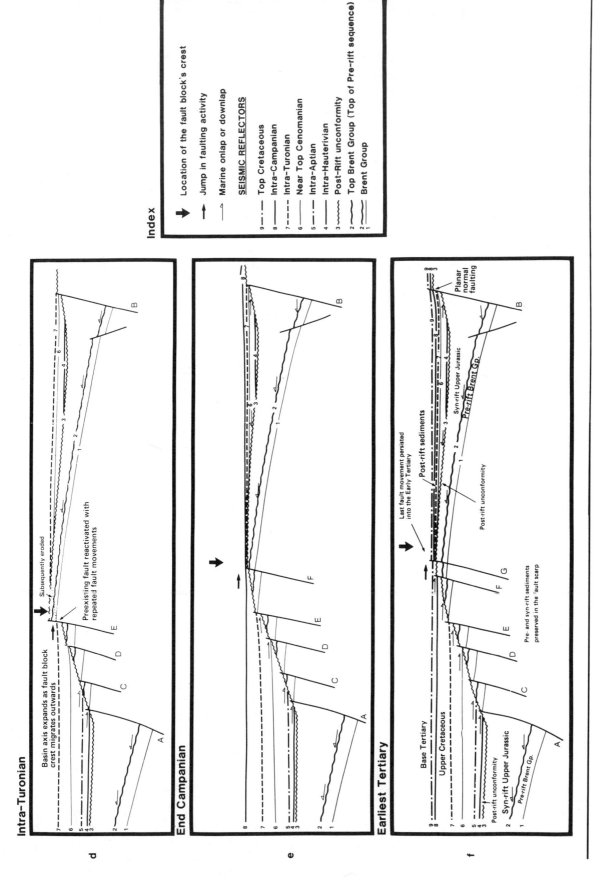

Intra-Turonian

Basin axis expands as fault block crest migrates outwards

Subsequently eroded

Preexisting fault reactivated with repeated fault movements

d

End Campanian

e

Earliest Tertiary

Base Tertiary

Upper Cretaceous

Post-rift unconformity

Syn-rift Upper Jurassic

Pre-rift Brent Gp.

Last fault movement persisted into the Early Tertiary

Post-rift sediments

Post-rift unconformity

Syn-rift Upper Jurassic

Pre-rift Brent Gp.

Planar normal faulting

Pre- and syn-rift sediments preserved in the fault scarp

f

Index

→ Location of the fault block's crest

↑ Jump in faulting activity

⌐ Marine onlap or downlap

SEISMIC REFLECTORS

9 — · · — Top Cretaceous
8 ———— Intra-Campanian
7 — — — Intra-Turonian
6 ———— Near Top Cenomanian
5 — · — · Intra-Aptian
4 ———— Intra-Hauterivian
3 〜〜〜 Post-Rift unconformity
2 〜〜〜 Top Brent Group (Top of Pre-rift sequence)
2 ———— Brent Group
1 ————

FIGURE 5.23 *Diagram showing the postrift development of the Oseberg structure, offshore Norway. Reprinted by permission of The Geological Society of London from Badley, Egeberg, and Nipen, 1984.*

nation with tilting produced during the syn-rift stage, produced the Oseberg structure and trap (fig. 5.23).

Figure 5.11, a seismic section across a fault from the Horda Platform, offshore Norway, is an example of how a single line can give a clue to both basin type and basin history. The fault shows reverse drag and antithetic faulting—characteristics of listric normal faulting—affecting reflection e, f, and g, and with normal drag—characteristic of planar normal faulting—affecting reflectors b, c, and d. The faulting was basement involved and the fault zone, which dips 70° W, appears to have been coincident for both the listric and planar normal movements over the 2-km interval observable in the seismic section. Since the fault is basement involved, the listric normal movements are indicative of rifting. The normal drag affecting the younger reflectors is indicative of planar normal movements during the postrift phase. The unconformity separating the two sequences that exhibit reverse and normal drag would be the postrift unconformity.

Chapter 6

Data Preparation and Preliminary Studies

The objectives and scope of seismic section interpretations vary so greatly—from regional interpretations to production geophysics—that it is difficult to give hard and fast rules as to how they should be accomplished. This part of the book, however, attempts to describe some primary guidelines that will aid efficient interpretation. Seismic-interpretation skills take time to acquire. They require the learning and development of techniques, good work practices, and exposure to a wide variety of areas and different seismic surveys.

Every interpretation project divides into three stages.

1. The preparation stage involves acquiring all the available background information relevant to the interpretation acquired and preparation of the seismic data itself
2. The actual interpretation
3. Presentation of the results

In any interpretation project it is essential to start by finding what is required and expected. The following are fundamental points:

Is a complete analysis required, or only a detailed study of a specific horizon, etc.?

For what geological horizons are maps desired? It may not always be possible to produce these maps directly from the seismic records (e.g., when there is no reflector at the desired level). In such cases the required maps will have to be derived indirectly, at a later stage, from the seismic horizon maps.

Establish the purpose of the maps. Detailed reservoir mapping for reserve estimates requires a much higher degree of accuracy than general prospect maps. There is little point in expending hours of effort on a study of the minutest details if such accuracy is not required in the end product.

Establish deadlines for the project and make a timetable, setting realistic targets for the project stages. Discuss and adjust the interpretation program if the timetable deadlines become unreasonable. Depending on priorities, a happy medium must be found.

Perhaps the most important preparation of all is to start a project file or note book. Record details of the seismic lines, wells, maps, etc.; and, during the interpretation stage, record features of interest in the data, such as mis-ties, etc.

This is the absolute minimum of information needed to begin an interpretation. Much can be achieved from a systematic analysis of the seismic data alone. However, other relevant information, which is usually available—such as well data and outcrop geology—should be incorporated. The following few pages briefly review typical back-up data and its uses.

SHOTPOINT MAPS

Before looking at the seismic data it is always helpful to know where it comes from: for this we need shotpoint maps. Shotpoint maps show the locations of the seismic lines. They show the line number and/or name and then every 10th, 50th, 100th, etc. shotpoint with a suitable symbol (depending on the map scale and spacing of the original seismic shotpoints).

Shotpoint maps have four uses:

1. They form the base map for later contouring.
2. They show line orientation and line spacing.
3. They give the interpreter a picture of the survey layout.
4. They provide the intersection points between lines from different surveys, information that is not always available from the section headings.

Especially for the latter reason, shotpoint maps are important during the preinterpretation stage. It is essential that all lines to be used in the interpretation are plotted on the same map at an appropriate scale. Computer plotting is facilitated by the digital navigation data available for most modern surveys. Digitizing of shotpoint maps to facilitate computer plotting for surveys where navigation data is unavailable is not especially time consuming. Alternatively, shotpoint maps can be drafted manually. Appropriate scales depend on the intended use of the maps. To calculate line intersections, the scale should be no more than 1:50,000, preferably 1:25,000. To plot trends, faults, etc., 1:50,000 is usually a convenient scale for a reference map during an interpretation; but for regional work, 1:100,000 may be more appropriate; or for very detailed work, 1:25,000. To facilitate efficient contouring, shotpoint maps should be scaled so that lines are well spaced and the posted time values are uncluttered. For 3-D mapping, 1:10,000 is a suitable scale. For conventional 2-D surveys with grid density of about 1 × 1 km, 1:25,000 is recommended, and for wider grids, 1:50,000. Mapping at 1:100,000 is only advisable for very widely spaced regional grids. Variants on these conventions may be in common usage locally (e.g., in the United States, Imperial Units, with scales of 1:10,560, 1:63,360, etc., are used in preference to metric units).

TYPES OF SEISMIC SECTIONS

Once it is clear which survey(s) are to be interpreted, the choice of which type of seismic section to use must be made. Sometimes there may be no choice as only one version of the data is at hand; but often migrated and unmigrated, normal or reversed polarity sections, in full or half scales are available. The choice of which to use will depend on a number of factors; it is always advisable to view the different versions to assess the relative merits of each display.

Migrated sections should be used when available, but a thorough comparison with unmigrated lines should be made to check the data quality of the migrated lines. In some cases, where the migration has not worked well (e.g., poor velocity control), the unmigrated lines may be of better quality. In complexly structured areas both types of data should be available for comparison during the interpretation. Using migrated lines in structured areas (where dips are more than about 15°) will introduce significant mis-tie problems.

Half-scale sections (5 cm or 2½ inches to 1 second) are useful for regional work and for providing an overview in the reconnaissance stage of a detailed interpretation. If an interpretation is done with care and the horizon picks are marked precisely, the accuracy obtainable may be within reasonable limits. However, for detailed studies, especially those involving interpretation of subtle variations in the wavelet shape, etc., the use of full scale (10 cms or 5 inches to 1 second) sections is advisable.

If both versions are available, the choice between normal or reversed polarity will depend on a number of factors. If the new grid is to be incorporated with previous surveys, mixing polarities is not recommended. If a free choice is available, normal polarity—a compressional wave displayed as a trough—may be preferable. In most areas acoustic impedance increases with depth and the majority of significant (i.e., tops of sequences) reflecting boundaries will have positive reflection coefficients. These are displayed as troughs on normal polarity lines. It is easier to pick, and mark, a boundary in a trough and to see subtle changes in the trough shape than in the blackened peaks. However, if direct hydrocarbon indications are anticipated, reversed polarity is more appropriate, because the flat spots will appear as strong subhorizontal black peaks. Each area must be judged on its merits and the appropriate choice made.

If a choice of display is available, the most suitable for detailed work is a combination of wiggle trace plus variable area where the details of the trough are preserved as well as the alignment of the peaks. All of the examples shown in the text are of this type. Figure 6.1 shows examples of commonly used displays.

The standard seismic trace displays the seismic response; the peaks and troughs indicate changes in both acoustic impedance and reflection strength. Differences in reflection strengths are shown by varying amplitudes of the peaks and troughs, although the differences can only be estimated since scaling factors are applied to the very low and high amplitudes to give seismic sections a balanced appearance. In most situations the information carried by this simple display is adequate, but there are many situations where more information is required. For example, when evaluating a bright spot as a possible indicator of a gas sand, it is crucial to know the polarity of the reflection and useful to know the relative amplitude of the reflection. In many cases diagnostic reflector relationships are not developed and polarity cannot easily be determined. To overcome this problem, a series of special displays have been developed; these are often in color, although grey tones are sometimes used.

Amplitude displays show the relative strength of reflections. Normally, amplitude differences are obscured by the automatic gain control during processing (fig. 6.2). Amplitude is affected by differences in reflection coefficients as well as by the acquisition and processing. For example, amplitude is affected by energy source, detector sensitivity, cable loss, instrument sensitivity, spherical spreading, transmission losses, scattering, reflector shape, and attenuation. All of these factors must be taken into account before a display of reflection amplitude is produced. Used in conjunction with a display of instantaneous polarity (a display showing whether the polarity is positive or negative at the maximum reflection amplitude) it is possible to evaluate bright spots. For example, a bright spot from the top of a porous gas sand overlain by relatively uncompacted claystone should have a strong reflection with negative polarity.

Instantaneous phase is a useful display when it is important to follow a particular reflection through a difficult area or to establish reflector relationships. Instantaneous phase is a value associated with a point in time on the seismic pulse and is independent of reflection strength. Because of this, weak reflections often show much better continuity on this display. The display is usually made by assigning color or grey shades to peaks, troughs, and zero crossings. Figure 4.36 shows an example of a section processed to display instantaneous phase.

Instantaneous frequency is also associated with a point in time on the seismic pulse, with the frequency in hertz being displayed as a color or grey tone. This type of display often shows great lateral and vertical variability, mainly because frequency is very sensitive to noise. An averaging technique is often used to make the displays more interpretable. Instantaneous frequency displays can be used as a correlation aid but are most useful in con-

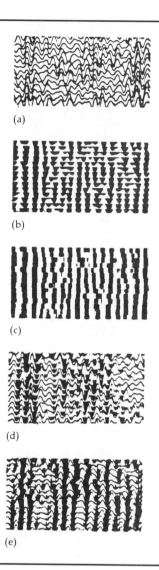

FIGURE 6.1 *Display modes:* (a) *wiggle trace,* (b) *variable area,* (c) *variable density,* (d) *wiggle trace superimposed on variable area,* (e) *wiggle trace superimposed on variable density. Reprinted by permission of the SEG from Sheriff, 1973.*

junction with other types of display. In particular, they help the evaluation of bright spots. Lower frequencies are often seen below gas sands, perhaps due to the absorptive effects of the gas on the higher frequencies.

Velocity displays show interval velocity in terms of color or grey shades. They can be useful for identifying lithologies, correlating across faults, and detecting porous zones in reservoir intervals. Caution must be exercised in their interpretation, however, as imprecision in the calculation of interval velocities, which is based on an empirical relationship between reflection amplitude and velocity, can produce geologically implausible shapes for intervals. All too frequently, velocity displays are interpreted without proper regard to this.

These are the main color-coded displays in fairly com-

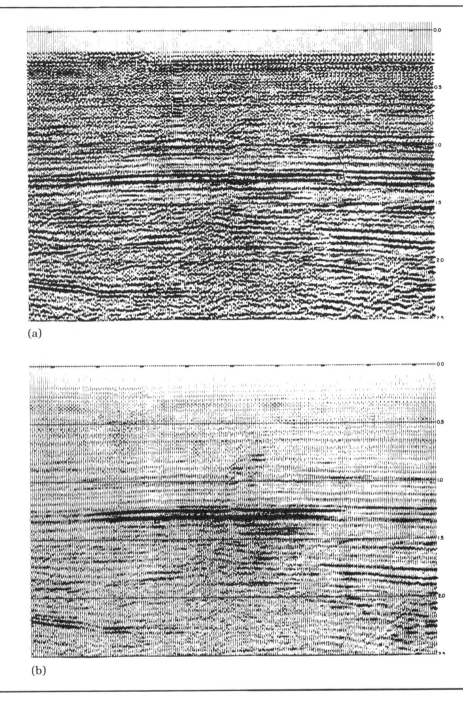

(a)

(b)

FIGURE 6.2 *Comparison of automatic gain control and true-amplitude processing, Gulf of Mexico. (a) Amplitude-destroying processing, using automatic gain control. (b) Amplitude-preserving processing. Reprinted by permission of Teledyne Exploration Company from Barry and Shugart, 1973.*

mon usage, but others, such as dip, rate of dip change, cross dip, etc., have been used. Taner and Sheriff (1977) give examples of the interpretation of color displays. Displays of reflection attributes will become a more common tool for the interpreter as interactive graphics terminals come into more general use.

THE SECTION LABEL

The seismic section labels for each survey should be studied to find out how the data were acquired and subsequently processed. By this stage it may seem a bit late in the day to be concerned about this. After all, the sections are lying on the table waiting to be interpreted and it is a lucky interpreter who has easy access to reprocessing facilities. However, one of the most disconcerting things that can happen to an interpreter is to see the results of reprocessing on a poor seismic section that he has already used. As figure 3.1 shows, the differences can be amazing and lead the interpreter to the inevitable conclusion that the more one understands of processing the better.

The information given in the label can be a useful guide to the nature of the data and its probable limitations. Because of the multiplicity of acquisition and processing techniques employed by the numerous seismic contractors, it is difficult to give a guide to seismic section labels. The brief details below are intended as a general guide to the type of information given and their typical implications in terms of the seismic data. If in doubt about a special feature of a particular survey, it is best to contact the contractor directly for a detailed explanation. A typical seismic section label is shown in figure 6.3. The label is divided into five main headings:

1. General line details
2. Recording and field data
3. Spread diagram
4. Processing
5. Display parameters

GENERAL DETAILS

The seismic section label contains at least the following information: survey location, survey identifier, line number, the type of section (migrated time section, filtered stack, etc.), shotpoint range, and shooting direction. Apart from the date, which will give a good indication of the data quality to be expected (technology has improved, but not every survey lives up to our high hopes), the other information is useful but has no direct bearing on interpretation.

The line-numbering system used in the Norwegian North Sea is an example of how useful information can be conveyed by the seismic section label. Each survey name consists of the following: the operating company; the year (abbreviated to two digits, e.g., 84) and the survey number (1, 2, 3, etc.). From the line number it is possible to

tell the line direction and relative position of the line. The line numbers are prefixed by 1, 2, 3, or 4 denoting EW, NE–SW, N–S, or NW–SE line directions, respectively; and line numbers always increase in northerly or easterly directions. For example, NH 8202–304 would be the fourth N–S line from the western boundary of the second survey shot by Norsk Hydro in 1982.

Positioning is a potential problem in remote areas, both on- and offshore. For marine data, two navigation systems are usual, a primary system and a back-up (often satellite navigation) of lesser accuracy. If navigation problems have occurred, this can cause serious mis-tie problems at line intersections. In cases where the mis-tie is serious or critical it may be necessary to consult the survey quality control report to check for navigation problems.

Many different types of source are used both on- and offshore, each with its own characteristics and attributes. They will affect the seismic results, hopefully in a uniform way for the whole survey. Experience shows that some sources produce better results than others in particular areas. Local knowledge and past experience is the best guide to evaluating a particular source. The shot interval, usually around 25 m (80 ft) for detailed surveys, affects the time spacing and scale of the line. Regional data can be shot with intervals of 50 m (160 ft) or more. This produces a foreshortened section and may show less detail than a line with a 25-m spacing. The recording geophones/hydrophones are clustered together into groups; 48 or 96 are common for marine cables, which are usually about 2500 m long. The recording fold, the degree of coverage for each CDP or CMP, is determined by the following relationship:

$$\text{recording fold} = \frac{(\text{no. of groups}) \times (\text{group interval})}{2 \times (\text{shotpoint interval})}.$$

(6.1)

A sample interval of 4 ms is considered sufficient for the recording of frequencies up to at least 65 Hz. The recording rate places an upper limitation on the frequencies that are recorded. Traditionally, the high-cut recording filter was set at about 25% of the sample rate frequency (e.g., ± 62 Hz for a 4-ms and ± 125 Hz for a 2-ms sample interval). If higher frequencies than these are used in an attempt for higher resolution, they are recorded at the cost of increased higher-frequency noise from the field. A high-resolution survey would be indicated by a sample interval of 2 ms. A low-cut filter of 6–8 Hz is normally used to cut out ground roll, cable noise, etc. Occasionally, no low-cut filter is used, as, for instance, in surveys where special processing to produce inverted seismic traces is attempted.

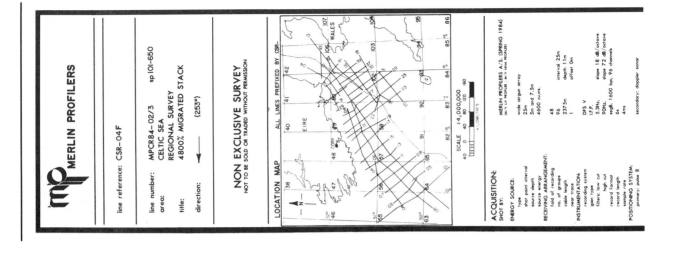

MERLIN PROFILERS

line reference: CSR-04F

line number: MPCR84-02/3   sp 101-650
area: CELTIC SEA
REGIONAL SURVEY
title: 4800% MIGRATED STACK
direction: ⟵ (253°)

NON EXCLUSIVE SURVEY
NOT TO BE SOLD OR TRADED WITHOUT PERMISSION

LOCATION MAP   ALL LINES PREFIXED BY CSR-

SCALE 1:4,000,000
40 0 40 80 120 160
KILOMETRES

ACQUISITION:
SHOT BY: MERLIN PROFILERS A/S. (SPRING 1984)
(M/V LIV PROFILER, M/V NINA PROFILER)

ENERGY SOURCE:
  type   wide airgun array
  shot point interval   25m
  source depth   5m and 7.5m
  source energy   4600 cu.ins.

RECEIVING ARRANGEMENT:
  fold of recording   48
  no. of groups   96   interval 25m
  cable length   2375m   depth 11m
  near trace   1   offset 0m

INSTRUMENTATION:
  recording system   DFS V
  gain type   I.F.P.
  filters: low cut   5.3Hz,   slope 18 dB/octave
  high cut   90Hz,   slope 72 dB/octave
  record format   seg8, 1600 bpi, 96 channels
  record length   6s
  sample rate   4ms

POSITIONING SYSTEM:
  primary: pulse 8   secondary: doppler sonar

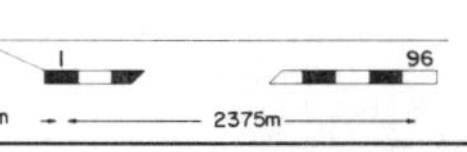

PROCESSING:

PROCESSED BY: MERLIN PROFILERS LTD., WOKING, ENGLAND (SPRING 1984; CONTRACTS 487, 496)

1. DEMULTIPLEX
2. SOURCE SIGNATURE COMPENSATION:
   - input — calculated far-field signature
   - desired output — fitted minimum phase Gaussian filter
3. FK COHERENT NOISE ATTENUATION:
   - pre-fk amplitude scaling — +12dB/s exp. to 3.0s
   - offset dependent mute
   - rejection dips — +6 to +50 ms/trace; −4 to −50 ms/trace
4. STATIC CORRECTIONS:
   - source and receiver depth — +11ms
5. FK MULTIPLE ATTENUATION
6. DECONVOLUTION BEFORE STACK:
   - type — minimum phase least squares inverse
   - autocorrelation window length — 3500ms
   - max. prediction lag — 240ms
   - min. prediction lag — 20ms
   - post-deconvolution inverse scaling — −12dB/s exp. to 3.0s
7. NMO CORRECTION:
   - velocity derivation — contoured semblance spectra
   - offset dependent mute
8. STACK:
   - type — standard mean amplitude CDP
   - coverage — 4800%
   - space variant geometrical divergence compensation
9. DECONVOLUTION AFTER STACK:
   - type — minimum phase least squares inverse
   - autocorrelation window length — 4500ms
   - max. prediction lag — 240ms
   - min. prediction lag — 20ms
10. WAVE EQUATION MIGRATION:
    - finite difference solution — 48ms depth step
    - pre-migration filter — 6(24)–80(36) Hz (dB/oct)
    - migration velocity derivation — interval velocity model
11. SPACE TIME VARIANT FILTER:

at sp 101	time (ms)	low cut Hz (dB/oct)	high cut Hz (dB/oct)
filters linearly interpolated	4	12(24)	70(36)
in space and time.	1200	10(24)	70(36)
cuts and slopes specified	2800	8(24)	55(36)
at −3dB point.	4000	8(24)	35(36)

12. TWO DIMENSIONAL FILTER:
    - number of adjacent traces — 7
    - passband — +5 to −5 ms/trace
    - percentage input feedback — 66
13. AMPLITUDE BALANCE:
    - a) general amplitude trend analysis and compensation
    - b) trace equalisation
      - type — Robust AGC

DISPLAY:

system	SCIITEX laser plotter
horizontal scale	1:25,000 (20 traces/cm)
	1:50,000 (40 traces/cm)
vertical scale	10 cm/sec
	5 cm/sec
gain	4 dB
bias	5 %
polarity	compression : negative : trough
datum plane	sea level
shotpoint location	source position

FIGURE 6.3 *A typical seismic section label. Courtesy Merlin Profilers Ltd.*

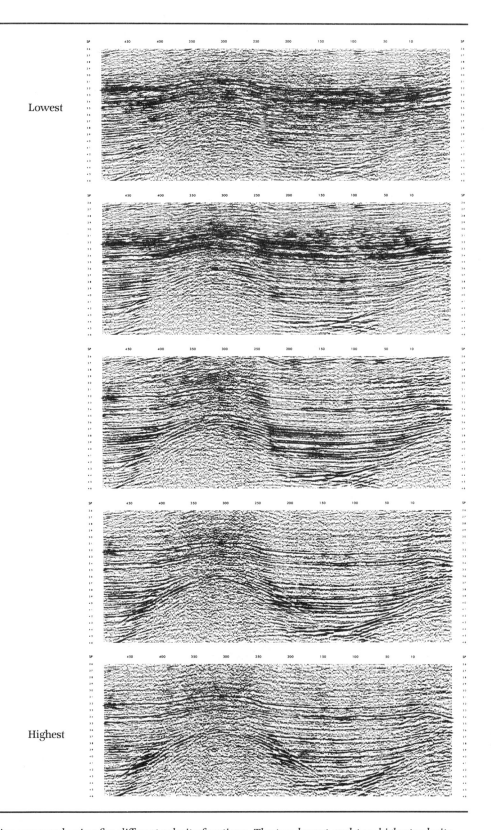

Lowest

Highest

FIGURE 6.4 *Part of a seismic section processed using five different velocity functions. The two lowest and two highest velocity functions produce poor results. The third function is perhaps the best. Courtesy Merlin Profilers Ltd.*

PROCESSING

The processing sequence should be of interest to the interpreter; it can give some indication of what the interpreter might reasonably expect from the data. Some of the processing steps that particularly affect the data, or its appearance, are discussed below.

Deconvolution. Deconvolution is designed to shape the pulse and attenuate multiples. The section label usually gives details of the deconvolution(s) applied during processing. The deconvolution operators (they are a type of filter) can be applied both before and after stack. Two main types are used, deterministic deconvolution and predictive deconvolution. Deterministic deconvolution, or wavelet processing, requires a knowledge of the propagating wavelet. It is capable of producing a pulse of any desired shape (e.g., zero-phase) with an appropriate bandwidth. In general, it produces predictable results. The difficulty of recording or determining the propagating wavelet is a disadvantage of the method.

Predictive deconvolution uses statistical methods to calculate the operator. The method attempts to predict event shapes and occurrences in the seismic trace by using past knowledge of event shapes and occurrences obtained by the statistical studies of the seismic traces. Predictive deconvolution is the easiest and cheapest method to apply, but does assume that the reflection coefficient series is random, which may not always be the case.

In predictive deconvolution the gap interval or prediction length is the length of trace unaffected by the deconvolution. Short gaps may provide the greatest resolution, but they often go hand in hand with increased noise levels. If predictive deconvolution is used for multiple attenuation, the gap length cannot be greater than the period of the multiple. For example, if the gap is 32 ms, then the deconvolution will not change the pulse shape over this interval or attack any short-term multiples with a period less than 32 ms.

The operator length is the length of trace over which the deconvolution is effective as it is successively moved down each trace, and it should be long enough to cover the period of the longest multiple that is to be attenuated. The length determines the maximum period of multiple that can be attenuated by the deconvolution. Multiples with a longer period will escape the deconvolution and we have to hope that they will be removed by stacking.

Derivation or design window (gate) is the interval of trace statistically analyzed in the design of the deconvolution operator for predictive deconvolution. Often several intervals in an overlapping sequence are used. The extent of the window can give an indication of the processing objectives. For example, if the target interval lay between 2.0 and 3.5 s, traces from this interval might be used in the design of the deconvolution operator. The processing should be at its optimum, all other things being equal, for the interval 2.0 to 3.5 s, but not necessarily for shallower and deeper parts of the section where a different operator might have been more appropriate.

Velocity Analysis. Velocity analyses are used to determine stacking velocities and are a very important step in the processing procedure. Figure 6.4, part of a seismic line processed using five different velocity functions, shows the dependence of seismic data quality on choice of the correct velocity. Good quality velocity analyses usually result in good seismic data but it should always be remembered that the stacking velocities are not geological interval velocities. Normally, velocity analyses are spaced at approximately 1–3-km intervals, but closer spacings are used in complicated areas where significant lateral velocity changes are expected. It is a good idea to check the quality of the velocity analyses on one or two lines in the survey. This can be done simply by checking the plausibility of the velocity picks made by the contractor for stacking. Velocity analyses are usually available for each survey. The velocity picks can be checked against the seismic interpretation, especially if the interpreter has some knowledge of the expected interval velocities.

Stacking. The combination of CMP traces into a single trace is the main line of attack against multiples and also attenuates other forms of noise. Several types of stacking procedure are often employed. An improved stack can be obtained by selective weighting of samples when the characteristics of the noise are known.

Vertical stacking, in which consecutive records are summed, channel for channel, is used to simulate a larger energy-source array. Its main application is with land data to build up energy levels when using Vibroseis.

Horizontal stacking, in which adjacent channels are summed, simulates a larger receiver array. It decreases the CMP fold of the stack and is used when the noise characteristics are such that a greater attenuation is obtained by summing traces in line order rather than CMP order.

Migration. Migration is commonly performed on modern seismic data. There are many types of migration used in conventional 2-D processing; attributes of some of the more common methods are detailed in the following:

Kirchhoff summation has good performance with steep dips but has poorer performance with low signal-to-noise (S/N) ratio data.
Finite difference (a form of wave-equation migration) has good performance with low S/N ratios and is adaptable to horizontal velocity gradients, but is relatively expensive and has difficulty with steep dip.
Frequency domain migration is inexpensive and has good performance with steep dips, but the method exagger-

ates errors caused by poor velocity control. It also has poor performance with severe velocity gradients and is unable to deal with horizontal velocity gradients.

If the velocity distribution used for the migration is approximately correct, each of these methods produces about the same results (fig. 3.24). It is to be hoped that the most suitable method will be chosen for each survey.

Time-Variant Filter. The time-variant filter is a cosmetic procedure used to suppress noise existing outside the frequency spectrum of the desired signal. It improves the signal-to-noise ratio, but if well chosen has only minor effect on the shape of the pulse. The filter is necessary because the frequency of primary reflected seismic signals decreases with time, due to greater absorption of higher frequencies. It is, therefore, desirable to use a time-variant filter whose passband decreases in frequency with increasing reflection time. Where there is appreciable structure, the onset times of the filter are varied so as to keep the frequency content (and therefore the character) of a given reflection approximately constant.

Muting. Muting, or ramp, is performed on the first part of the traces of a common-depth-point group to cut off refractions and noise caused by geometric and other effects. These are most severe on the far traces. The severity of muting varies, and the first traces can be completely blanked off in shallow water. This results in the first event seen on a marine seismic section being well below the theoretical time to the sea bed. Muting produces lower fold data near the surface part of the section and it can be 2 s or more before the data is at full fold. Normally, this would only be critical in an interpretation of shallow reflections where the fold is low (less than twenty), but the effects of muting on the data fold should always be borne in mind when investigating shallow reflections.

Display. The most important feature of the seismic display is the polarity. Although invariably referred to as being "SEG normal" or "reversed polarity," often it is not directly stated as such, especially on older seismic sections. Instead, wording is arranged around the same theme. All of the following are examples of normal polarity:

Polarity: compression; negative; trough
Processing polarity: positive number gives black peak
Polarity: normal [SEG standard] compressional wave displayed as a trough [white]—[this leaves the interpreter in no doubt].
Polarity: compressional pulses recorded as negative numbers on tapes and plotted as troughs [white] on playback

Usually the reference datum is specified. Marine surveys are normally corrected (i.e., for gun and cable depths, delays, etc.) back to mean sea level. However, occasionally time zero is taken as the zero correction of the gun and cable depth. To correct back to sea level can involve adding as much as 10 to 15 ms. Even when applied, datum correction is sometimes incorrect, as is evidenced by the way some surveys mis-tie to wells within the area with a consistent static shift.

The bias and gain indicate respectively the percentage of the peaks on the wiggle trace that are filled in black (25–30% bias is common) and how much the data has been scaled in display. Both are cosmetic and are changed easily.

PREVIOUS SURVEYS
The seismic data set for interpretation may consist of just one survey and its associated data (shotpoint maps, velocity data, etc.), or may come from a new survey to be incorporated into an older data grid based on earlier surveys. The decision to use or not to use previous surveys will depend very much on the problem to be solved. The aim of a seismic interpretation is to extract from the seismic data the maximum amount of geological information, especially in terms of structure, stratigraphy, and geological history. The success of this will depend partly on the density of the seismic grid. Seismic interpretation uses a grid of two-dimensional vertical sections between which are blank areas where no data is available. The density of the grid is obviously the controlling factor on accuracy of the interpretation. The closer the grid, the tighter the control, the greater the accuracy. A 5 km × 5 km grid, could, in theory, miss a feature up to 23 to 24 km² in extent. Such a grid would be of little use in searching for pinnacle reefs with a surface area of only 1 or 2 km². Therefore, if the new data is only an infill of an older grid, the previous surveys should be included. If, on the other hand, the new survey is a 3-D grid, with a line about every 75 m, it is unlikely that any old data will be used.

Onshore it is likely that any data, however old, will be used to make up the grid, as the high acquisition costs make all lines valuable. Twenty years later it may be quite impossible to reshoot a line or survey, even using Vibroseis, if, in the meantime, new settlements, construction works, etc., have been established. Reprocessing of the older data is often desirable if it is to be used. Offshore, where data acquisition is both cheaper and easier, older data is frequently disregarded. For example, in the northern North Sea, pre-1975 data is generally so poor when compared with modern data that it is rarely used.

VELOCITY DATA
Velocity is a parameter that plays a very central role in the seismic method. Detailed knowledge of velocity is required for normal-moveout corrections and migration. The interpreter uses velocity to help identify lithology and

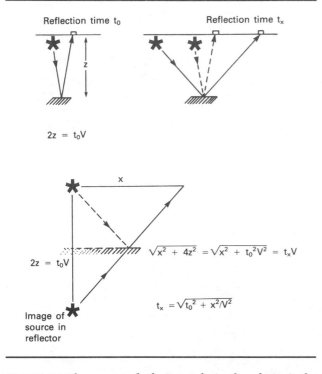

$$2z = t_0 V$$

$$\sqrt{x^2 + 4z^2} = \sqrt{x^2 + t_0^2 V^2} = t_x V$$

$$2z = t_0 V$$

$$t_x = \sqrt{t_0^2 + x^2/V^2}$$

Image of source in reflector

FIGURE 6.5 *The concept of velocity analysis: the velocity is the extra distance divided by the extra time. Reprinted by permission of IHRDC Press from Anstey, 1980a, fig. 8, p. 13.*

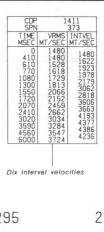

Dix interval velocities

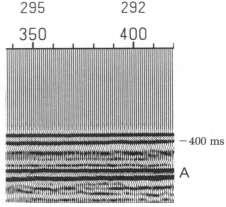

FIGURE 6.6 *Typical example of velocity analysis results displayed along the top of a seismic section. CDP, common depth point; SPN, shotpoint number; TIME MSEC, two-way time to reflector for which the normal moveout velocity has been calculated; VRMS, velocity root mean square, assumed to be equivalent to NMO for small offset; INTVEL, interval velocity calculated using the Dix equation. Courtesy Statoil.*

to convert seismic times to depth. Velocities can be calculated from seismic data using normal-moveout corrections. Normal-movement (NMO) velocities are used in the CMP stacking to bring the arrival time of a particular reflection to the same traveltime for different source-to-receiver spacings (offsets). As figure 6.5 demonstrates, the principle behind the calculation of NMO velocity is that the extra distance between source and receiver divided by the extra traveltime gives the velocity. For subsurface geometries that are relatively simple (flat layers, conformable dipping surfaces, etc.), NMO or stacking velocities have a fairly straightforward relationship to average and interval velocity. Dix (1955) showed that for uniform horizontal layers and small offsets, the NMO velocities are equivalent to the root-mean-square velocity ($VRMS$), the time-weighted root-mean-square value for a series of layers, and that interval velocity can be calculated from the equation:

$$\text{internal velocity} = \frac{(T_2 \times VRMS_2^2 - T_1 \times VRMS_1^2)^{1/2}}{(T_2 - T_1)},$$

(6.2)

where

T_2 = two-way time to deeper level,
T_1 = two-way time to shallower level,
$VRMS_{1-2}$ = calculated root-mean-square velocity to the respective level,

and $VRMS$ is the weighted root mean square of the component interval velocities. It is always greater than the actual interval velocity for a geological sequence, except where there is only one layer involved.

The Dix velocities are correct only for horizontal layered strata and are larger than the true interval velocities for dipping reflectors. Values for dipping reflectors can be corrected by dividing by the cosine of the dip. Also, the error of interval velocities calculated for thin intervals (less than 100 ms) may be unacceptably high. In favorable circumstances, however, interval velocity calculated from the Dix equation can be very diagnostic and helpful to the interpreter. They are especially useful because it can be estimated directly from seismic data. Velocity analyses to obtain NMO velocities for the processing are performed every kilometer or so along the seismic line. The results of the velocity analyses are often displayed along the tops of seismic sections, showing time as $VRMS$ (the assumption is made that $VRMS$ approximates NMO velocity), and Dix interval velocities (fig. 6.6).

168

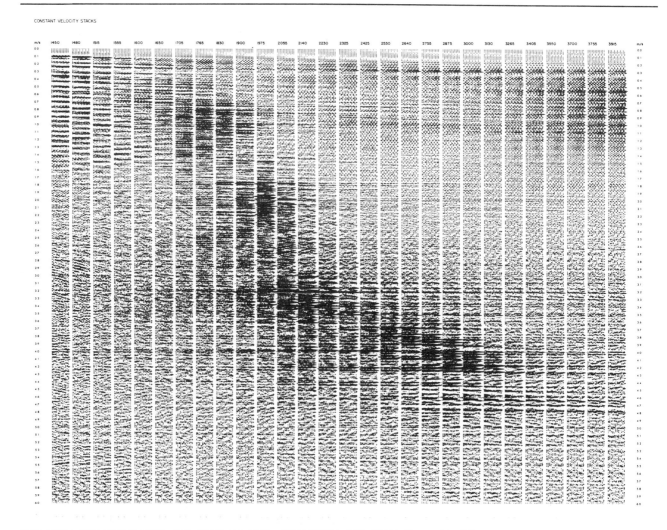

CONSTANT VELOCITY STACKS

FIGURE 6.7 *A constant-velocity stack. The data for a common midpoint gather are stacked for a wide range of velocities. The correct velocity will result in a reflection having its maximum amplitude. Courtesy Merlin Profilers Ltd.*

The Dix interval velocities displayed along the section top can be used if the interval velocities were calculated from the same reflections as those used as picks during the interpretation. Unfortunately, they are rarely coincident or consistent between velocity analyses. The levels picked during processing are usually made without reference to a specific reflection but, instead, are chosen on the basis of reflection strength at each location in the velocity analysis.

If the values displayed on the seismic sections are not adequate to determine the required interval velocities, velocities can be estimated using the raw velocity-analysis data. It is usually possible to obtain copies of the original velocity-analysis data. The data is presented in a variety of forms (constant-velocity stacks, corrected gathers, function-velocity stacks, etc.). Constant-velocity stacks show the CDP gather stacked for a series of constant velocities (fig. 6.7). The correct velocity for a particular time pro-

duces the maximum reflection amplitude. In a corrected gather display the correct velocity for a particular time flattens the reflection (fig. 6.8). For too high a velocity the reflectors dip down and for too low a velocity the reflections dip upward. To find the stacking velocity of a reflection, the corrected gather display is scanned to find the velocity that best flattens the reflection.

Perhaps the most convenient plots to use are those that show how well reflections from a particular CMP gather stack for a wide range of stacking velocities (fig. 6.9). The plots are constructed by stacking the CMP traces at small time increments down the traces, using a range of reasonable stacking velocities each time. The stacking veloci-

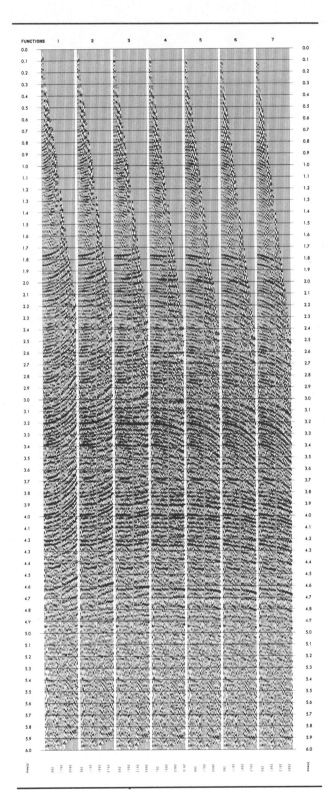

FIGURE 6.8 *Example of corrected gather display. Courtesy Merlin Profilers Ltd.*

ties define hyperbolic curves which are fitted to the traces. The best velocity provides the best-fit hyperbola (fig. 6.10). The results are presented graphically, showing time versus velocity and contours or some other statistical summary of the degree of stacking achieved by a particular velocity. The plots are interpreted by observing which velocity provides the best fit to the traces for a particular reflection. Problems arise with poor-quality data, where noise can totally obscure the velocity relationship. Multiples are a problem, especially as they generally stack at a lower velocity than primaries for a particular time. Figure 6.11a shows an example of a water bottom multiple completely dominating a velocity plot. Figure 6.11b shows the velocity spectrum after removal of the multiple.

The following tips may help interpretation of velocity plots:

1. If available, check relevant well logs to find the anticipated velocity breaks and changes.
2. Assume that velocity increases with depth unless a local decrease is expected.
3. Care must be taken to avoid picking the velocities of multiples and other noise. Pick on the high side of the contoured values to avoid picking multiples.
4. Pick strong reflections. The acoustic-impedance contrast must be reasonably large to produce a reliable correlation point on the velocity plot.
5. Check the velocities for geological plausibility by computing Dix interval velocities.
6. Look at the lateral interval-velocity picture from several locations along a section of the velocity analysis and check that it fits the geology.
7. Correct velocities of dipping reflectors by dividing by the cosine of the dip.

In practice Dix interval velocities are rarely more accurate than 400 m/s for a single observation and may be considerably less accurate for short intervals (100 ms or less). The inaccuracies in the Dix velocities usually become apparent when well–check shot data are available. There are a number of reasons for this:

1. Difference in the raypaths—check shots are near vertical and travel only one way
2. Inaccuracies, errors, and false geometric assumptions concerning the stacking velocities
3. Departure from the assumption of horizontal layering for stacking velocities

In regard to the last of these, Hubral and Krey (1981) have proposed an alternative method for obtaining interval velocities from surface measurements, which gives promise of being superior to the Dix method when the velocity layering is not horizontal.

In addition to the above problems, there are several

170

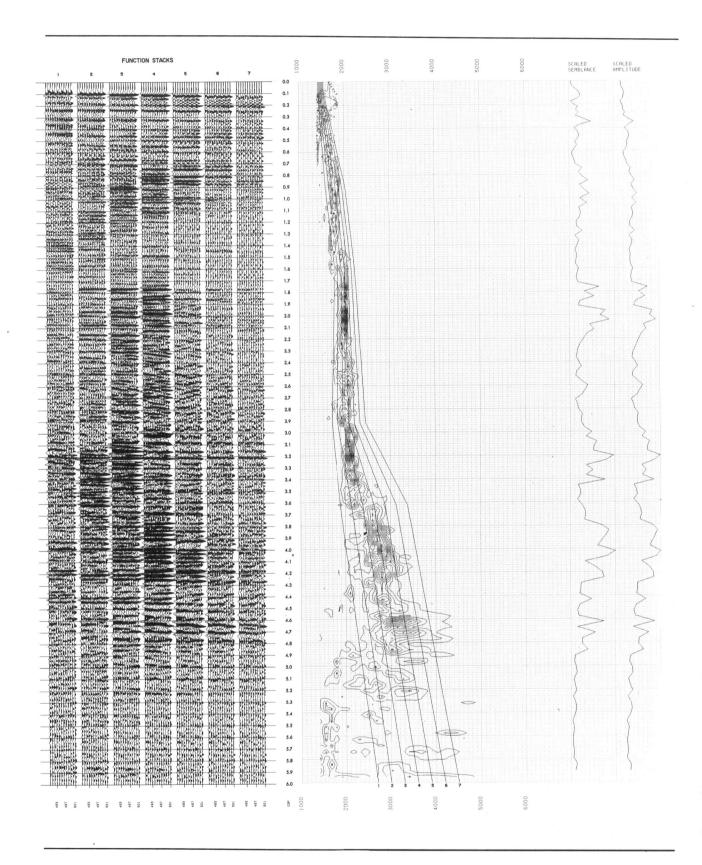

FIGURE 6.9 *Example of a velocity spectrum display. Courtesy Merlin Profilers Ltd.*

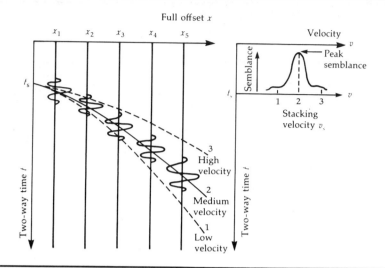

FIGURE 6.10 *Hyperbolic sweep of CMP gather to determine stacking velocity Vs at a time ts. This process is repeated at constant time intervals down the stack. Reprinted by permission of IHRDC Press from Robinson, 1983, fig. 2.29, p. 93.*

pitfalls of which the interpreter must beware when using Dix interval velocities for depth conversion; and there are certain geological situations when their use should be avoided (fig. 6.12). To obtain the best results, velocity analyses should be made with regard to the following points (Anstey, 1977):

1. Locate analyses at the crests and troughs of folds where conditions approximate uniform horizontal layering (1 on fig. 6.12). Velocity determinations on the flank (6 on fig. 6.12) would produce unrealistically high velocities.
2. Avoid CMP gather locations where the raypaths will have passed through faulted or disturbed zones (area 2 on fig. 6.12). However, within this constraint, analyses should be made on each side of the fault.
3. Avoid analyses at levels where there are divergent reflectors causing interference and distorting the deeper raypaths (area 3).
4. Avoid locations where raypaths will have traveled through an obvious near-surface anomaly (area 4).
5. Locate analyses over areas where intermittent reflections are visible at depth (area 5) as they may provide the only velocity information at depth.

Greater reliability can be obtained by statistical treatment of many observations. If the Dix interval velocities are to be used for depth conversion, it may be necessary to edit, smooth, re-edit and smooth again to produce a satisfactory interval-velocity map. The application of good

geological sense is often one of the best tools for reconciling a velocity distribution.

Velocity plots and Dix interval velocities have applications other than depth conversion. They can often provide a quick indication if a noticeable improvement could be expected from reprocessing the seismic section using a new set of velocities, and can sometimes help in tying reflectors across large faults, etc.

Anstey (1977) and Robinson (1983) are recommended for a detailed discussion of the topic.

WELL DATA

Well control is not essential for the successful interpretation of seismic sections; but, when available, it is an invaluable aid to the interpreter. It provides the link between lithology and seismic reflections and stratigraphic calibration of seismic-sequence boundaries. The quantity and quality of well data varies between wells and areas. In many pre-1970 wells the available data can be very sparse by present standards. During the past ten years there has been an encouraging tendency to collect all relevant well data comprehensively. The data comes in two main forms: continuous logs and analysis of actual rock samples (cuttings and cores obtained during drilling).

WIRELINE LOGS

Continuous wireline logs are produced by instruments lowered down a wellbore to sense remotely the physical properties of the rock formations immediately adjacent to the wellbore. Depending on their type, the tools are able to resolve individual beds ranging in minimum thickness from a few centimeters, to over 1 meter. A variety of logs are usually run in a well to measure such properties as resistivity, natural gamma ray radiation, acoustic proper-

172

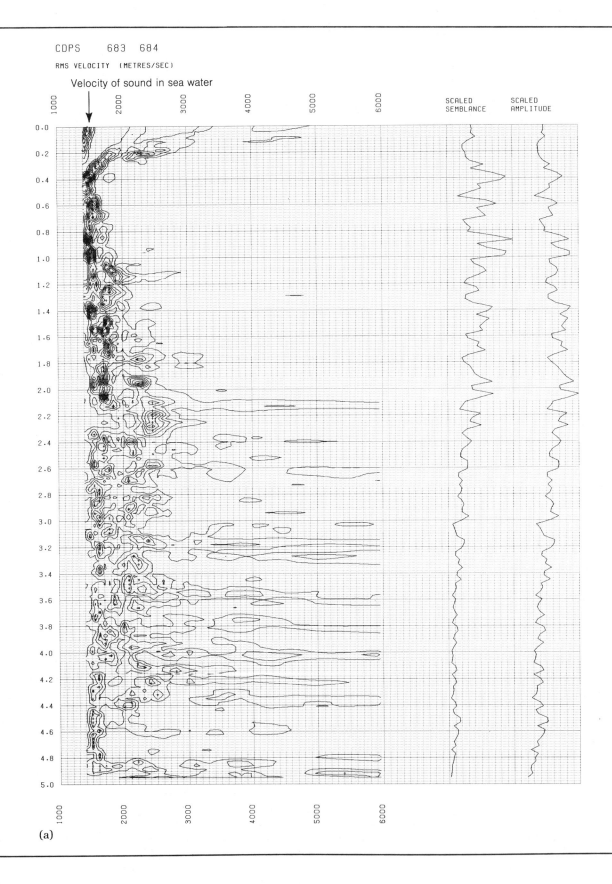

CDPS   683   684

RMS VELOCITY (METRES/SEC)

Velocity of sound in sea water

SCALED SEMBLANCE

SCALED AMPLITUDE

(a)

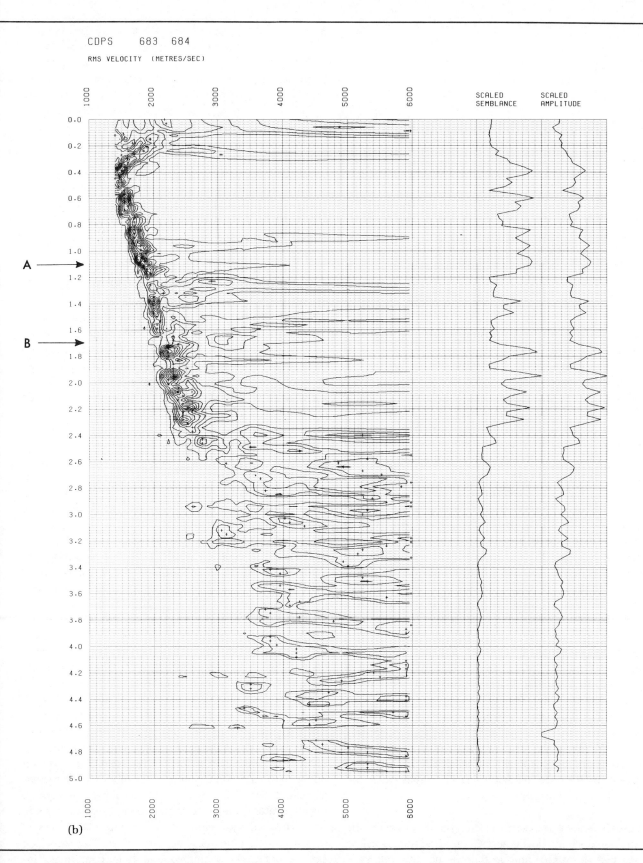

CDPS   683 684

RMS VELOCITY (METRES/SEC)

SCALED
SEMBLANCE

SCALED
AMPLITUDE

A →

B →

(b)

FIGURE 6.11 *Velocity analysis from a seismic line in the North Sea. (a) The water-layer reverberations (the vertical alignment below 1500 m/s) are so severe that no portion of the primary function can be interpreted. (b) The velocity analysis after prestack multiple attenuation of the unstacked traces reveals the primary velocity function. Courtesy Merlin Profilers Ltd.*

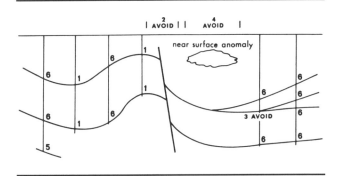

FIGURE 6.12 *Schematic geological section depicting areas for velocity analysis (regions 1, 5, and 6). Areas 2, 3, and 4 should be avoided. Reprinted by permission of IHRDC Press from Anstey, 1977; after Blackburn, 1980.*

ties, etc. Of these, the compensated density and compensated sonic logs are of the greatest interest to the interpreter. The compensated formation density log uses a gamma ray source to bombard the formation with gamma rays. Two detectors measure the intensity of back scatter from the formation which, after corrections, is approximately proportional to the electron density in the rock. This in turn can be equated to the actual rock density. Logs are invariably recorded on to digital tape, making computer manipulation of the data much easier.

The sonic log, which measures the traveltime of ultrasonic sound waves between two closely spaced receivers (varying from 0.75 m to about 3 m apart depending on the tool type), provides a value of rock velocity immediately adjacent to the borehole. The results are not normally displayed as velocity but in units of transit time over a one-foot interval—microseconds per foot (fig. 6.13). With luck, the sonic log will show the integrated traveltime (ITT) as ticks along one side of the scale grid containing the sonic log curve (fig. 6.13). The spacing between ticks gives the thickness of rock equivalent to one millisecond one-way time. The ITT is usually displayed with small ticks every millisecond and larger ticks every 10 milliseconds—both one-way time (OWT). Some logs display ticks only every 10 milliseconds OWT. In rare cases where no ITT is available, velocities can be obtained from the sonic curve, averaged over intervals and then converted to time thickness as required.

Useful as they are, the sonic log ITT times suffer the following disadvantages:

The sonic is not run to surface. Both on- and offshore the sonic log usually begins several hundred meters below sea bed or surface and so there is no time reference datum for the ITT times—the time from sea level or surface to the top of logs is unknown.

Any tool malfunction or gap in the log coverage will produce a break in the continuous velocity information.

The ITT assumes a constant velocity over a small interval. In fact, the sonic log can be badly affected by microfractures, vugs, borehole washouts (enlarged hole), and changed rock properties due to destressing of the rocks in the immediate borehole vicinity. Other errors may arise from instrumentation and calibration errors.

The velocities measured by the sonic tool may not be directly comparable to those affecting the seismic. The sonic tool investigates over small transmission distances at ultrasonic frequencies. The seismic method investigates over long transmission distances in layered, possibly dipping, strata, at much lower frequencies.

Not surprisingly, even when it is possible to make an overall tie between well and seismic section using the sonic log, discrepancies frequently occur in the detailed correlation. However, in the absence of further velocity information, much can be done with the sonic log alone or in combination with the density log. The curves from the sonic and density logs can be combined to produce a log of acoustic impedance. This is the first step towards producing a synthetic seismogram.

Sonic Log and Calibrated Velocity Log. To overcome the inherent uncertainties of the sonic log in tying the well to the seismic section, check-shot or velocity surveys were introduced (fig. 6.14). A geophone is lowered down the well and shots are fired at the surface. In this manner the exact traveltimes to known depths can be found. Check shots are made with a geophone clamped to the borehole wall at various depths. Usually check-shot recordings are made a few meters below important boundaries and at other points, such that recordings are made with a spacing of about 100 m. As the accuracy is not better than about 0.5 to 1 ms, closer spacings would produce unacceptable errors in interval velocity determination. Check velocity measurements are comparable to the seismic data, as they are measured over long transmission distance with typical seismic frequencies. Theoretically, only one good check shot is required to provide a time/depth reference datum for the sonic log integrated traveltimes. However, because of inaccuracies and other differences between continuous logged velocity and check shots, a number of calibration points are required. Even when a full suite of calibration points is available, there are usually small discrepancies between the sonic log integrated traveltimes and the velocity shot data. These differences are reconciled by a calibration procedure. Both sets of measurements potentially contain error. The sonic log can be affected by unfavorable hole conditions, instrumentation errors, and the difference in wavelet frequency and travel paths compared with the velocity sur-

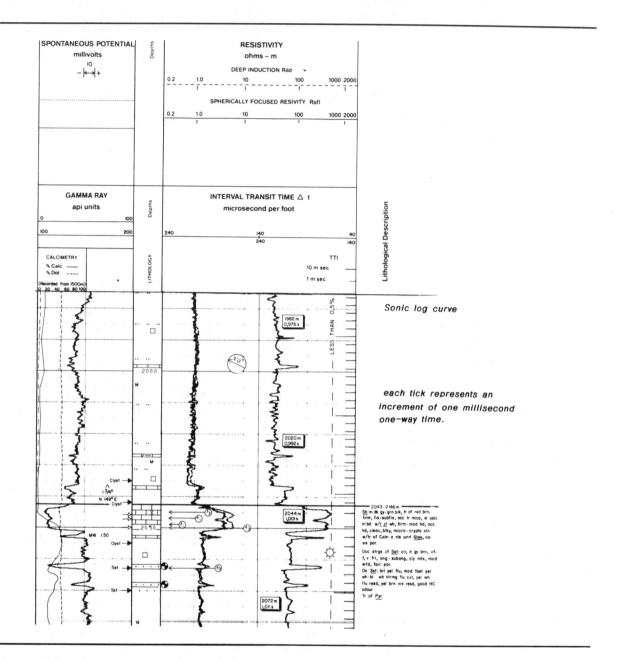

FIGURE 6.13 *Typical wireline-log suite (ISF sonic) including the sonic log. The ticks along the right side of the log are increments of one-way time. Courtesy Norsk Hydro.*

176

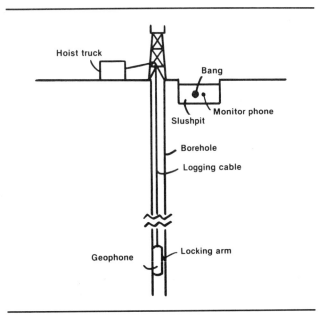

FIGURE 6.14 *The basic arrangement for a velocity survey in a borehole. Reprinted by permission of IHRDC Press from Anstey, 1980a, fig. 82, p. 105.*

vey. The velocity survey contractor often has insufficient lithological information to edit correctly problem sections of the sonic log. In such cases the tendency is to under-, rather than over-, edit. The editing process, often relying on subjective judgment, is an obvious source of potential, if small, error. The velocity survey results are also not free from error. Good check-shot data is likely to be within ± 0.5 ms, but errors due to raypath, location of survey points not coinciding with error trend changes, and the problem of where to pick the true arrival time on the received wavelet, are all potential sources of error.

Figure 6.15 shows part of a typical velocity log. The display shows the integrated traveltime (in either one- or two-way time), the edited sonic log curve and the check-shot points and times. The times are referred to a datum (e.g., mean sea level), which may be different from the log datum (e.g., log depths referred to the rotary table, RT, or kelly bushing, KB).

Not unexpectedly, following the calibration, it is quite common to find that not all check shots are in agreement with the corrected integrated traveltimes. The corrected integrated traveltimes have been adjusted to take into account possible error in the check-shot times. Unless the correction procedure is suspect, the corrected integrated traveltimes should be used. To find the traveltime to a given depth we simply read the corresponding integrated traveltime value—and trust that the calibration was good. If serious problems arise in making a tie between the well and seismic section, it may be necessary to go back to the

sonic and velocity survey calibrations to look for possible problems.

LITHOLOGICAL DATA

The second source of well information comes from the study of actual rock samples from the well. This material comes in three forms, ditch cuttings, sidewall cores, and conventional cores.

Ditch cuttings are rock fragments produced during drilling and collected in a sample that mixes rocks from several meters of drilled hole, and are used by wellsite geologists to make lithological logs. The bulk of micropaleontological and palynological age datings are made from this source. Both of these age-dating methods are relatively reliable at the level of geological stages, but become less precise for smaller time intervals. Both are also, to some degree, facies dependent. The difficulty in making definitive age determinations from ditch cuttings, is, in some instances, compounded due to too coarse a sampling interval and resulting dilution of the sample by caved material plucked from the borehole wall. Individual samples are usually grouped together into larger samples (e.g., ten 3-m samples grouped together into a 30-m interval), making it easy to miss a key horizon. Diagnostic fauna or flora are commonly very scarce, and it is also easy to overlook them in a diluted sample.

Sidewall core samples are small cylindrical samples, 1.5 cm to 2.5 cm long, obtained by a wireline tool after drilling. The samples are superior to ditch cuttings as they come from precisely (usually) known depths and, in comparison with the ditch cuttings, the individual samples are large. However, due to the high costs of rig time, it is unusual for more than one hundred sidewall cores to be taken in a well.

Full size *continuous cores* are cylindrical samples of rock up to 30 m long taken while drilling. They are the best form of sample and the least frequently taken. Many wells are drilled without any cores being cut.

The rock samples and wireline logs form the basis for a whole range of studies, ranging from subsurface correlations, facies analysis, stratigraphic studies, geochemistry, age dating, etc. The results of these studies may be available in a number of reports but are often summarized in a composite (sometimes called completion) log. The composite log usually comprises:

a. A lithological description, including paleontological information
b. Several log curves—typically, the gamma ray, spontaneous potential, resistivity, sonic, and caliper (a measurement of the borehole diameter), curves
c. The interpreted formation identification
d. Details of hydrocarbon shows and tests

The composite log is usually an excellent summary but

177

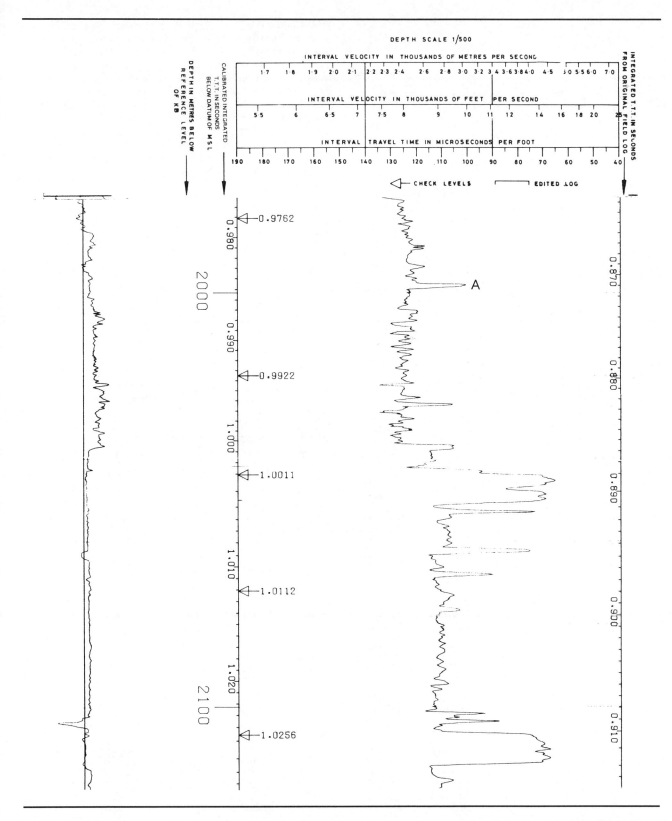

FIGURE 6.15 *Example of a calibrated velocity log. The integrated TTT (total traveltime) in seconds from the original field-log display on the left are the one-way times from the top of the sonic-log runs in the well. The calibrated times are shown to the left, referenced to a datum, in this case mean sea level. The check-shot locations are indicated by the arrows together with check-shot one-way time. The log depths are often set to a different datum from the calibrated times. Courtesy Norsk Hydro.*

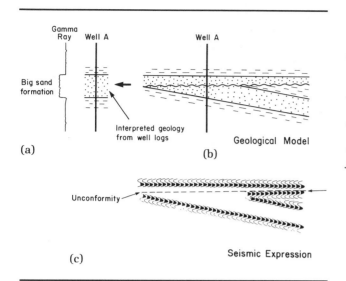

(a)

(b)

(c)

FIGURE 6.16 *Diagram illustrating potential difference between well stratigraphy and seismic stratigraphy.* (a) *A well has encountered a thick sand interval within a shale sequence. The sand cannot be subdivided on the basis of log response. The sand is duly given litho-stratigraphic formation status.* (b) *Geological model showing that in fact the sand consists of two bodies; an overlying and a subcropping unit. An unconformity separates the two sands. As the sands above and below the unconformity are very similar the unconformity is not recognized in the well logs.* (c) *Seismic expression: The unconformity can be seen easily and projected to its correct position in the well.*

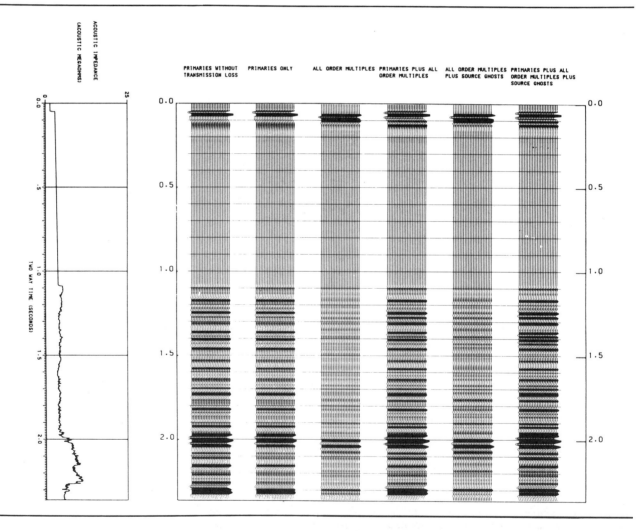

FIGURE 6.17 *Example of a synthetic seismogram. Courtesy Merlin Profilers Ltd.*

should be treated with a little caution as it mixes factual data (the log curves) with interpreted information—for example, interpreted lithology from ditch cuttings and log response, paleontological dates, and information boundaries.

It is the latter two categories that can cause problems for the interpreter. Unquestioning acceptance of formation boundaries and age dating on the composite log can be very misleading. Some composite logs may be from wells drilled when knowledge of the area was scanty and imprecise, and the interpretation could be wrong. This can be a serious problem, especially in new areas that may have few wells all drilled on structural anomalies (usually, very poor locations to provide a good insight into a basin's stratigraphy).

The well log stratigraphy is dominantly lithostratigraphic (arising mainly from the correlation of wireline logs guided by paleontological control), whereas the seismic derived stratigraphy is both chronostratigraphic and lithostratigraphic. This can lead to significant differences in the placing of sequence boundaries (unconformities) in the wells and on the seismic record. The seismic section can be the more powerful tool for demonstrating unconformity relationships (fig. 6.16).

SYNTHETIC SEISMOGRAMS

It is now fairly standard practice to produce synthetic seismograms for exploration wells. Their production requires edited versions of the sonic and density logs from which reflectivity coefficients are calculated for the well. The reflectivity coefficients are convolved with a suitable zero or minimum-phase wavelet with a frequency response and band width similar to the seismic sections. A typical synthetic seismogram display is shown in figure 6.17. Synthetic seismograms usually include a variety of different displays (traces showing primaries—i.e., reflections from acoustic-impedance boundaries—only, primaries with transmission loss, all-order multiples, primaries plus all-order multiples, primaries and short-term multiples, ghosts, etc.).Correlation of the synthetic traces to seismic sections is a trial-and-error procedure but the results are often extremely helpful in tying a well to a seismic section (fig. 6.18). Obviously, to tie, the synthetic seismogram should be displayed in the same polarity and have a similar wavelet shape to the real seismic data. If the seismic record has been processed successfully, most of the long-term multiples should have been removed. In such cases a synthetic seismogram display showing primaries and short-term multiples (those which affect the pulse shape but do not generate new reflections) often provides the best match to the seismic section. The synthetic seismogram not only helps to recognize individual reflections, but can also give a valuable guide to diagnostic reflection character. A drawback of many synthetic

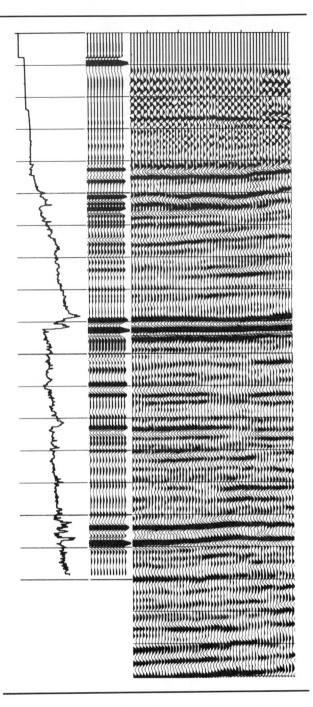

FIGURE 6.18 *Example of a tie between well log, synthetic seismogram, and seismic section. Courtesy Merlin Profilers Ltd.*

seismograms is that they are often made by constructing a wavelet with constant frequency for the entire display. Usually the synthetic wavelet which is convolved with the reflection series is chosen to coincide with the frequency range of the seismic wave over a particular interval—that

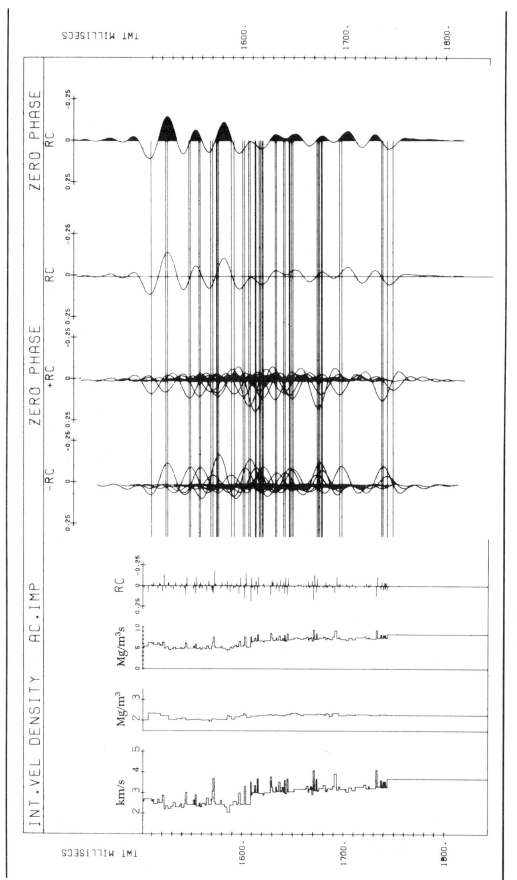

FIGURE 6.19 *Example of an expanded-scale synthetic seismogram. Courtesy Norsk Hydro.*

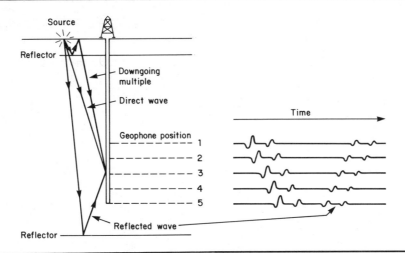

FIGURE 6.20 *Diagram showing principle of the vertical seismic profiles.*

containing reservoir zones, for example. Mismatches between the synthetic seismic wavelet and the actual seismic wavelet frequency can make it difficult to make a match between the synthetic and seismic section outside of the original target interval.

Although the synthetic seismogram helps the tie between well and seismic section, the commonly available display does not allow, except for widely spaced reflectors, an analysis of reflector origin. This can be especially important for detailed studies when the reflecting boundaries are so close that they produce a trace that is an interference composite. To analyze the effects of closely spaced reflecting boundaries, a synthetic seismogram displayed at expanded scale and showing the effects produced by the individual reflectors is required (fig. 6.19). In simple cases the origin of the reflector can be traced back to one acoustic-impedance contrast which makes the main contribution to the reflector of the composite trace. In other, more complex cases, several acoustic-impedance contrasts are equally important in forming the composite reflector and geological reasoning is necessary to decide which are of significance in the study area. As a general rule the significance of events of short duration (less than half a cycle) should be accepted only if they can be traced between more than two wells in the immediate area. Attributing a reflector's origin to a particular acoustic-impedance contrast can result in a lead or lag to the real two-way time of the event. The lead or lag will depend on wavelet type and interference from neighboring acoustic-impedance contrasts.

Following the above process to its logical conclusion leads to seismic modeling. A well only gives information at its location and sometimes, to make a tie, it is necessary to consider lateral thickness changes and their effect on the seismic. Ideally, it should be possible to model such changes and compare the results with the seismic section.

Neidell and Poggiagliolmi (1977) and Meckel and Nath (1977) give examples of 2-D modeling and its applications.

VERTICAL SEISMIC PROFILES

Useful as they are, synthetic seismograms derived from check-shot data and well logs suffer from several limitations. They are essentially interpretive insofar as the input wavelet is estimated, as are other effects such as transmission losses, etc. The matching of synthetic seismograms and seismic sections at well locations is partly a matter of good judgment, but there is also an element of trial and error.

A more sophisticated comparison between the seismic section and well results can be obtained by converting the velocity check-shot data into a vertical seismic profile (VSP), a technique pioneered by the Russian oil industry. Vertical seismic profiling uses the same setup as a standard check-shot survey, except that more geophone locations are required, typically at a regular spacing of no more than 30 m (100 ft), and the recording lasts for several seconds. Figure 6.20 illustrates the principle of the technique. A geophone, clamped to the borehole wall, receives both direct downgoing waves from the source shot and downgoing multiples from the underside of major acoustic-impedance contrasts (particularly the surface). On a typical VSP display, with increasing time displayed horizontally and depth vertically, the downgoing rays appear as events whose traveltime increases with depth (fig. 6.20). Reflected arrivals (upcoming waves from the reflectors beneath the geophone) appear as reflections with increasing traveltime toward the surface. An example of a primitive display taken from Anstey (1980a) is shown in figure 6.21. AD is the downgoing

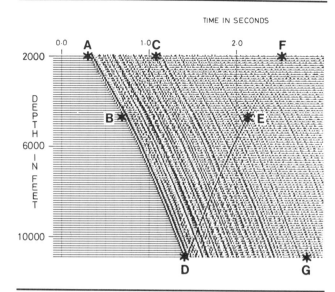

FIGURE 6.21 *A VSP with very strong downgoing reverberations. Courtesy Seismograph Service Limited.*

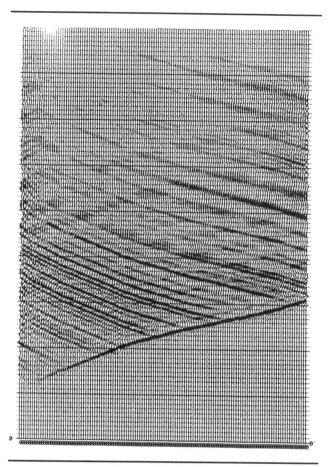

FIGURE 6.22 *A VSP with processing to enhance the downgoing direct signal and the upcoming reflected signals. Courtesy United States Geological Survey.*

direct wave, paralleled by numerous multiple reflections. Upcoming reflections cut up across from left to right (e.g., BC, DEF). The reflections can be seen better by squinting along the alignment. Further processing can be applied to enhance the reflections and attenuate the downgoing waves (fig. 6.22). Figure 6.23 shows an example, taken from Balch et al. (1982), of a processed VSP and how it can be tied to a well lithology log. A portion of conventional seismic profile runs horizontally across the top of the figure. Reflections can be tied to the well (e.g., the well labeled Madison Group) by simply following the event back down the VSP to its origin and comparing this with the acoustic impedance and lithology changes in the well. Alternatively, starting at the well, reflections arising at an acoustic-impedance boundary can be traced back up to the surface to see where they appear in the total seismic response. An alternative display is shown in figure 6.24. The upcoming reflections have been enhanced and each trace has been delayed by the time of the direct downgoing signal. The display looks like a seismic section but the horizontal scale is depth down the borehole. If an event is not horizontal on this display, it indicates that the reflector dips; but the dip direction cannot be determined from the display. The relative ease of correlation between well and seismic section using a VSP not only removes much of the trial and error associated with the matching of seismic and synthetic seismic sections, but also offers the following advantages:

a. Reflections can be tied directly from the seismic record to the well log.

b. Multiples are readily identified.

c. Dip, but not its direction, can be found. This can provide confirmation of wireline dipmeter surveys.

d. Faults, or other boundaries, can be detected by offsets of events on the VSP. However their direction relative to the borehole cannot be determined.

e. Reflections beneath the well's terminal depth (TD) can be obtained and evaluated.

f. Reflection coefficients can be calculated accurately.

g. Detailed interval velocity can be calculated.

h. An evaluation of what the surface seismic section can and cannot resolve can be made.

i. It is possible to evaluate the bulk porosity of an interval if the lithology and interval velocity are known.

Vertical seismic profiles offer a wide variety of applications to seismic exploration problems. Kennett et al. (1980), Hubbard (1979), and Gal'perin (1973) discuss their application.

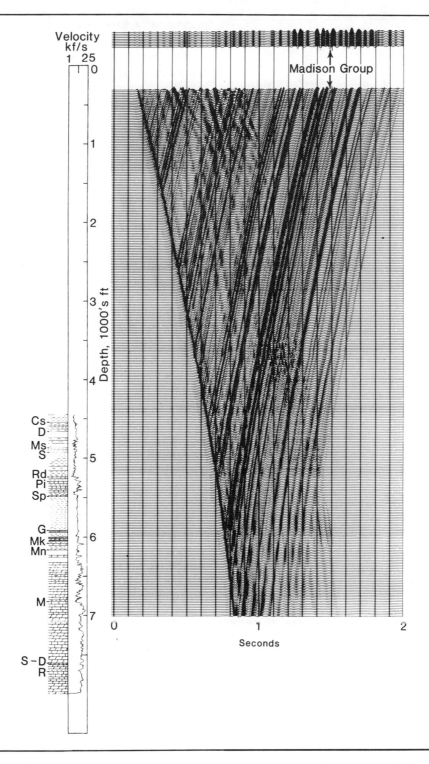

FIGURE 6.23 *Vertical seismic profile from the Sam Garry Madison No. 1 well, Bell Creek oil field, Montana, showing tie from lithology log on the left to surface seismic data drawn across the top. Reprinted by permission of the SEG from Balch et al., 1982.*

184

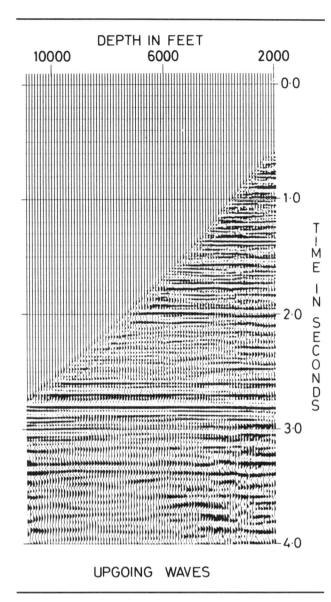

DEPTH IN FEET

10000   6000   2000

TIME IN SECONDS

UPGOING WAVES

FIGURE 6.24 *Selective enhancement of the upcoming reflections of Figure 6.20. Courtesy Seismograph Service Limited.*

SEISMIC REFRACTION

The technique of seismic refraction was the main seismic method used a few decades ago. Since the 1960s refraction seismics have been replaced by the now ubiquitous seismic-reflection method. It is unlikely that many interpreters will be required to interpret seismic-refraction data, but it still has a place in exploration for special applications such as:

Mapping horizons that underlie complex geological structures like salt domes, igneous intrusions, etc.

Mapping horizons beyond the normal depth range of commercial reflection seismic sections

Providing control data for reflection interpretations

However, refraction seismics are still in everyday use and are an essential part of the data acquisition for reflection seismics on land where the method is used to determine the thickness of near-surface velocity layers for use in static corrections.

The refraction method is based on the effect of seismic raypaths being bent at velocity discontinuities in accordance with Snell's Law. Snell's Law states that $V_1/V_2 = \sin a/\sin b$, where V_1 and V_2 are the seismic velocities on either side of a boundary. At the critical angle of a, when $b = 90°$, the seismic wave is refracted along the plane of the boundary. In the normal case where velocity increases with depth, the first arrival will travel a refraction path that gets deeper into the surface as the offset distance increases. From such data, the refraction velocity in each layer and the depth to each refracting horizon can be calculated. Musgrove (1967) and Dobrin (1976) describe refraction methods, field techniques, and case histories.

MAGNETIC METHODS

Magnetic methods are based on the fact that some rock types are highly magnetized (e.g., most basic igneous rocks) and that the magnetic effect of these rocks distort locally the Earth's magnetic field. Magnetic data are relatively inexpensive to acquire and can be obtained by airborne surveys. They are usually collected as regional reconnaissance surveys or as magnetic profiles surveyed along the course of actual seismic profiles. The data are collected by comparing local values of the magnetic field strength against a reference, usually the total Earth field. Differences between the local and reference fields are used to compile an anomaly map, with contours showing the value in gammas (1 γ = 10^{-5} oersted) above or below the reference. Magnetized material, such as volcanic or igneous rocks, will show as highs on an anomaly map. The magnitude of an anomaly will depend on the size of the magnetized body, strength of its magnetic field, and the depth to which it is buried.

Magnetic anomaly maps can often be used as a very cost-effective way to locate fault trends, basement highs,

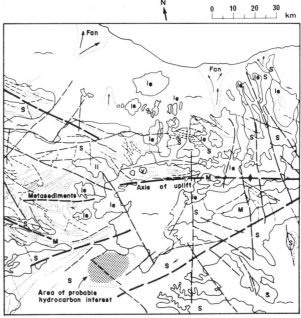

FIGURE 6.25 *Example of Landsat interpretation in hydrocarbon exploration in North Africa. Courtesy Geomorphological Services, Ltd.*

relative depth to basement, volcanic and igneous rocks, etc. They can be invaluable, especially when used in the early stages of an investigation to locate prospective areas and establish the broad structural framework for a region. The Society of Exploration Geophysicists (1971) and Dobrin (1976) describe magnetic methods in exploration.

GRAVITY METHODS
Gravity methods, like magnetics, are used mainly for reconnaissance work, especially on land where acquisition costs are low. Offshore, the collection of gravity data is more complex and costly because of the necessity for elaborate corrections and calibrations. Regional gravity surveys enable the delineation of sedimentary basins and calculations of total sediment thickness. Gravity and magnetic surveys are often integrated to provide a more detailed interpretation.

Gravity methods, similar to magnetics, compare local variations in gravitational attraction against a reference field. Dense rocks, such as igneous intrusions, volcanics, etc., produce local gravity highs; less dense rocks, such as sediments or granites, produce local gravity lows. Corrections are made for the height of observation (the free-air correction), the gravitational effect of the layer of rocks between the observation site and sea level (Bouguer correction), and the gravitational effects of the terrain. The resulting anomaly maps, of Bouguer anomaly values, are contoured in milligals. In suitable cases gravity data can be used to test the plausibility of a seismic interpretation. For example, gravity modeling can be used to estimate the depth to top basement, or perhaps identify whether a

shallow high consists of crystalline basement or sediments. A special publication of the Society of Exploration Geophysicists (1971) describes and discusses gravity methods applied to exploration.

SURFACE GEOLOGY
Surface geology can be a valuable source of information in both onshore and offshore areas. If the outcrop geology is relevant, it can provide much detailed information which can be extrapolated and used to model the subsurface. Typically, the outcrop geology can give details of stratigraphy, lithology, facies relationships and associations. These findings can often be extrapolated to subsurface conditions, to predict potential acoustic-impedance boundaries, structure, etc. In favorable situations, it may even be possible to correlate a prominent outcropping lithological marker (i.e., one possessing a significant acoustic-impedance boundary at either top or base) with a suitably located seismic line.

Outcrop geology can also be relevant to offshore areas, even in situations where there is no direct continuity between the two (e.g., when a marine basin is bordered by a major fault zone). Even in these cases the often thinner onshore record frequently reflects the lithofacies and the stratigraphic relationships developed offshore. The interpreter should be thoroughly familiar with details of any relevant onshore geology before starting an interpretation. Special attention should be given to lithofacies and strati-

186

graphic relationships. Of course, there are many instances when the outcrop geology onshore has little relevance. For example, the Precambrian and Paleozoic
metamorphic rocks of southern Norway give little hint of
the thick Mesozoic and Tertiary sediments present only a
few kilometers away offshore.

PHOTOGEOLOGY AND SATELLITE IMAGERY

Photogeology and satellite imagery can provide detailed
regional onshore data concerning tectonics and structural
geology, outcrop geology, lithology, stratigraphy, and
significant geomorphological features. It provides the
overview, placing the outcrop geology into a linking regional framework (fig. 6.25). It also often has the ability
to detect deeper structural lineaments that can give important clues to the deeper structural grain, not evident
from outcrop studies. Currently, Landsat is the chief
source of satellite imagery. In favorable situations Landsat
can be used to correlate faults between seismic lines.
Landsat has imaging sensors which detect radiation in
the green, red, and near-infrared spectral regions. Each
Landsat image covers approximately 34,000 km^2 (13,000
square miles). Numerous display options are available,
including false color, achieved by mixing the images obtained from the different spectral bands. Several other
satellite imaging systems are due to be launched in the
near future. Satellite imagery provides an inexpensive
method of obtaining a regional overview and can be invaluable to the seismic interpreter as an aid to defining
trends. Halbouty (1976, 1980) gives details of the interpretation and applications of satellite imagery to exploration.

Chapter 7   The Interpretation

MAKING A START

At this stage the interpreter should have a list of all the
data available for the interpretation of a seismic section
and should have studied all the available background
material—relevant geological and geophysical reports,
etc. If the selection of lines or surveys for interpretation is
obvious, this is the time to go ahead and order a set of full-
scale (migrated if available) lines. Usually, migrated lines
are preferable; but a check on data quality should be
made by ordering some unmigrated lines for comparison
with the migrated data. In rare cases the migrated data
are of much poorer quality (due to poor velocity control
during the processing, etc.) and better resolution is obtained using unmigrated lines. Generally, it is unnecessary to order a full set of unmigrated data. Individual
lines can be ordered later in the interpretation where a
check is desired or if problems are experienced with the
migrated version.

If, however, it is unclear which surveys or lines to
use—sometimes up to six or more surveys of various vin-
tages can be available for an area—it is better first to
order a set of half-scale lines for all surveys. In any case
the half-scale sections are most useful later in the interpretation for a review of all the lines and for gaining an
impression of the area's seismic character, structures, etc.
The half-scale lines can be checked and compared, and a
selection of lines and/or surveys made. Often the older
data have been superseded by newer lines; in other cases
they may provide a valuable infill to the newer survey
grids.

Once a final selection of seismic data is made, a new
shotpoint map(s) should be prepared showing only those
lines used in the interpretation. If computer facilities are
available, this can be done easily by editing the navigation
data and replotting the shotpoint maps. Alternatively, the
shotpoint maps can be hand drafted.

For an analysis of the well logs it is normally sufficient
to obtain copies, if available, of the composite, compensated sonic, compensated formation density, and velocity
survey logs. Other logs may be required for special studies. In some cases, especially in relatively unexplored

188

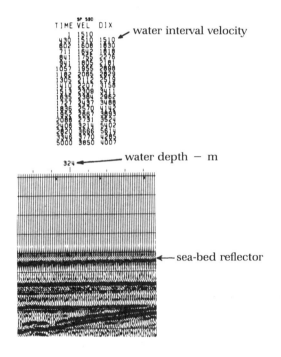

2.8 - 4.2	8 - 35	18/24
3.8 - 5.2	7 - 30	18/24
4.8 - 6.0	5 - 25	18/24

DISPLAY: GAIN = 11DB   BIAS = 30 %

POLARITY: **NORMAL** (S E G STANDARD) COMPRESSIONAL WAVE DISPLAYED
AS A TROUGH (WHITE)

HORIZONTAL SCALE   VERTICAL SCALE
FULL SCALE SECTIONS   1 : 25.000   FULL SCALE SECTIONS 10 CM/SEC.
HALF SCALE SECTIONS   1 : 50.000   HALF SCALE SECTIONS   5 CM/SEC.

BAR SCALE   SP.1   25M   40
            0   500M 1KM

(a) Read the seismic-section label.

water interval velocity

water depth — m

sea-bed reflector

(b) Calculate the traveltime in water
to find the sea-bed response.
This should always be positive.

$$\text{two-way time} = \frac{\text{distance}}{\text{velocity}} \times 2$$

$$t = \frac{324 \times 2}{1510} = 429 \text{ milliseconds.}$$

trough = compressional wave = normal polarity (SEG)

FIGURE 7.1 *Determining polarity.*

areas, it may be worth checking the basis for the formation tops given on the composite log.

At this stage, before any detailed analysis of the data has begun, it is advisable to keep a very open mind concerning the conclusions of previous seismic interpretation reports. This is especially important in relatively unexplored areas. The current project most probably has access to new data and information unavailable to prior interpreters. They may have come to erroneous conclusions based on the data available to them, and it is important not to be unduly influenced by previous findings. Keep an open mind!

SEISMIC POLARITY

Try to establish or confirm the polarity of the seismic display and, if possible, determine the type of wavelet aimed for by the processing.

Under the current SEG convention on normal-polarity sections, compressional reflections are displayed as troughs, but as peaks on reverse-polarity sections (fig. 2.6). Polarity and phase can usually be determined using one or more of the following techniques (fig. 7.1):

1. Polarity can usually be determined by reading the seismic label. This usually gives both the recording and display polarity. The deconvolution operators usually indicate the type of phase (minimum phase or zero phase).

2. Polarity can be checked by observing the nature of the reflection from an acoustic-impedance boundary of known sign. For example, the sea-bed reflector can be a good polarity indicator, because it will always produce a compressional reflection. The exact two-way time to the sea bed can be found by dividing twice the water depth (usually displayed along the top of the seismic section) by the velocity of sound in water. If the seismic section has been calibrated correctly using this method, it is often possible to confirm not only polarity, but also the processing phase (fig. 7.1). However, the sea-bed reflector can be spoiled during processing by muting of the shallow reflections. This is quite common in older data and in water less than 100 m deep. With land data it is better to use a strong reflection (if one is developed in the upper half of the seismic section) that from a boundary of known acoustic-impedance contrast. For example, the positive reflection coefficient expected at the top of a massive limestone beneath a thick claystone sequence could be used as a calibration point.

3. Perhaps the best method of determining polarity is to use a good well-to-seismic section tie, backed up by synthetic seismograms and/or vertical seismic profiles. Techniques for tying wells to seismic sections are discussed later in this chapter.

STATIC SHIFTS

When several surveys are involved it is common to find systematic differences in the seismic times to a given reflector at line intersections. These differences arise through miscalibration back to a reference datum, and must be resolved before beginning the interpretation. Older marine data, especially, may not be corrected to a sea-level reference datum. Systematic mis-ties can be 60 ms or more when seismic times are compared with times observed in the wells. In such situations it is not uncommon to find that the water depths calculated from the seismic sections are in conflict with the water depths measured by the ship's echo sounder. (The latter are recorded on each section below the shotpoint numbers.) Factors that may be contributing to this error include the following:

a. The echo sounder may have been set to record the depth below the ship, instead of below the sea-level datum.
b. The ship's position is determined at the antenna. As suggested in figure 7.2, this may be appropriate for the echo sounder, but a setback is required to relate the ship's position to that of the corresponding common midpoint.
c. The reflection times may not be corrected for the depth of the source and the streamer below the sea-level datum.
d. The sections may not have been processed to bring the maximum of the reflection envelope back to the correct traveltime. Without this processing, the time necessary for the reflection pulse to build up to its maximum envelope represents a lag, which may be several tens of milliseconds. The echo sounder, working with sharp-fronted pings of sound, is much less susceptible to this problem.

In modern work, well controlled and processed, none of the above should happen. All measurements should be referred to sea-level datum; all positions should be referred to the common midpoint identified by the shotpoint number; and all data should be processed so that the maximum reflection envelope occurs at the correct reflection time.

Frequently, however, we have to work with old data, and must harmonize reflection times at intersections between lines of different vintage. Then the sea floor, if deep enough to be recorded as a reflection by the streamer, gives us a good way of assessing the lag present on the reflection times.

First we must assess the setback problem by comparing observations on dip and strike lines. Then, with the locations corrected, we turn to the times. Figure 7.3 shows how a dipping sea floor may be used to calculate reflection lag time. At the two ends of the section, A and B, the

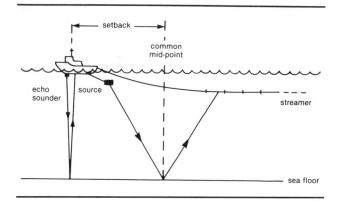

FIGURE 7.2 *The setback distance between positioning antenna and common midpoint. Reprinted by permission of IHRDC Press from Badley and Anstey, 1984, fig. A1-1, p. 163.*

water depths given by the echo sounder are 832 and 607 m. The corresponding reflection times for the sea floor are 1168 and 863 ms. Dividing the two-way difference of each echo-sounder depth by the difference of reflection times, we find that the local velocity in sea water is 1475 m/s. (We hope that the echo sounder was using the true velocity, properly measured by the velocimeter on the ship.) The correct reflection time at point A is therefore (2 × 832)/1475, or 1128 ms. Since our picked time was 1168 ms, we have a first estimate of the reflection time lag on this survey: 40 ms. The true zero time of our section should not be at AB, but at A'B', 40 ms later.

The same exercise performed on intersecting lines from another survey may yield a different lag (because of a different source, different instruments, and/or different processing). By correcting both surveys for their individual lags, we would hope to improve the line ties.

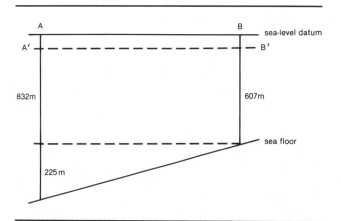

FIGURE 7.3 *A dipping sea floor may be used to calculate the reflection lag time, for sections not wavelet processed. Reprinted by permission of IHRDC Press from Badley and Anstey, 1984, fig. A1-2, p. 165.*

In practice, after establishing and correcting the lags, one survey showing a good tie to the well information is used as a reference, and the times of all other surveys adjusted to those of the reference survey by applying appropriate positive or negative static shifts. Once established, the static shifts must be used consistently throughout the interpretation.

Unfortunately, not all static shifts are systematic (e.g., onshore, where differences in weathering-zone corrections occur). In such cases the interpreter must make the best of a bad job, recording all mis-ties in the interpretation diary, so that they can be dealt with when preparing contour maps.

INITIAL GEOLOGICAL REVIEW

On completion of the data calibration, attention can be focused on the geological aspects of the seismic survey. At this point it is very tempting to tie any available wells into the seismic grid immediately. If possible, avoid the temptation for a little longer and have a good look at the seismic section, allowing it to give its own message before introducing any preconceptions that inevitably arise out of the well ties. Instead, using half-scale line if available, select successive dip lines (or every second, third, etc., depending on line spacing) and lay them on the floor or hang them on the wall. This should provide a good overview of the seismic section and give a good idea of the main structural features and also of the data quality, resolution, variability, etc. throughout the area.

Using the full data set, check each line for its quality, especially noting both lateral and vertical variations. Plot this data on a map. The map will have several uses: easier selection of lines for display; defining areas where the interpretation should be easy; helping in long-distance correlations; helping estimate a work schedule. Areas of poor data quality can arise for a number of reasons, ranging from bad data acquisition and processing to unfavorable geology. In the former case, if a problem is recognized and diagnosed at an early stage it may be possible to reprocess the data before proceeding with the interpretation. If the cause is geological, little can be done.

Nevertheless, changes of data quality can sometimes be helpful. For example, a sudden lateral change from good to poor data quality can be a direct indication of hydrocarbons in an underlying structure (fig. 4.52).

The next check is for likely multiple problems. Modern processing should have removed or severely attenuated most multiples; but they can still be a problem in detailed work, when the partly attenuated multiple(s) have the same strength as a weak primary event. Sometimes it can be helpful to mark the multiples, or where they are predicted, so as to avoid possible trouble later in the interpretation. Criteria for recognizing multiples were discussed in chapter 3.

Once likely data quality problems have been recog-

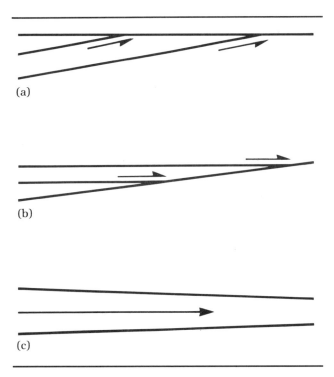

FIGURE 7.4 *Code for making sequence boundaries and reflection terminations. (a) Truncation and toplap—an arrow with the upper part of the arrowhead drawn. (b) Baselap: onlap and downlap—an arrow with the upper part of the arrowhead drawn. (c) A two-sided arrowhead is used for a termination not related to a sequence boundary.*

nized, the next stage of the review should concentrate on providing an overall picture of the area, its main features, and likely problems. The full seismic data base should be used and every line inspected. The major structural elements (dip trends, faults, horsts, grabens, basin axes, flexures, etc.) should be recorded on a map. It should be possible to subdivide the area vertically into stratigraphic intervals and laterally into structural provinces. The lateral subdivision into basins, highs, and so on is usually fairly straightforward; but the vertical subdivision is more involved and constitutes one of the main tasks facing the interpreter. Vertical subdivision is accomplished by recognizing seismic sequences. Seismic sequences, related terminology, and their significance are discussed in detail in chapter 4. Each seismic sequence should form a coherent unit corresponding to a depositional sequence, bounded by unconformities. To define and correlate a depositional sequence, the boundaries must be found and traced. The boundaries will usually be unconformities identified by discordant relationships between the reflectors. To locate sequence boundaries, view the section at a low angle along its length, first in one direction and then in the other—this often helps emphasize reflector relationships. Using a fine, sharp, red pencil, sequence boundaries can be indicated on seismic sections (fig. 7.4) with the following code:

A half-arrow with the tick downmost is used at the upper sequence boundary for toplap or truncation.

A half-arrow with the tick uppermost is used at the lower sequence boundary for baselap.

A complete arrow is used for a termination that neither toplaps, truncates, or baselaps.

The nature of the discordance is also the best indication of whether an unconformity results from erosion or deposition. However, in some cases no discordance can be demonstrated and character change can be used to locate sequence boundaries, as, for example, the boundary between the Zechstein and Triassic in figure 4.27. It will not be possible to recognize every possible seismic sequence in an area for a variety of reasons. Firstly, not all sequences may have seismically visible boundaries. If there is no change in acoustic impedance across a boundary, no reflection will be developed. Secondly, diagnostic discordant relationships, or significant character changes, may not be developed in the area or on the available seismic lines. Discordant relationships are often best developed at basin margins or in the vicinity of structures. Where the reflectors are parallel and there are no diagnostic character changes, it is impossible to recognize sequence boundaries; and it may be necessary to go outside the study area to find the discordant relationships. Just as with onshore geological outcrop mapping, where one outcrop can be a key locality for demonstrating critical geological relationships, a single seismic line may hold the key to an interpretation. Thirdly, many of the boundaries, even if accompanied by significant acoustic-impedance change, will be too closely spaced to be individually resolved. This becomes more of a problem with depth and the attendant loss in resolving power. Fourthly, in poor data areas, or because of depth factors, noise in the section obscures the critical reflector relationships, which in some cases can be quite subtle. These are only some of the factors that may frustrate all attempts to detect sequence boundaries.

However, the preceding approach should identify the main structural features and gross geological relationships, and provide a sound basis for subsequent detailed interpretation. Excepting in areas that are well known, a study of the seismic section alone will not be sufficient to conclusively identify the age of reflectors and lithologies. For this we require well information.

TYING WELL AND SEISMIC DATA

Although there are several intuitive approaches to reflector identification, there is no substitute for a good well-tie. Tying well and seismic data is an essential step in an interpretation and the process begins with an analysis of the data collected in the well.

In preparation for tying well data to the seismic section, a thorough review and analysis of the available well data,

including wells adjacent to the area, is essential. The results of the review are used to:

1. Calibrate the seismic section to a reference datum: The well times are assumed to be correct (unless there is evidence to the contrary) and systematic deviations in seismic time are corrected by an appropriate static shift.
2. Detect intersurvey static shifts: If older marine data is being used, it is possible that the seismic data are not corrected to the sea-level reference datum. This results in a systematic mis-tie between well(s) and seismic sections for the entire survey, and can produce seismic times up to 60 ms greater than those observed in the wells. Other systematic mis-tie effects can result from delays introduced during the processing and not accounted for in the calibration. Nonsystematic mis-ties can arise because of phase distortion, wavelet interference, or incorrect static corrections. It is too late to correct for such nonsystematic effects in the interpretation.
3. Provide a preliminary identification of the seismic sequence boundaries and other reflectors for both stratigraphic age and local lithology
4. Provide a detailed analysis of reflector origins

The well-log stratigraphy is dominantly lithostratigraphic (arising mainly from the correlation of wireline logs with subordinate paleontological control), whereas the seismic-derived stratigraphy is both chronostratigraphic and lithostratigraphic. This can lead to significant differences in the placing of sequence boundaries (unconformities) between the well and seismic section (fig. 6.16). Also, wells are often drilled at stratigraphically anomalous locations. The seismic section is the more powerful tool for demonstrating unconformity relationships. However, in unfavorable circumstances (e.g., closely spaced reflecting boundaries), interference can produce a composite waveform and a tie to the well is no longer straightforward. Before proceeding with the interpretation, discrepancies between well and seismic stratigraphy should be noted and, if possible at this early stage, resolved.

Even if synthetic seismograms are available, it is recommended that a well tie is first established using times and tops extracted from the available well logs. This approach involves a full consideration of the stratigraphic implications of the seismic section. Jumping straight in with a synthetic seismogram can focus too much attention on matching reflections and character, as opposed to a consideration of why they are there in the first place. Vertical seismic profiles are more satisfactory, as they allow a direct comparison between a measured seismic trace and the well. However, there is again a danger of concentrating too much on matching reflections and

TABLE 7.1 *Well name: Anywell-1*

Stratigraphic/ lithologic tops	Depth (meters)	Acoustic-impedance contrast	Anticipated seismic response*	Seismic two-way time (millisecs)
Pliocene	679	small +ve		732
Massive sand	948	large −ve		1007
Base Massive sand	1392	medium +ve		1401
Oligocene	1460	small −ve		1475
Paleocene Tuff	1824	large +ve		1800
Cretaceous Chalk	2021	large +ve		1946
Lower Cretaceous	2100	medium −ve		2048
Kimmeridge Clay Fm	2135	large −ve		2071
Upper Jurassic sand	2186	none		2108
Middle Jurassic coals	2344	medium −ve		2200
Lower Jurassic shales	2325	small +ve		2198
Lower Jurassic coals	2599	small −ve		2342
Terminal depth (T.D.)	2800	—		2502

* Anticipated seismic response for normal (SEG) polarity section

character and not enough on the geology that generates them. Even if synthetic seismograms and a vertical seismic profile are available, the following procedure is still recommended.

Obtain copies of the completion log, together with calibrated velocity log and density log if detailed studies are required. If no sonic log, synthetic seismogram, or well velocity is available, the interpreter has a problem. A formation density log can be used to give a very qualitative indication of the relationship between the geological section penetrated by the well and the equivalent seismic section. If there is some confidence in velocities derived regionally from seismic and well data, the gamma ray, spontaneous potential (both reflecting lithological changes), formation density, or even resistivity depth scale can be converted to time and used as a guide for tying the seismic section to the well. Where a reasonable log suite is available, the likely problems should not be so serious. If a completion log is not available, use the sonic log and obtain preliminary formation tops from the area geologist. In any case, always discuss the well results with the area geologist before beginning the interpretation. Well results are often reinterpreted and revised as more information becomes available, and the completion-log tops may not correspond to the latest interpretation. Work through the composite log noting depths to important (relevant to the interpretation) stratigraphic tops and significant acoustic-impedance changes. If a reduced-scale sonic log, two-way time log (TTL), or a plot of acoustic impedance on a synthetic seismogram display is available use them to help locate the acoustic-impedance changes. Tabulate the results in the format shown in table

7.1 with columns for tops, depth, acoustic-impedance contrast, anticipated seismic response, and two-way time.

TOPS AND DEPTHS

The use of subsea depths or depths to a reference datum, rather than drillers depth, is recommended. Tabulation of both stratigraphic tops and acoustic-impedance contrasts is necessary as they do not always correspond. Stratigraphic tops may have no seismic response at the well location. Moreover the stratigraphic tops based on paleontology could be wrong, as generally the paleontological resolution is much poorer than that of the seismic or may not correspond to a significant acoustic-impedance change. For example, in the northern North Sea, reflections from tuff beds in the Paleocene/early Eocene Balder Fm provide an excellent regional marker horizon. The top of the Balder Fm is picked by geologists at the shallowest occurrence of volcanic tuff (fig. 7.5). There is usually no significant acoustic contrast at this level. The main acoustic impedance occurs several tens of meters deeper. Simply tying the seismic record to the top Balder Fm will result in a tie 20–50 ms above the main seismic reflection. Significant acoustic-impedance changes should be used to supplement the stratigraphic tops for correlating the well and seismic times, and locating the lithological changes associated with the main reflectors. Select only major acoustic-impedance changes or those that may be especially relevant (near or within an objective horizon or some other critical level). It is not necessary to select every change on the log—the main purpose is to supplement stratigraphic tops and provide adequate control for well-to-seismic data correlation. We should also remember that reflections from the top and base of units thinner than half of the seismic wavelength will interfere. Tuning thickness and maximum amplitude occur at one-quarter of the wavelength for units with higher or lower acoustic impedance than the overlying and underlying sequences. Units thinner than about one-thirtieth of the wavelength, no matter how great the acoustic-impedance contrasts, may not produce a reflection (figs. 2.12 and 2.13). Methods for estimating seismic wavelength are shown in figure 2.15. If we assume that velocity is a good guide to likely acoustic-impedance change, significant acoustic-impedance changes may be detected using the sonic curve. The sonic log is often displayed on the composite log. As mentioned above, a reduced-scale sonic curve, or better still, acoustic-impedance curves produced as part of a synthetic seismogram display, are ideal for detecting acoustic-impedance boundaries. Select some acoustic-impedance changes in the shallower section (1.0–2.5 s), as it is generally easier to use these points to confirm the correlation between well and seismic time and to detect static shifts. Remember to use the caliper log to check that the velocity changes are real and not caused

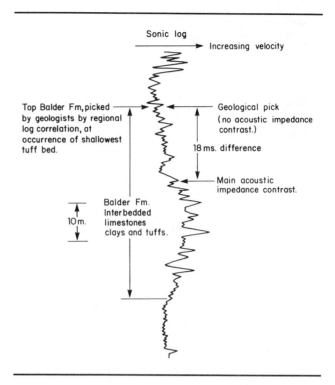

FIGURE 7.5 *Tie between the geological and seismic picks of the Early Tertiary volcanic tuff Balder Fm. in the northern North Sea.*

by bad hole conditions. Deeper events are much more likely to be influenced by processing factors, structure, etc., and are sometimes difficult to correlate with the seismic section without reference to shallower horizons. In the vicinity of the objective(s), or if there is some uncertainty in the sonic-derived acoustic-impedance boundaries, use the density log to supplement the sonic log. Sometimes, the density varies in the opposite sense to velocity and changes in acoustic impedance and, therefore, reflection strengths do not correspond to the velocity changes. This is often the case with salt layers. The density log can be used to verify the results of the sonic log, and to locate other acoustic-impedance changes due to density variations not producing a change in the sonic curve.

ANTICIPATED SEISMIC RESPONSE

The anticipated seismic response depends on the polarity of the seismic display. For lines of normal polarity: (a) an increase in acoustic impedance should give a trough (white) at the boundary, and (b) a decrease should give a peak (black) at the boundary. Indicate with a symbol in the table (table 7.1) whether a peak, trough, or no response is expected.

TWO-WAY TIME

A problem can arise in calculating the seismic two-way time when there is no calibrated velocity log relating time to depth. Using the ITT on the sonic log alone, it is possible to calculate interval velocities and elapsed time between the reflections; but a fixed time-depth reference is still lacking. One possible way around the problem, given suitable data, is to hang the tie on a prominent reflector of fairly certain origin and fix all other levels above and below by reference to this datum. For example, in areas of the North Sea where Upper Cretaceous chalk is developed, the top chalk reflector can often be used as a datum on which to hang sonic-log-derived times. A perfect fit should not always be expected because the error in the ITT can be significant. If a calibrated sonic log is available, the task is much simpler; the times corresponding to any depth can be read directly from the log. However, note that the times given on the log are frequently one-way traveltime to the seismic data, but the depths may correspond to a different datum (the drilling rig kelly bushing or rotary table, for example). Also note that the calibrated traveltime values should be used. No further adjustment for small discrepancies with check-shot times is necessary.

MAKING THE TIE

From the table of depths, times, and anticipated acoustic response prepare a well-tie strip on film (or any suitable transparent material) with the same time scale as the seismic section. The well-tie strip can then be overlain on the seismic section at the well location. Before doing this, however, the following should be taken into consideration:

Are dipping reflectors present at the well location and involved in the well tie? If they are, then we can only hope to have a good tie at the well location if the tie is being made to a migrated seismic section. If we are tying the well to an unmigrated line, the tie point will not be at the well location but at some distance, downdip from the well location (fig. 7.6). The actual distance downdip depends on the reflector dip. The tie can be more complicated if the well is not located on the seismic line and some of the reflections are dipping. The same considerations apply as before for unmigrated versus migrated lines, but even with migrated data there is the added complication that the best tie point is not necessarily the shotpoint where the seismic line passes closest to the well. The best tie point is found by contouring the dipping reflector locally around the well location and then using the contour trend to establish the best tie point (fig. 7.7). If there are several dipping reflectors, with different dip directions, there could be several well-tie points on the seismic line, each one suited to a particular reflector dip direction.

Once the best tie point has been established, a tie is made by overlaying the well-tie strip at the well location

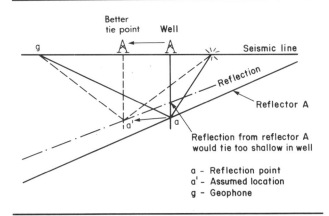

FIGURE 7.6 *Tie of well to seismic data for a dipping reflector and unmigrated seismic section.*

and observing the match. Does the well strip tie the seismic section, with the anticipated seismic response corresponding to at least some of the simpler reflectors (originating from a single acoustic-impedance contrast); and do unconformities concur between the well and the seismic stratigraphy? We should remember that on seismic sections processed with a minimum-phase type of wavelet, reflections do not even begin until after the two-way time of the reflection. Picks made with this type of seismic wavelet will always be late with respect to traveltime.

If, after taking all these considerations into account, the well strip and seismic section do not tie, try the following:

1. Check that the well is located correctly on the base map.
2. Check the shotpoint intersection at the correct well location.
3. Check the seismic polarity.

If all the above are correct try the following:

4. Move the well strip downward (to increase observed times) to counteract any static shift left in the seismic section. Mis-ties can be caused by incorrect normal moveout and/or static correction; incorrect corrections for weathering or other low-velocity data corrections on land; and, offshore, the possible use of incorrect data corrections for gun and cable depths. It should not be necessary to subtract time from the strip (i.e., move it upward) to make a tie, although this could be necessary if the seismic section has been overcorrected during calibration.

When making the tie, concentrate on flat or low-dipping, strong reflectors, originating from a single

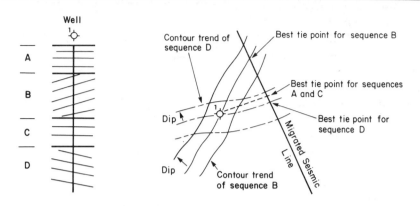

FIGURE 7.7 *Tie of well to seismic data for dipping reflectors when well is located some distance from the seismic line.*

acoustic-impedance contrast in the shallow part of the section. Unfortunately, a static shift established in the shallow section may not remain constant, but may vary with depth due to phase distortion caused by processing, instrumentation effects, incorrect velocity-log calibrations, migration effects on dipping strata, and so on.

An earlier review of the seismic section should have located the main sequence-boundary unconformities. Pay special attention to these unconformities and other sequence boundaries and their tie to the well stratigraphy. It is most important that significant differences between the geology derived from well logs and seismic survey are resolved, or good explanations found for the discrepancies, before proceeding with the interpretation.

At this stage it is very useful to incorporate and tie any synthetic seismograms and vertical seismic profiles to the seismic section. This may help resolve outstanding problems and give a more detailed correlation to both reflectors and character. The choice of which synthetic seismogram display to use is a matter of trial and error, but the polarity and type of wavelet should be the same as was used for the seismic processing (e.g., zero phase, minimum phase, etc.). Often a version showing primaries and short-term multiples provides a good match. The synthetic seismogram can be overlaid onto or spliced into the seismic section at the appropriate location. A good well tie is one in which there is a good correlation of shape and amplitude for peaks and troughs between the synthetic seismogram and seismic data. When comparing real and synthetic data, emphasis should be placed on correlation of high-amplitude and continuous, rather than discontinuous, reflections.

In most cases a reasonable tie will have been established and the main reflectors dated with some confidence. However, detailed correlation between seismic re-

sponse and the more closely spaced acoustic-impedance boundaries may still be uncertain and require a more detailed analysis of reflection origins using an expanded-scale synthetic seismogram.

HORIZON SELECTION

By this stage the initial interpretation should have established a stratigraphic framework for the main interpretation; recognized the main sequence boundaries; and, with the introduction of well data, should have allowed calibration of seismic times to a common datum and resolved, or at least highlighted, potential stratigraphic problems. The interpreter should now be in a good position to judge which reflections and unconformities must be mapped to describe fully the geology and hydrocarbon potential of the area. The choice will obviously be influenced by the objectives of the interpretation, but must be chosen with regard to good geological sense. If the area is relatively unexplored, all reflections at sequence boundaries, and those illustrating special geological features should be picked and carried throughout the grid. For specific problems where only one level may be of interest, it is still advisable to pick additional reflectors, both above and below the target level—even though they may not be digitized and mapped. They provide a framework and constraint during the interpretation and can help prevent silly mistakes. These are all too easy to make if all attention is focused on an horizon without consideration to its seismic/geologic context.

Not only is it desirable, but there may also be some pressure exerted externally, to select a reflection as near as possible to the top objective level. This can sometimes lead to problems. Often this is impossible, because no reflection is developed. In such cases it is better to pick some other horizon that can be related to the objective by thickness (time or depth) assumptions rather than carry a phantom pick (a totally guessed pick). Only in exceptional circumstances (e.g., when data quality is extremely poor), is it permissible to use a phantom pick. The use of phantom picks is a throwback to the bad old days when data was poor and noisy. The method, still unfortunately in common use, is essentially a deliberate attempt to use the seismic section solely as a structural tool. A justification for the phantom picks is often based on the mistaken belief that a phantom horizon is an indication of structural attitude at some level of constant geological time—implying that phantom horizons will cross transgressive or regressive lithostratigraphic boundaries. It is invariably better to select a reflection that is real, shows good character and continuity, and can be followed with confidence throughout the area. It is usually safer to derive a map mechanically from a reliably picked reflection, than to construct a map based entirely on guess work and erroneous assumptions concerning the relationship between geological time and lithology.

In addition to the horizons selected for mapping, other reflections are often included in an interpretation. These reflections would be easier to follow than those that are sequence boundaries. Characteristic reflections are especially helpful in a complexly faulted and structured area where sequence-boundary evidence may be rather localized. There is a need for a balanced approach to any interpretation and a judicious use of all available evidence. As a final word, it should always be remembered that mapping solely on the basis of reflection character is less reliable than using reflection relationships. Character can change or become ambiguous for nongeological reasons (filtering, etc.). Real reflection relationships reflect real geology. As a final step in the initial interpretation, it is useful to add more details of interesting reflection configurations, and so on, to the sketch map of structural elements.

Finally, to highlight possible problems, the interpreter should develop a preliminary geological history for the area that fits the seismic or well stratigraphic framework so far established. Pay especial attention to the timing of events. The geological model should be tested by sketching a series of cross-sections that illustrates the area's geological development. Inconsistencies or incompatibilities in the geological model soon become obvious. A good model will help focus the interpretation on the critical reflections.

SECTION FOLDING

Even at this advanced stage, when the data has been reviewed, wells tied, and horizons selected, there is one final and extremely tedious job remaining. The sections have to be neatly folded at the line intersections so that the lines can be tied. With luck, the line intersections will be indicated on the sections. If two or more surveys are involved, we may not be so lucky and the intersections must be found from the shotpoint map or a computer listing of intersections calculated from the navigation tapes. A deci-

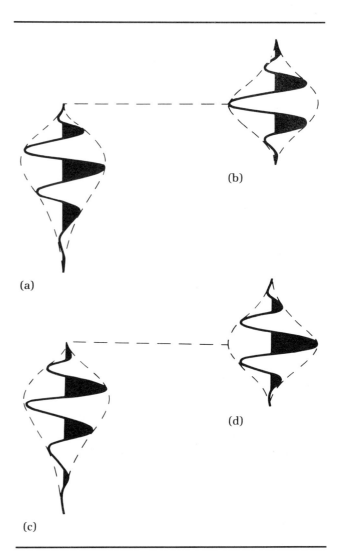

FIGURE 7.8 *Idealized reflection pulses before and after processing to the zero-phase form. (a) Normal polarity before. (b) Normal-polarity zero phase. (c) Reverse polarity before. (d) Reverse-polarity zero phase. Reprinted by permission of IHRDC Press from Badley and Anstey, 1984, fig. A2-1, p. 167.*

sion must be made regarding which lines to fold. It is best to fold the dip lines and tie these to the strike lines. Reflection continuity is likely to be better on the dip lines, which makes it easier to extrapolate the picks. If the dip varies, some lines may be partly folded, alternating between the dip and strike parts of the sections. It is impossible to give hard-and-fast rules for folding sections; each case will vary and it is largely a matter of common sense to fold lines in the most efficient way. But one practical hint—beware of simply folding the sections square with the paper edge. It is surprising how often the sections are printed at an angle to the paper's edge. Care should be taken that the folds are perpendicular to the section and not simply to the edge of the paper on which it is printed.

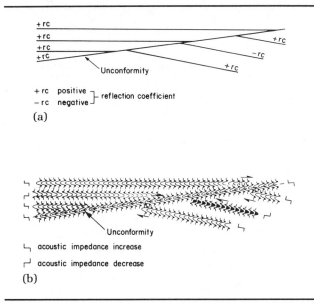

(a)

+ rc positive ⎤ reflection coefficient
− rc negative ⎦

(b)

⌐ acoustic impedance increase

¬ acoustic impedance decrease

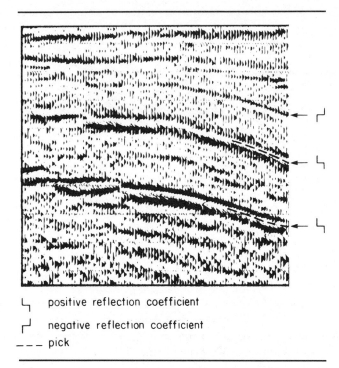

⌐ positive reflection coefficient

¬ negative reflection coefficient

- - - pick

FIGURE 7.9 *Idealized reflection relationships at a sequence boundary for a zero-phase wavelet. Local interference effects are not shown. (a) Geological model showing reflection coefficients of the reflectors. The unconformity is assumed to have a large positive reflection coefficient compared with the truncated and onlapped reflectors. (b) Seismic expression: Ininterference between the lead- and follow half-cycles of the unconformity zero-phase reflection causes both onlapping and truncation reflections to terminate before reaching the unconformity.*

FIGURE 7.10 *Seismic section showing examples of acoustic-impedance boundaries located using the symmetric nature of the zero-phase wavelet.*

PICKING—THE EFFECT OF WAVELET SHAPE ON WHERE TO PICK

The interpretation proper begins at this stage. During the data review, sequence boundaries may have been indicated on some sections, and reflection relationships marked with the red arrow code shown in figure 7.4. However, this will have been done only sparingly and not in a methodical manner. To complete the interpretation, all the selected horizons and perhaps some others, have to be carried throughout the seismic grid. One of the first questions to answer is where on the wavelet should the horizons—acoustic-impedance boundaries—be marked. Knowledge of the shape of the seismic wavelet can be an important guide to the positioning of sequence boundaries and picks. For well-processed marine seismic data, it is often possible to identify the seismic wavelet from the shape of strong reflections or from reflection relationships. For land seismic data, however, recognizing the wavelet shape is often difficult and, not infrequently, impossible. For example, the wavelet shape of Vibroseis seismic data is usually not known. In such cases, application of the techniques discussed in the following will be difficult or not possible. Two main wavelet shapes are commonly produced; zero and minimum phase (fig. 7.8). Zero-phase wavelets are produced by wavelet processing

that shapes the reflection pulse to a form symmetrical about the maximum of its envelope. This manipulation is termed phase "zeroizing" or "bringing to zero phase." Thus a discrete reflection, looking like figure 7.8a, is reshaped by processing so that the reflection pulse and its envelope are nominally symmetrical about the envelope maximum—that envelope maximum may coincide with a white trough (fig. 7.8b) or a black peak (fig. 7.8d).

The visual effect of the zero-phase process is not major; reflections move earlier, and their form becomes a little sharper. This can make it harder to locate sequence boundaries, as the wavelet interferes with both baselapping and truncating reflections (fig. 7.9). However, the process (to the degree that it works) does make it easier for the interpreter to decide where to pick on the waveform itself. On marine sections shot in deep water, the success of the zero-phase process can be assessed from the sea-floor reflection; because this reflection is usually fairly discrete, its form should approximate zerophase symmetry. Where we have this comfort, there is no doubt where we should pick a reflection; we must pick the peak or trough that lies at the envelope maximum (fig. 7.10). No other pick is permissible on a discrete reflection. If the envelope maximum is at a trough, we must pick the trough; if it is at a peak, we must pick the peak.

Of course, reflections are not always discrete; often we can see a band or complex of reflections that merge together into one long wave train. Then we scan all the lines

198

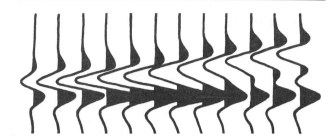

FIGURE 7.11 *Two zero-phase reflections come together, illustrating the subtle changes in waveform attributes that result. Reprinted by permission of IHRDC Press from Badley and Anstey, 1984, fig. A2-2, p. 168.*

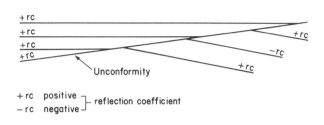

+ rc   positive ⎤
− rc   negative ⎦ reflection coefficient

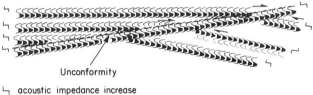

Unconformity

⌐ acoustic impedance increase

⌐ acoustic impedance decrease

FIGURE 7.12 *Idealized reflection relationships at a sequence boundary for a minimum-phase wavelet. Local interference effects are not shown. Geological model showing reflection coefficients of the reflectors. The unconformity is assumed to have a large positive reflection coefficient compared with the truncated and onlapped reflectors. Seismic expression: The minimum-phase reflection from the unconformity interferes with the truncated reflections, which terminate against the follow half-cycle of the unconformity reflection. The onlap reflections, however, continue onto the unconformity surface and their terminations can be used to locate accurately the sequence boundary.*

of the survey, and ask whether (in general) the reflection train shows just one envelope maximum, or two; is there a "saddle" in the envelope? If there is, are we justified in making two picks, corresponding to the two envelope maxima—provided, of course, that the extra effort brings some exploration benefit.

A particular case where we might wish to do this is at the top and base of a reservoir layer. When a layer thins, we may obtain the reflection appearance of figure 7.11. The reflections from top and base can be seen separated at the right; there is a saddle in the envelope. Using the envelope, we pick the top as a white trough, and the base as a black peak. This does not quite yield the correct answer, but any other course yields an answer that is much worse.

What if the layer is not thick enough, anywhere, to show us the top and base separately? Then we do not have the three or four traces on the right of figure 7.11. We go to pick the envelope maximum, and find that it does not correspond to a peak or a trough. This tells us that we have a thin layer, and that our reflection is actually an interference between two reflections. If the layer is our target, we pick both the trough and the peak. This is not perfect, but it is the best we can do.

If we have a long reflection train that does not show any saddle in its envelope, the train is almost certainly composed of three or more reflections. What can we say? The interpreter just does what seems reasonable, taking into account whatever is known about the geology and the importance of that level in the exploration play. Probably most interpreters would pick the first major peak or trough to show good continuity, and label that pick "near-top yellow complex."

Now what about sections without wavelet processing, or sections in which the success of the processing is in doubt? The traditional approach has been to pick the first clear trough of each reflection—the trough in order to make the color visible, and the first trough to minimize

possible lag. However, if the wavelet is a minimum-phase reflector, relationships at an unconformity can often be a very good guide as to the exact position of the boundary. Figure 7.12 shows how onlaps can be traced almost directly onto a sequence boundary, their terminations marking its position. Truncation and toplap, on the other hand, are poor indications of the boundaries' positions, because they terminate against the sequence boundary follow half-cycle some distance short of their true terminations. Onlap is the best criterion for locating boundaries with minimum-phase data. Figure 7.13 shows a sequence boundary located using the onlap criterion.

A boundary with a positive reflection coefficient is best drawn at the onset of the compressional wavelet (top of the trough for normal-polarity data) for a section processed to minimum phase; for a zero-phase section, the boundary should be drawn at the center of the trough. If the boundary has a negative reflection coefficient, the same rules apply and either the onset or center of the black peak should be marked. If a soft wax-based crayon with suitably selected color or a soft pencil is used, there

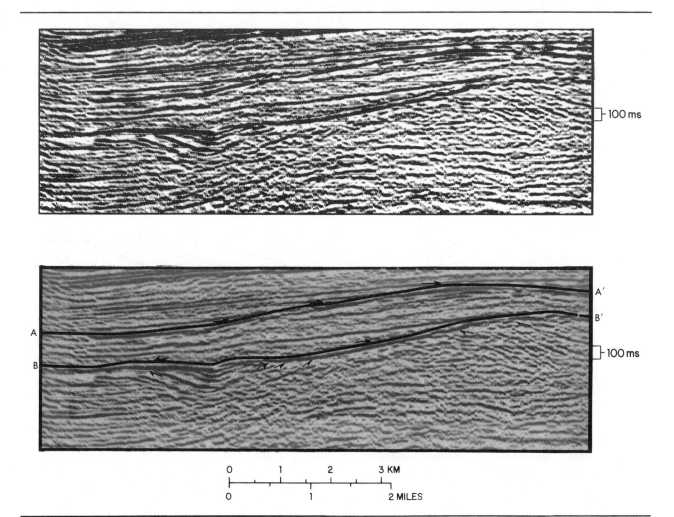

FIGURE 7.13 *Example of a normal-polarity (SEG) minimum-phase processed seismic section. Onlap relationships position the unconformity B–B′ at the onset of a trough, demonstrating that acoustic impedance increases across the unconformity. Truncations beneath unconformity B terminate against the black (peak) follow half-cycle. If the truncation terminations were used, the unconformity pick would be too low. Onlap relationships also indicate a positive reflection coefficient for the sequence boundary A–A′. Courtesy Merlin Profilers Ltd.*

should be little problem about seeing the boundary drawn on top of the black peak. Reflector terminations are best indicated by a red arrow at the end of the reflection, even though the boundary causing the reflection may extend beyond the arrow's tip (e.g., on truncated reflections on a minimum-phase section).

There are situations where the boundary, determined from reflector relationships, is a very weak continuity reflection. This is common with intermediate-type wavelets that are neither minimum phase or zero phase. In these cases the best continuity is always found near the maximum of the wavelet envelope. The lag to the better

continuity part of the reflection can be used as a guide to locating the true boundary. In situations where there are no diagnostic reflector relationships, pick any convenient point on the reflection—peak, trough, or zero crossing—that is near the envelope maximum.

All of the foregoing must be seasoned with realism. In many poor-record areas, the interpreter has no choice—anything at all that has some appearance of continuity will be picked gratefully.

Even when we have decided where to pick on the waveform, problems usually arise where there is a change in the reflection character. For example, the reflection splits and the decision has to be made—where does the pick go. Geology can often come to the interpreter's aid. The following rules have been found to be useful and correct in the majority of cases.

1. For a surface that is being onlapped or downlapped, stay down when picking against the onlap or downlap direction (fig. 7.14).

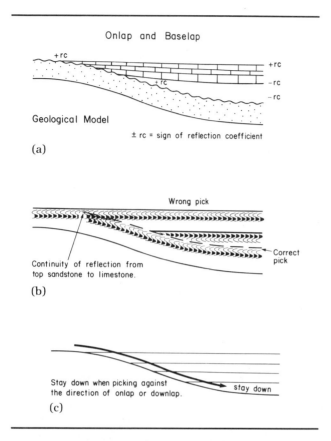

Onlap and Baselap

Geological Model

± rc = sign of reflection coefficient

(a)

Wrong pick

Continuity of reflection from top sandstone to limestone.

Correct pick

(b)

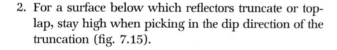

Stay down when picking against the direction of onlap or downlap.

stay down

(c)

FIGURE 7.14 *Picking criterion—onlap and downlap. (a) Geological model: A sandstone of intermediate acoustic impedance is onlapped by shales of low acoustic impedance, and limestone of high acoustic impedance. The reflection coefficient signs are indicated on the diagram. (b) Seismic expression: The top sand reflection, the sequence boundary defined by the onlap, changes polarity due to the varying reflection coefficients between the sandstone, limestone, and shale. The apparent continuity between the top sand and top limestone reflections is a potential trap for the unwary interpreter. (c) A general rule when following an onlapped sequence boundary is to stay down when picking against the onlap direction.*

2. For a surface below which reflectors truncate or toplap, stay high when picking in the dip direction of the truncation (fig. 7.15).

These rules are intended for guidance only and the interpreter will find instances where the rules do not apply. As always, geological plausibility is the best criterion.

LOOP TYING

Once the picks have been settled the loop-tying can begin. The interpretation is best begun in an area where the seismic response is good and the horizons selected for mapping are well developed. This often results in an interpretation beginning in off-structure areas. Here, the seismic stratigraphy can have more importance than the

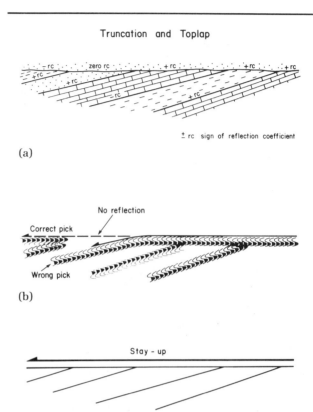

Truncation and Toplap

± rc sign of reflection coefficient

(a)

No reflection

Correct pick

Wrong pick

(b)

Stay - up

(c)

FIGURE 7.15 *Picking criterion—toplap and truncation. (a) Geological model: An interbedded sequence subcrops an unconformity overlain by a sand. Signs of the reflection coefficient are indicated. There is no acoustic-impedance contrast between the sands. (b) Seismic expression: The unconformity has a positive reflection coefficient to the right, no reflection where it is subcropped by sand, and a negative reflection coefficient to the left. A potential interpretation pitfall would be to take the unconformity pick along the top limestone reflection. (c) A general rule when following a surface in the direction of truncation or toplap direction is to stay high.*

well control (because the wells are often on the structural highs where the sequences are usually thinner and seismic resolution poorer). The objective of line-tying and interpretation is to trace the lateral continuity of each selected event. The most prominent feature of an event is its alignment, rather than the details of the pulse shape. Events can be traced laterally until there is a break in continuity such as a fault, pinchout, truncation, poor data area, etc. However, rather than attempting to follow each event as far as possible it is better to adopt a more methodical approach and follow loops around the seismic grid. Select a dip line where the events are well developed and fold the sections at intersections with the strike lines. Transfer the picks onto a strike line and carry to the next dip line. Sometimes, it is possible to carry the picks

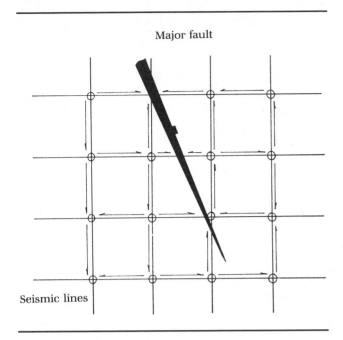

Major fault

Seismic lines

FIGURE 7.16 *Sketch showing how loop-tying through a grid is used to correlate picks around a major structural feature.*

through several strike-line intersections; but it is best not to carry the picks too far. The picks transferred to the new dip line are traced to the next strike-line intersection and then back again to the original dip line, thus closing a loop. If the picks fit, gradually expand the loops in a methodical fashion until the entire grid is tied. If not, backtrack, locate the mis-tie and try again to close the loop. Careful progress, with methodical checking and backtracking, has no substitute. Although it may seem tedious, it will be well rewarded by the results and confidence in the interpretation.

Often major structural features such as faults or salt walls can only be crossed by tying loops until an area of continuity is found (fig. 7.16). Sometimes no way around major structural features can be found and correlations from one side to the other cannot be established without well data. Nevertheless, an attempt can be made to match the seismic section on either side by jump correlation and/ or matching the sequence boundaries. A jump correlation involves using the reflection character as a guide to correlation. To make a jump correlation, fold a section so that the undisturbed area on each side of the structural feature are juxtaposed. The correct correlation may be obvious (fig. 7.17). Doubtful cases should be treated with suspicion since the character of a reflection is highly de-

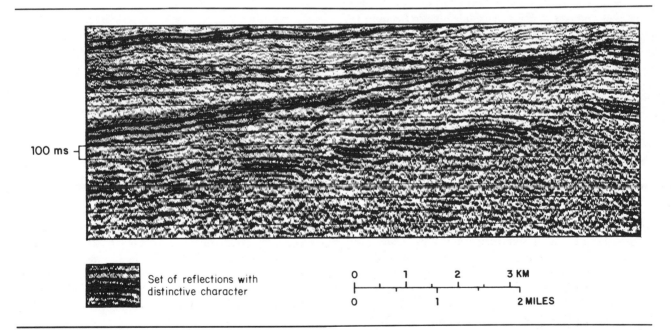

100 ms

Set of reflections with distinctive character

0 1 2 3 KM

0 1 2 MILES

FIGURE 7.17 *Character correlation: Example of distinctive seismic character enabling high-confidence correlation across several faults.*

pendent on processing parameters, which can change significantly across a major feature.

Alternatively, it may be possible to follow a reflection by using the area's structural evolution as a guide. For example, locally in the northern North Sea, in different tilted fault blocks between which no direct line tie can be made, the top of the prerift sequence in different tilted

TABLE 7.2 *Shorthand notation for seismic facies mapping*

Code system

(A) *Upper sequence boundary*

Te — erosional truncation
Top — toplap
C — concordant

(B) *Lower sequence boundary*

On — onlap
Dwn — downlap
C — concordant

$$\frac{A - B}{C}$$

(C) *Internal cycle configuration*

P — parallel	M — moulded
D — divergent	Ob — oblique progradational
C — chaotic	Sig — sigmoid progradational
W — wavy	Rf — reflection free
Dm — divergent moundy	Sh — shingling

SOURCE: Adapted from G. K. Ramsayer, Seismic stratigraphy, a fundamental exploration tool: Offshore Technology Conference, Houston, 1979.

fault blocks can be recognized by the onlap of syn-rift sequence reflections (Badley et al., 1984).

Seismic correlation often depends on recognition of sequences of reflections. If one reflection in a sequence terminates or changes in character while other reflections in the sequence retain their continuity, the most likely cause is lateral facies change. Minor thickening and thinning can produce subtle changes in reflection sequences, as can local and temporal changes in the sensitivity of the seismic system itself, due to operational or overlying geological conditions.

It is good practice to pick and correlate too many reflections rather than concentrate on one or two. Many reflections will prove to have limited lateral extent but may be of great help in achieving a proper geological understanding. The decision as to which of the picked reflections should be timed and mapped can be made at a later stage.

The internal structure and reflection parameters of a seismic sequence can also be highly diagnostic and can add an extra dimension to interpretation. Mapping of the internal reflection configuration is the first step. The configurations can be categorized according to relationships at the upper sequence boundary (concordance, toplap, truncation); the lower sequence boundary (concordance, onlap, downlap or simply baselap, dip direction of onlap or downlap); and on the basis of the dominant geometry within the sequence (parallel, divergent, prograding, etc.). Ramsayer (1979) developed a coding system for the description of different types of internal configurations and boundaries. The type of upper boundary (A), the type of lower boundary (B), and the internal

configuration (C) are abbreviated in the following manner:

$$\frac{A—B}{C}$$

Table 7.2 lists a modified version of Ramsayer's code. An example of such a notation is:

$$\frac{Te—Dwn}{Sig}$$

This notation indicates erosion truncation along the upper boundary, downlap along the lower boundary, and a sigmoid progradational internal reflection configuration. These notations are posted on a shotpoint map together with arrows indicating the directions of onlap and downlap (fig. 7.18). The limits of different configurations are connected to show the extent of each seismic facies. Isopach contours of the seismic sequence are usually included on this type of map together with other descriptive data, such as reflection continuity, amplitude, and reflection spacing.

COMMON INTERPRETATION PROBLEMS
Even in areas where the data are good, the interpreter will usually be faced with some interpretation problems. Some of the more common problems are discussed in the following.

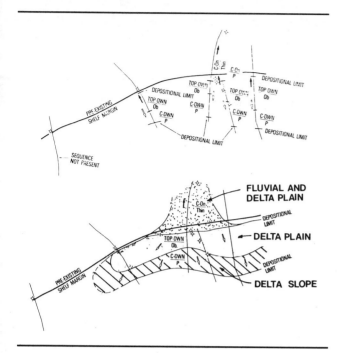

FIGURE 7.18 *A seismic stratigraphic map. Reprinted by permission of the Offshore Technology Conference from Ramsayer, 1979.*

INTERFERENCE

Interference results when reflectors are more closely spaced than one-half of the seismic pulse wavelength. Recognition of interference effects can be critical to interpretation, as illustrated by the following example. Figure 7.19 shows part of a seismic line tied to a well with the anticipated seismic tie and response indicated. The section is processed to a minimum phase and is of normal polarity, but note that, although the tie of well to seismic data is good, the amplitude of the first half-cycle (which ideally should predominate) at many of the tie points, is much less than the first and second follow half-cycles. This is an indication that the wavelet is quite long. This presents no serious problems down to 2000 ms. Below 2000 ms, however, the close spacing of some acoustic-impedance boundaries has resulted in interference and distortion of the seismic signal. For example, the peak anticipated at 2075 ms is not present; instead, a trough is developed. The strong reflection present at 2109 ms is more of a problem. It has high amplitude and is very dominant. However, according to the acoustic-impedance log (not shown) no strong reflection would be anticipated. A further strong event occurs at 2180 ms, 12 ms above the position where a weak peak is anticipated. These strong events certainly lend some character to the section and might seem like a stroke of luck; in fact, the events are artefacts. We can demonstrate this by comparing the section with a line from a more recent survey (fig. 7.20). The original line was acquired in 1977 and is quite

good for its age. The new line was shot in 1981 and shows very high resolution. The two strong events that dominate the interval 2100–2200 ms have disappeared. They were the result of constructive interference from the convolution of the rather long minimum-phase wavelet with closely spaced reflecting boundaries. So beware! All may not be as it seems!

FOLDS AND FAULTS

The appearance of folds and faults on seismic sections can be considerably distorted, especially on unmigrated sections. Only a true dip line will show the proper cross-sectional form. On unmigrated sections:

a. Anticlines appear too broad, but the anticline crest is in its proper subsurface position.
b. Synclines are narrowed; and if the syncline has a buried focus, the limbs will overlap to give a bow-tie effect. The synclinal axis is in its proper subsurface position.

Faults almost always have inclined fault planes which will be properly represented only on a seismic line crossing the fault trace at right angles. Even on migrated sections, it may be difficult to ascertain whether a fault dips at 40° or no fault is present. The resulting map is not very different, but if the production geologist expects a sealing fault, he may be hoping for a more definite answer. Diffraction patterns on unmigrated seismic sections are often useful in locating the fault plane precisely—the fault plane should pass through the apex of the diffraction hyperbola. The closer the direction of the seismic line to the strike of the fault trace, the shallower will be the apparent dip of the fault.

The failure to interpret faulting properly, especially on sections oblique to fault traces, is a common error in seismic interpretation. Figure 7.21 shows an example where a curved fault plane occurs twice on the same seismic line. Fault planes should be treated as steeply dipping horizons and be tied at line intersections. It is vital to maintain and update a sketch map showing the faults during the interpretation of a complexly faulted area. The fault pattern should also be sensible. Sometimes reflections appear to extend for a short distance across a fault plane owing to the diffraction effects. The resulting appearance can resemble a high-angle reverse fault. Caution should be exercised in marking reverse faults unless there is independent evidence for their existence. However, when they do occur and become low-angle thrusts, the fault plane may lie subparallel to the bedding and interpretation can become extremely complex. Structural differences above and below the thrust plane could mimic the seismic expression produced above and below an unconformity. Often special processing is necessary in such structurally complex areas.

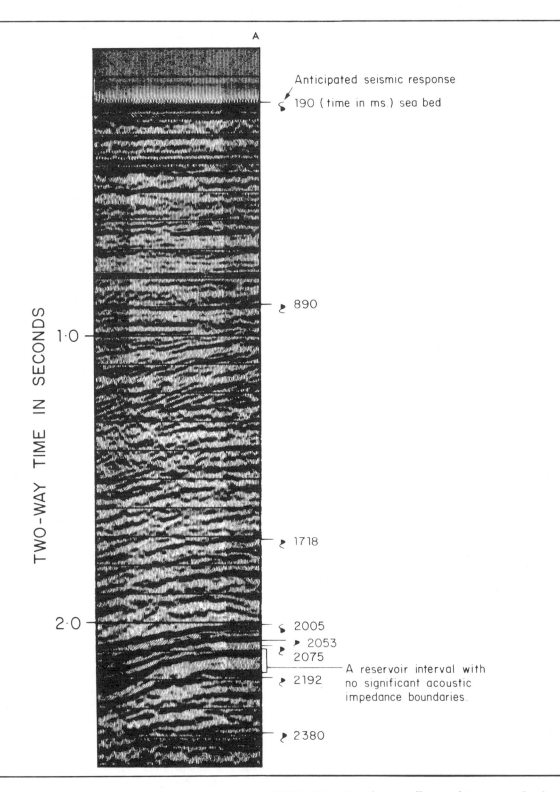

FIGURE 7.19 *A North Sea well,* A, *tied to a normal-polarity (SEG), minimum-phase seismic section showing the main acoustic-impedance boundaries, anticipated seismic response derived from well logs. Courtesy Norsk Hydro.*

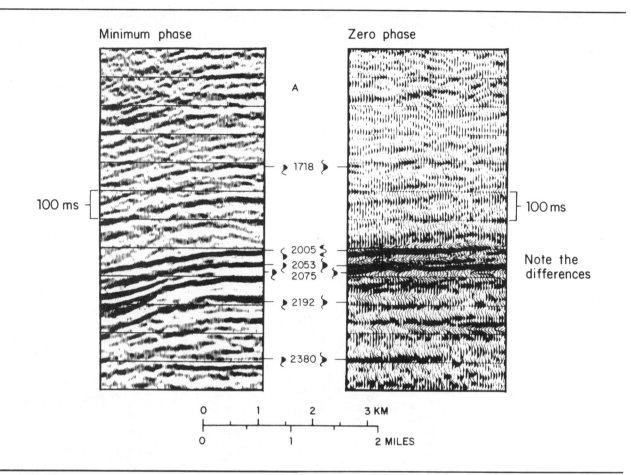

Minimum phase   Zero phase

A

1718

100 ms   100 ms

2005
2053
2075

Note the
differences

2192

2380

0   1   2   3 KM

0   1   2 MILES

FIGURE 7.20 *Comparison of minimum-phase and zero-phase seismic lines at well A of figure 8.10. Courtesy Norsk Hydro.*

Strike-slip faulting causing lateral displacement along the fault trace is also difficult to detect. Strike-slip faulting may be suspected when mapping shows offset of major structural features. An understanding of the regional structural framework is important in arriving at an acceptable interpretation.

Interpretation in some areas is made more complex by later tectonic events (e.g., fault and tilting after deposition of a unit). Often sections are made more interpretable if the later structural effects can be removed. This is usually most simply done by taking a photocopy, then cutting and splicing (fig. 7.22) to restore the earlier structural/depositional configuration.

Attempts to interpret stratigraphic details from seismic data can only be made when the structural effects have been fully interpreted. Elucidation of an area's structure is vital in hydrocarbon exploration. One of the main aims must be to accurately map structure and delineate possible traps. Attempts to interpret stratigraphic details from seismic data can only be made when the structural effects have been fully interpreted.

MIS-TIES

Mis-ties are almost inevitable in any interpretation, and they are a nuisance; but with luck they will not be too serious. Mis-ties occur within a survey and between surveys for a variety of possible reasons, which, in any given case, may be impossible to identify. However, perhaps the most common serious mis-ties are caused by incorrect positioning of line intersections on the sections! Always check this first. If this is not the cause then the mis-tie is probably real. The most common causes of mis-ties are briefly listed below:

Navigation and Surveying Errors. On land, mis-ties are less likely to arise than at sea, where the quality of navigation can vary considerably. Uncertainty in positioning can be as much as 100 m at line intersections. Streamer feathering—caused by currents sweeping the cable from its desired path—can add to the problem. If the mis-tie(s) is serious it may be necessary to consult the original survey data to establish which line is most likely to be in error.

Polarity Conventions. Reconciling mis-ties due to different polarity displays between different surveys is a common

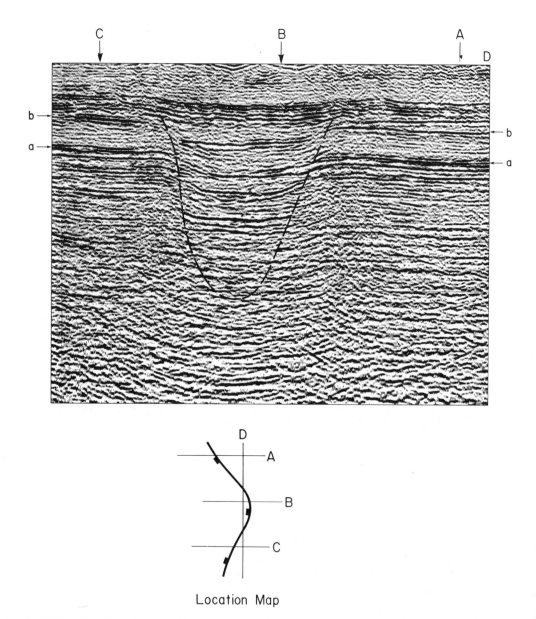

Location Map

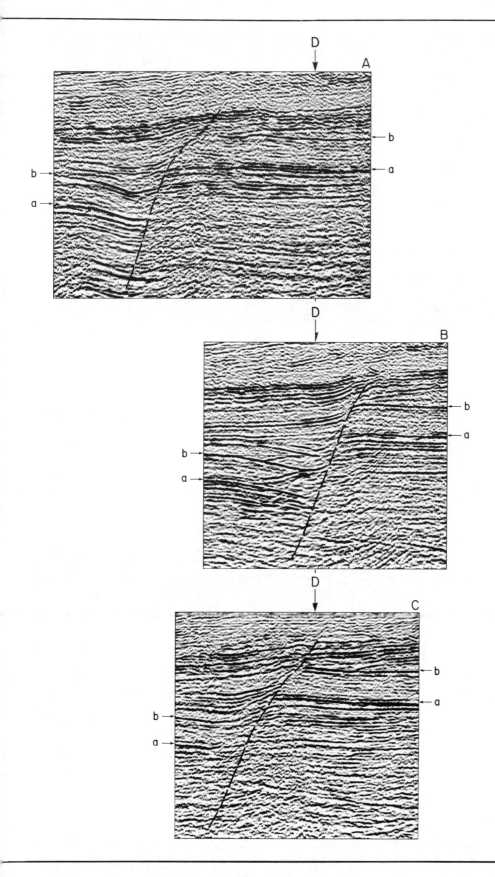

FIGURE 7.21 *Fault appearing twice on one line. Courtesy Statoil.*

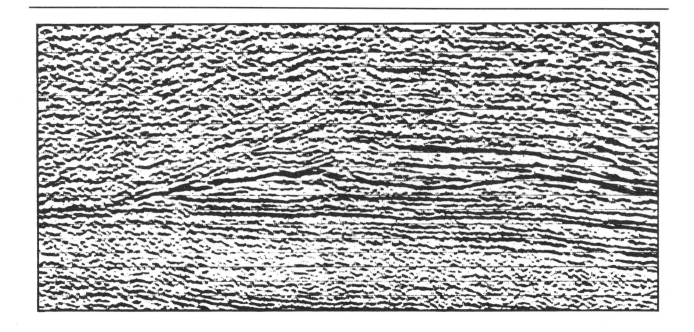

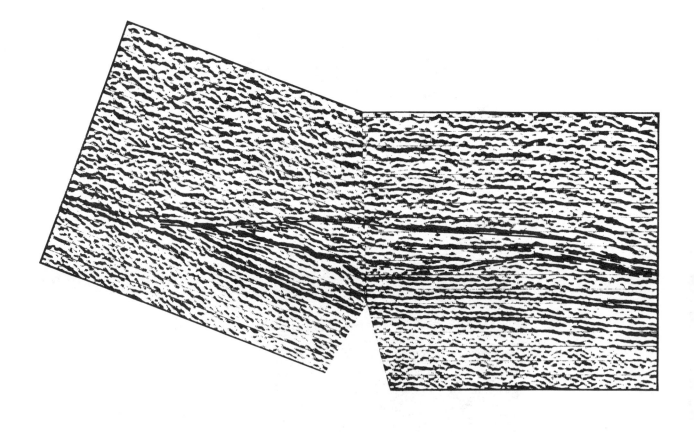

FIGURE 7.22 *The role of scissors as an exploration tool. Restoration of the structure before faults simplifies interpretation of the reflection relationships. Courtesy Saga Petroleum.*

problem when the polarity display of older data is not stated; as frequently happened before the use of the SEG standard became commonplace. Various methods for determining polarity are described at the beginning of this chapter.

Processing Problems. Static corrections, differences in stacking velocities used on two intersecting lines, mute pattern differences, differently phased deconvolution operators, and wavelets of different phase, are only some of the causes of mis-ties induced by processing. The causes of processing mis-ties are difficult to determine, but if the mis-tie is between two surveys and is found to be consistent, a standard static shift can be applied to reconcile the difference.

Diffractions. Mis-ties are often observed at intersections near small faults. This can be caused by interference between reflections and diffractions, especially on the line oblique to the fault trace where the diffraction may not have been successfully attenuated.

Migration. Perhaps the most common and totally expected cause of mis-ties is the conventional 2-D migration process. On a dip line, the reflection occurs updip from the vertical through the point of observation on the surface, but a normal, unmigrated section displays the reflection on the vertical. The process of migration moves the reflection a distance h, back where it should be. No problem— on a dip line; but on a strike line, the reflection still comes from updip of the vertical plane. However, since the reflection appears to have no dip, the process of migration leaves it substantially unchanged (fig. 3.21). Thus migration changes the reflection times on dip lines, but does not change them on strike lines. It follows that sections that tie properly on unmigrated sections do not tie, in general, on migrated sections. The mis-ties become significant for dips greater than about 15°. So what should we do? We like the improved clarity of the faults on migrated sections. We accept that where a reflecting surface is very rough, migration is necessary before we can even begin to pick it. But we are reluctant to lose that confidence-building check we get by tying unmigrated sections at the line intersections.

The optimum course depends on the circumstances. Where the structures are smooth, gentle, and unfaulted, there is no problem. In fact, there are few prospective areas where the structures are smooth, gentle, and unfaulted. Consequently, the vast majority of seismic sections are clarified by the migration process. What do we do, then, when the unmigrated sections can be picked, but the migrated sections are more clear locally? One choice is to pick the unmigrated sections, and use the migrated sections to guide our picking. Then we proceed to the migration of the unmigrated contour map. In this

last stage, it helps if we can specify, from the migrated sections, the true position and throw of the faults.

As the complexity of the geology increases, we come to some point where the improved clarity of the migrated section outweighs the comfort of exact line ties. If we have a grid of lines that are close to being on dip and on strike, and if the faults are generally on strike with the structure, we pick and time the migrated dip lines first. Next we pick and time any strike lines that happen to cross the dip lines in zones of low dip—there we expect good ties. Then, in the vicinity of the other line intersections, we search the dip-line sections for any identifiable reflection feature (perhaps a small fault) that is recognizable on both migrated and unmigrated sections; and we assess how far the migration process has moved it. This (the distance h) tells us where the line intersection really is in the subsurface. Then we time the reflection on the strike line; we do not use the absolute reflection times, only the differences of reflection time relative to the times at the line intersections. These differences are then posted on the map in the time subsurface position of the line strike line (which is, of course, the distance h updip from its surface position). Finally we contour the absolute reflection times from the dip lines, using the time differences on the strike lines to guide our contouring between the dip lines.

In the real world, however, many lines are neither on strike nor on dip, reflection quality is variable, and faults cross all the lines at unfavorable angles. So the interpreter does the best possible, aided by a first rough map showing the highs, the lows, the steep dips, the shallow dips, the flat areas, the fault locations, the zones of bad data, and any other obvious anomalies, which provide a crude picture of the structure, and the likely effects of migration and mis-migration.

The important thing in all this, of course, is that the interpreter should think out and understand the allowances to be made at the line intersections.

Poor Data. Another very common cause of mis-ties, especially onshore, where data is often poor compared with typical marine seismic, is the difficulty of simply crossing poor data areas and emerging on the other side still on the correct pick. There is little that can be done in such cases other than trying to make the picks as plausible as possible in the poor data areas.

Chapter 8

Contouring and Mapping

Proficiency in contouring—the quest for a two-dimensional representation of a three-dimensional surface—is a basic skill that should be in the armory of every explorationist. There is a surprising variety of approaches to what at first seems a simple task of joining points of the same value with lines. The various techniques that can be applied to the contouring problem in general, their advantages and disadvantages, plus some peripheral applications of contour maps are described and discussed in this section. Before delving into the technicalities of contouring, it is perhaps a good idea to review briefly the shapes characteristic of typical geological surfaces. Shape is the key to contouring. Contouring attempts to accurately depict shape by honoring data values; it also endeavors to convey any geological message that shape may carry. But the shape shown by seismic data can be misleading. For example, anticlines appear too broad on filtered stack sections, mis-ties cause all sorts of mischief, and so on. Slavish adherence to all data points, giving equal weight to each, may give an accurate contour map of the data but provides no guarantee of a geologically meaningful shape for the mapped surface. The art of contouring, and it is an art, is to use the data values honestly, while at the same time keeping in mind the desired geological shape.

Seismic interpretation is different from most other forms of geological mapping. It uses a grid of two-dimensional vertical sections (this is still the case for 3-D migrated surveys) between which are blank, or dead, areas where no data is available and which can only be sampled by shooting extra lines. In the absence of extra data, these dead areas are infilled by extrapolation from the neighboring lines. The grid density is obviously a controlling factor on the accuracy of the interpretation and is important for recognizing structural anomalies. The denser the grid, the better the control, the greater the accuracy. A 5 km $\times$ 5 km grid, could, in theory, miss a feature up to 24 km^2 in extent. Such a grid would be of little use in searching for pinnacle reefs with a surface area of only 1 or 2 km^2. Grid density must be compatible with structural complexity. An otherwise gently structured area would be extremely difficult to interpret with

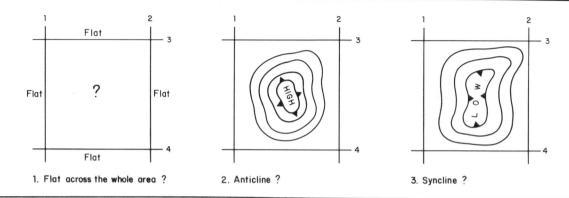

1. Flat across the whole area ?   2. Anticline ?   3. Syncline ?

FIGURE 8.1 *Contouring dilemma—no structure? Sketch showing alternative interpretations that could be made for the blank area between four intersecting lines.*

lines more widely spaced than 2–3 km if it were criss-crossed by faults with a density of several per line kilometer. The following examples illustrate some of the constraints placed on an interpretation by the line spacing.

Figure 8.1 shows four lines each showing flat, featureless reflectors. There are at least three possible interpretations:

1. The intervening area may be flat.
2. The intervening area may contain a structural high.
3. The intervening area may contain a structural low.

Which of these is the most likely geologically? This will obviously depend on the line spacing, the structural style of the area, and the potential significance of a "missed" structure represented by alternative (2). If the lines in figure 8.1 were spaced 10 km apart, a potential structural closure of at least 64 km² could be hidden between the lines. If structures of this order of magnitude had been detected on other lines in the area (structural trends indicated that they could be present in the area of fig. 8.1), it would be wise to shoot an infill line to clarify the situa-

tion. If, on the other hand, the general area is one of monotonous dip, then the likelihood of any structure occurring within the intervening area would be considered extremely low and an infill line would be unjustified. As the grid becomes denser, the potential significance of a missed structure becomes less important. There comes a stage when, in all but exceptional cases (e.g., within a field), the potential size of any missed structure is of no economic significance. This is an important consideration, for it leads us to acknowledge that there is an acceptable level of inaccuracy, which we can tolerate in our interpretation and resulting contour maps. A sound appreciation of the acceptable level of inaccuracy is one of the most vital factors in determining the efficiency of an interpretation.

The second example (fig. 8.2) again uses four intersecting lines and is in marked contrast to the first example. It illustrates the dilemma that can occur in correlating the

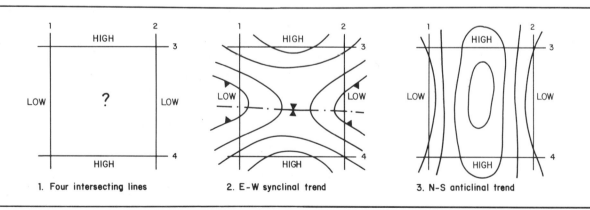

1. Four intersecting lines   2. E–W synclinal trend   3. N–S anticlinal trend

FIGURE 8.2 *Contouring dilemma—anticline or syncline? Sketch showing alternative interpretations that could be made for the area between structures observed on four intersecting lines.*

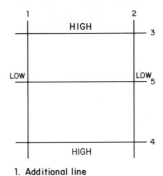

1. Additional line

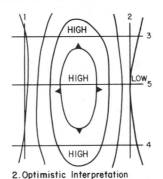

2. Optimistic Interpretation

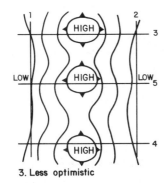

3. Less optimistic

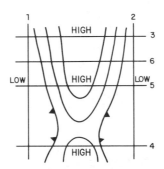

4. A further line confirms closure
to the north. An additional line
between 4 and 5 would be necessary
to confirm the closure in the
optimistic interpretation (2).

FIGURE 8.3 *Contouring dilemma—shoot an infill line. Sketch
showing how an infill line confirms closure to the N. An additional line between 4 and 5 would be necessary to confirm
the closure in the optimistic interpretation.*

structures observed on the lines. The two east–west lines show a syncline, the two north–south lines show an anticline. There are two potential interpretations:

1. The intervening area is crossed by a north–south trending anticline.
2. The intervening area is crossed by an east–west trending syncline.

The two interpretations are diametrically opposed, but both are possible in the absence of further information. The same considerations apply as in the first example. What are the geological likelihoods? If the area has a pronounced east–west structural grain, the synclinal possibility would be favored. The line spacing is again important with regard to the economic potential of a wrong interpretation. An additional factor not present in the first example is that a decision must be made. The contours must be joined and somehow cross the intervening area. In the first example, it was possible to ignore the problem and assume the intervening area to be flat without taking further action. In the second example, if the line spacing is such that the size of the anticline could be economically significant, then an infill line should be shot.

Figure 8.3 assumes that the structures are potentially significant and an additional east–west line has been shot to reveal an anticline. The presence of a north–south anticlinal trend is now confirmed. It is still possible that the anticline consists of an alignment of separate highs but this can only be resolved by shooting an additional east–west line. The scope for alternative structural interpretations becomes smaller with increasing grid density. The coarseness of the grid compared to the size of the structures to be delineated and their economic potential must always be carefully considered.

The third example (fig. 8.4) illustrates the difficulties that can arise when contouring an undulating horizon. The problem is to establish the structural trend or grain. It is common for structures to show some form of alignment or grain due to the natural elongation of many features (faults, flexures, folds, etc.). Their pattern can be random or a combination of trends, but trends should be

214

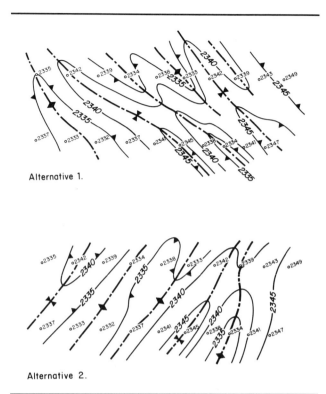

Alternative 1.

Alternative 2.

FIGURE 8.4 *Contouring dilemma—what is the structural trend? Two alternatives are possible.*

expected in most areas. The exceptions are areas where the structures do not have a linear configuration, but are more nearly circular and discontinuous. This can arise in areas of salt tectonics, reef development, volcanics, and gently undulating surfaces caused by differential compaction and velocity effects. In these cases the fold axes do not join up, they are discontinuous, and can only be correctly interpreted if the grid size is small enough to give several cross-sections through each feature. Figure 8.4 shows two parallel lines that can be contoured with opposing trends. Either interpretation could be correct and additional control would be required to resolve the dilemma. Alternatively, the area between the lines could be left uninterpreted and only the high areas marked on the lines. This is visually unsatisfactory and the leaving of blank areas should be reserved for areas of very poor data quality or for areas of major doubt caused by wide gaps in the control. Often it is possible to recognize dominant trend(s) within an area and use these to extrapolate into areas of uncertainty. In such cases the degree of uncertainty should be indicated by appropriate contour symbols or remarks on the map.

Often the best guide to establishing trends can be faults and/or folds. When they are large and persistent, their correlation through a grid can greatly assist both interpre-

tation and contouring. However, there are instances where it can be difficult to establish fold and, especially, fault patterns. The correlation of fault lines across areas of no control can cause considerable problems (Fig. 8.5). In some cases a fault may have a recognizable character (similar morphology, amount of throw, etc.) from line to line. In other cases, especially where faults are numerous, a decision has to be made using trends established nearby or at deeper levels in the section where the relationships are clearer.

The foregoing brief discussion has highlighted some of the common contouring problems and shows how line spacing is a most critical factor. If the grid is too coarse the map only shows an hypothesis and not an interpretation. The potential size of a missed structure or an ambiguity will be a major consideration in determining if more data should be collected. Whatever the outcome, it is the duty of an interpreter not only to attempt to resolve such problems and to display or annotate a map so as to leave no doubt as to the confidence that can be placed on the interpretation—whether it be the whole or only part of a map.

MECHANICAL CONTOURING

The contouring problem can be solved mechanically. The advent of computers over the last twenty years has led to their widespread use to draw maps from digital data sources. Initially, this seems a good idea and the answer to all contouring problems, freeing the interpreter of this seemingly mundane task. It should be possible to automate, and thereby significantly speed up, the contouring process and so remove human bias and subjectivity from it. However, it is debatable how desirable it is to eliminate the last two factors and there are inherent problems in the automated contouring process.

Mechanical contouring of seismic data faces two main problems. Firstly, the seismic data forms a far from ideal grid for automated contouring (excepting 3-D surveys which, from a grid-spacing viewpoint, are in many respects good candidates for mechanical contouring). Secondly, mis-ties, varying from small to significant, will occur at practically every line intersection.

Ideally for mechanical contouring, the data points should be evenly distributed throughout the area. However, conventional 2-D seismic data has a one-dimensional structure depicting the surface in a continuous form (the line) from which a two-dimensional structure (the map) has to be created. The transformation from line information to the required map involves some form of interpolation. This is achieved in two main ways by automatic contouring systems:

1. Simulation of the manual approach to contouring by using methods such as area partitioning into some form of triangulation of the data points, or by using

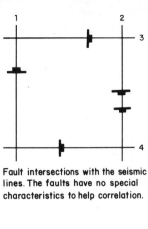

Fault intersections with the seismic
lines. The faults have no special
characteristics to help correlation.

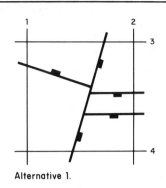

Alternative 1.

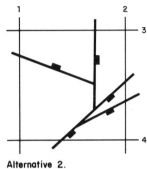

Alternative 2.

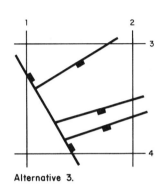

Alternative 3.

FIGURE 8.5 *Interpretation dilemma—which fault pattern is correct? Five fault intersections affect the four lines. The faults have no special characteristics to help their correlation. Three of many possible interpretations are shown.*

direct contour determination
2. By using the computer's ability to store two-dimensional data sets as grids (tables, arrays, networks, etc., depending on terminology)

Both approaches produce end products that can vary greatly for a variety of reasons inherent in the particular method applied. This is discussed below. Currently, the system based on the latter process has the most widespread use throughout industry, although the manual mimic methods are gaining in popularity and may offer significant advantages in accuracy.

The mis-tie problem is more of a hiccup but is, potentially, a serious handicap to the automation process. Obviously, under ideal conditions each data point should have a unique value. This is true for many observations that are contoured (e.g., geochemical analyses and meteorological data), but seismic grids consist of lines that intersect. At each line intersection there are two possible values available for contouring; and, inevitably, discrepancies between the values do occur. The discrepancies have their origins in a multitude of possible causes—picking error; digitizing error (which, it is to be hoped, is

small and randomly distributed); small differences in the real time to a particular event on sections involved, due to processing effects; etc. If, as we would hope, the mis-ties are small and randomly distributed, they will be amenable to statistical treatment. But, whatever the cause, they can produce their own artefacts and also introduce a pre-contouring phase into the automatic procedure. If the main criterion for using automatic contouring is speed, the time involved in resolving mis-ties, or the assumptions required to automate their removal, should not be overlooked when evaluating the pros and cons of manual versus mechanical contouring.

Assuming that the mis-tie problem has been surmounted, the next consideration is how best to automate the contouring procedure.

GRID CONTOURING

Grid contouring is still the most widely used contouring technique. The term "grid" implies a network of values arranged in a rectangular mesh and calculated in such a fashion that the values at the grid nodes (where a given row and column pair intersect) are accurate samples from the seismic surface that is being contoured (fig. 8.6). The grid is so arranged that its rectangular area coincides with the map area to be contoured. The estimation of the values at the nodes is the major problem associated with the first phase of the contouring process—interpolation.

216

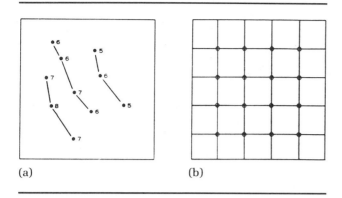

(a)   (b)

FIGURE 8.6 *Sketch showing how seismic data can be gridded prior to mechanical contouring. (a) Seismic lines. (b) Seismic data gridded for automatic contouring.*

The second phase is the lacing, in a smooth fashion, of the contours through the regular grid that has been created, automatic labeling, and generation of commands to drive the plotting device. The most general technique used for contouring grids is the contour lacing approach, where each contour in the grid is found, threaded through the grid, and sent as vectors plus any appropriate labeling and annotation to the hardware device which may or may not perform a vector/raster conversion before display. The process is illustrated in figure 8.7 where a small portion of the grid has been considered—namely, one grid cell. Linear interpolation is used to determine whether there is a contour entering the cell on any of its sides. Obviously, if there is a contour entering there will also be a contour leaving the cell. Thus an entry and exit point can be marked and a line drawn between them to show the location of the contour within the cell. This sounds simple but problems can arise—as in figure 8.8, where a saddle occurs and there is no determinate solution to the correct choice of location of the contour lines on the basis of the information at the grid cell nodes. The solution to this problem may be wrong in geological terms, in that a

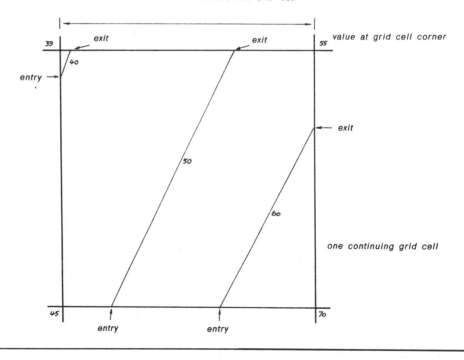

FIGURE 8.7 *Diagram showing how linear interpolation is used along the side of each grid cell to calculate exit points (the entry points for the next cell) for contours.*

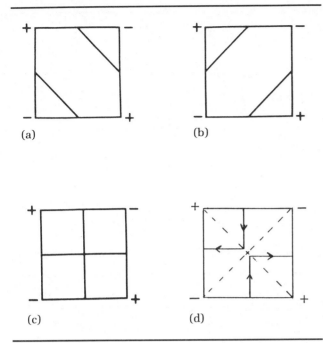

(a)   (b)

(c)   (d)

FIGURE 8.8 *Typical computer contouring problem—a saddle. (a) and (b) are two possible solutions. The problem is solved by estimating the value at the grid cell center (c), dividing the cell into four triangles (d), and calculating the contour position using the "high ground to the right" rule. This may not always produce the geologically correct solution.*

value is estimated for the central location in the cell thus dividing the rectangle into four triangles that are always fully determined. Then by following a "high ground on the right" rule the position of all contours can be determined uniquely.

Contour Smoothing. Figure 8.9 shows a portion of a map created using the techniques outlined above. All the contour line vectors are long because the size of the grid cell used to create the map is large. Thus the map is very unappealing and is only barely interpretable. The solution to this problem can take one of two courses: either resolution of the grid mesh can be increased by regridding until every cell of the grid has a side length of less than a few millimeters—thus creating reasonably short vectors giving the appearance of a smooth curve—or the line has to be smoothed in some other way. Smoothing a line in vacuo can be a very dangerous thing to do, as figure 8.10 shows—the same piece of map from the previous figure has had each line on the map smoothed by using a cubic spline technique. It is possible to make the lines individually smooth, but it is not possible to ensure absolutely that they do not cross. The solution, demonstrated in figure 8.11, is to create a surface "patch" that fits every grid cell in such a manner that the course of a contour through a grid cell can be determined by refer-

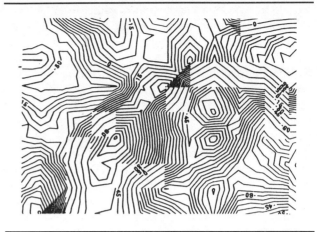

FIGURE 8.9 *Map contoured using the techniques described in the text.*

FIGURE 8.10 *Same map as figure 8.9 but with each line smoothed using a cubic spline technique (note how some contours overlap).*

FIGURE 8.11 *Same map as figure 8.9 but contoured using the surface "patch" technique for every grid cell instead of linear interpolations to the grid cell edges as used in figure 8.9.*

218

ence to interpolations on the patch, rather than by linear interpolations to the grid cell edges. The patch function (either local or global) will generate a surface that honors exactly not only every grid node value but also estimated first derivatives, thus ensuring continuity over the whole area, and hence a smooth surface.

Fault Depiction. A perennial problem with automated contouring is the representation of faults and other discontinuities in the surface being contoured. It is not possible to stipulate that a surface continuous in the first derivative is essential, and then to say that faults must also be included. The many attempts to achieve some form of compromise between these opposed objectives have usually resulted in the need to segment the data set into a number of areas that are both gridded and contoured independently and then plotted as one map. A few versions have attempted to generate weighting functions for a projected-distance-weighted-average (PDWA) interpolation. These functions are effectively almost discontinuous in the area of a fault because they introduce the concept of barriers into the data as in figure 8.12. In these cases the calculation of the distance weightings in a complex seismic map, although possible, takes an inordinate amount of computer time.

In grid terms, the problem of developing faulted structures is related to: (a) computer time, and (b) the problem of making the contours run up to a fault and no further, without the need for elaborate masking techniques. This is essentially an unsolved problem, but definitely one of interest to seismic interpreters!

ALTERNATIVE CONTOURING STRATEGIES

There are several objections to the grid methods outlined above:

1. Considerable computer time is needed to interpolate a large regular grid to represent relatively few data points.
2. Lack of flexibility in responding to variable data densities in different parts of a map.
3. Non-honoring of data points caused by an insufficiently fine grid in order to keep the computer time down to reasonable levels.
4. Difficulty in representing fault information adequately on a continuous surface has led to the intensive development in recent years of alternative methods of generating contour maps.

The two most widely known methods are (1) those based on triangulation of the data set, and (2) the process of contour following without either grid or triangulation as a guide. The latter method found favor because it simply skipped all gridding stages and looked for contours by hill-climbing techniques. A local PDWA or a global inter-

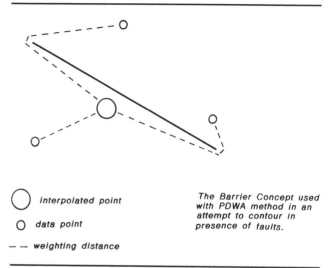

○ interpolated point

○ data point

– – weighting distance

The Barrier Concept used with PDWA method in an attempt to contour in presence of faults.

FIGURE 8.12 *The projected-distance-weighted-average (PDWA) method and faults. The barrier concept is used with the PDWA method in an attempt to contour in the presence of faults.*

polation function was used to hunt by binary bracketing methods for the precise location of a given contour, working on the complete raw data set. Incremental movement along, and iterative search for, the contour, once it was found, was then used to trace the contour through the map area. This method proved quite effective but rather heavy on computer time. In part for this reason, in part because it had none of the side benefits of the regular rectangular grid (for instance the possibility for the generation of rock and pore space volumes), and in part because of the difficulty of inserting fault lines and barriers into the scheme, the method is rarely used now.

Triangulation Contouring Techniques. The human cartographer, given a scattered data set to contour, will subconsciously visualize a set of triangles in the area under consideration that help to locate the contour being traced. These triangles have no existence but provide a structure the cartographer can use to estimate position of the contour line relative to other data points. It would seem likely that an automated approach that did the same would have considerable benefits, particularly as it would always honor all data points (since the data points would form the vertices of the triangulation). This approach is summarized in figure 8.13, where the data points connected by a triangulation are then contoured using linear approximations across the planar facets of the triangles that have been created. There used to be little interest in the automatic triangulation of seismic and other data sets because (1) it appeared impossible to generate the same triangulation, and hence the same map, from the same set

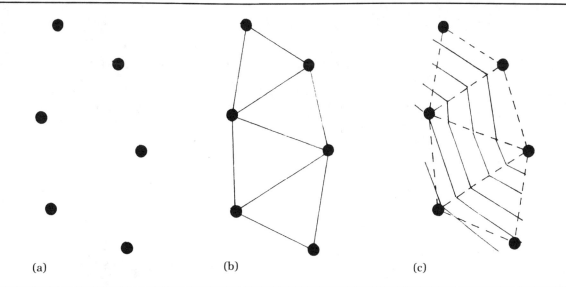

(a) (b) (c)

FIGURE 8.13 *Contouring by triangulation.* (a) *The data points.* (b) *Triangles based on the data points.* (c) *Resulting contours.*

of data, independent of the starting point of the triangulation process, and (2) the time taken for automatic triangulation was exorbitant. (Although the time taken for gridding is related to the square of the number of data points, some of the methods of automatic triangulation were at best related to the cube!)

Improvements in the last ten years have led to reliable triangulation procedures that produce the most equilateral (and therefore unique) set of triangles possible in a time linearly related to the number of data points, and without the need for large computer memory requirements. For any given data set, it is now faster to generate unsmoothed contours from an automatic triangulation procedure than interpolation of a grid. At the same time, all data points are honored, the resolution of the map varies with the data density, and maps can be joined together without error at the margins. However, smooth contouring from triangles presently takes two to five times longer than smooth contouring of a regular rectangular grid.

Another reason for the upsurge of interest in triangulation techniques has been that they are ideally suited to fault insertion. If the dummy fault points are entered as data, the triangulation process will include them and will automatically relate them to the rest of the data set. Then, as in figure 8.14, the triangulation can be "unzipped" so that there is no direct connection in the data structure between the two halves of the fault. Contouring can then take place and the result will be a perfect edge to the fault, depending only on the input resolution of the fault line.

There has been some criticism of triangular techniques for seismic shotpoint line contouring because of the very long, thin triangles generated. An example of this problem is given in figure 8.15. There are presently experiments under way to deal with both this problem and that

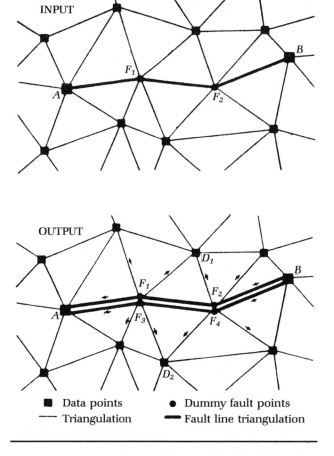

FIGURE 8.14 *Computer contouring—triangulation and faults.*

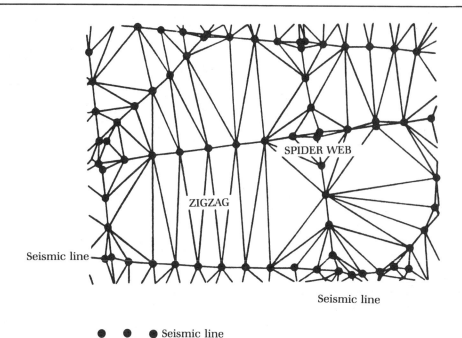

Seismic line

FIGURE 8.15 *Triangulation of seismic data: Diagram showing how wide line spacing of seismic data can produce unfavorable (very long and thin triangles) triangle networks.*

of mapping large seismic suites (more than 100,000 points) without large memory machines. The solution has been to partition the data automatically and uniquely into sets of polygonal areas (faults included) enclosed or partially enclosed by a seismic, fault, or border line. These polygons are then infilled with PDWA estimates at critical locations if the triangles are too thin, then triangulated and contoured.

COMPUTER CONTOURING

The widespread use of machine contouring does not mean that all the problems have been overcome, merely that computers are available and will allow production-line mapping without employing a large number of extra staff.

Data Danger Signs. There are a number of situations outlined in figure 8.16 where the data are not very suitable for automated contouring:

1. Where mis-ties between seismic lines have not been sufficiently resolved to suppress an annular pattern of contours around the intersections, the only real solutions are to correct by hand or by computer graphics, or to use a generalizing technique, such as trend surface analysis, to resolve the local problem before contouring the data.

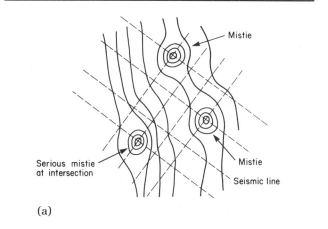

(a)

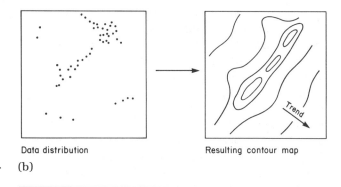

Data distribution

Resulting contour map

(b)

FIGURE 8.16 *Examples of data unsuited to computer contouring. (a) Effect of mis-ties on the contour patterns. (b) Variability of data density influences the contour pattern.*

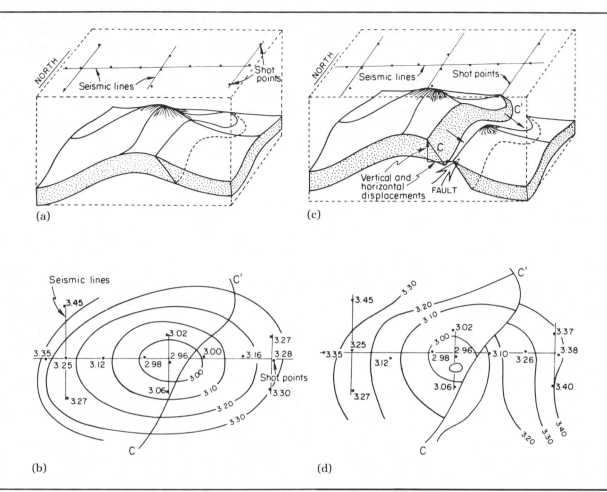

FIGURE 8.17 *An example of a situation unsuited to computer contouring:* (a) *Block diagram of a hypothetical dome-shaped structure crossed by five seismic lines.* (b) *Contour map of the structure; line CC′ represents a fault with negligible displacement.* (c) *The same dome but there is now substantial displacement along fault CC′.* (d) *Computer contour map misrepresents the structure because contours on fault blocks were fitted independently of each other. Reprinted by permission of the AAPG from Berlanga and Harbaugh, 1981, fig. 4, p. 427.*

2. Sometimes the variation of data density in different locations on the map is so extreme that one area of a grid may be over-dense while another area has insufficient detail to cope with the variability in data values. The only possible solution to this problem is to create a number of maps, at different scales, of the areas of differing data density.

3. Figure 8.17 illustrates perhaps the most serious potential shortcoming of computer contouring—the lack of geological intelligence. While this condition may occasionally afflict the interpreter, it is a characteristic of currently available computer contouring packages. Figure 8.17a shows a dome-shaped structure crossed by five seismic lines. Both computer and manual contouring would produce a good representation of the structure. However, this is not the case when the dome is faulted. The interpreter contouring the structure would realize that contours should close against the fault on both its up- and downthrown sides and thus correctly depict and predict the shape of the faulted surface. The computer contouring program, on the other hand, has neither geological sense, nor a memory of the shape it has con-

toured on the upthrown side of the fault. In cases where there is insufficient seismic coverage to depict the structure accurately, the computer-drawn contour map, although honoring the data points, has produced neither a geologically correct solution nor one that would identify a prospective structure on the fault's downthrown side. So be especially cautious of using computer-generated maps to identify potential traps.

Is It Worth It? Is computer contouring "worth it"? The answer today is a qualified "yes," "in the right circumstances." Perhaps in another ten to twenty years continued improvements in computing power will make this answer redundant. However, today we are still faced with

222

considerable problems if computer contouring is applied in unsuitable circumstances. Computer contouring is definitely not suited to:

a. Data grids where mis-ties are unavoidable: Consider, for example, a highly structured horizon that has been interpreted using migrated seismic lines. Unavoidable mis-ties will occur between dip and strike lines. To contour such data correctly requires cross-reference between the migrated and unmigrated lines; and this is beyond the capabilities of any current automated system.
b. Densely faulted grids where one or more horizons are to be mapped: Two problems related to the fault pattern arise in these situations. Firstly, the fault pattern on a particular horizon. Although there are techniques that can contour a faulted surface, the resulting fault pattern is dependent on the decisions of the contouring routine, which takes no account of geology. There are many instances where a particular fault can be recognized by its associated geological features, of which the least important may be its throw magnitude, which would be considered the main criterion by a computer mapping routine.

There are, however, techniques for handling the faulting problem. They are cumbersome but do allow the computer to cope. For example, the fault pattern can be determined by hand, digitized and then incorporated with the data grid to be contoured. In such circumstances, it is relevant to ask if, after the expenditure of time reconciling mis-ties and establishing the fault pattern in preparation for machine contouring, it would not have been quicker simply to contour by hand. This decision becomes especially relevant if, within a grid, more than one related horizon, sharing a common fault pattern, has to be contoured. Contour trends should, in many cases, share some continuity in shape from surface to surface. Also, the fault pattern must be positioned on each map so as to correctly portray the fault pattern as it successively cuts the horizons. Preparing a data base that takes these factors into account is extremely time consuming and tedious. Only if the mapping project is extremely large is it likely that computer contouring for complexly structured and faulted multiple horizons is worthwhile.

Computer contouring of seismic data comes into its own for:

1. Mapping unfaulted horizons with relatively simple structure: Computer contouring is ideal for producing isopach maps. In these cases, sorting out mis-ties lends itself to automated routines and it is possible to produce large volumes of work.
2. Very large interpretation projects: Here, computer-generated maps can provide a first look for initial assessments.

3. Mapping velocity functions derived from seismic data: Here, computer contouring can be used only after the data has been edited to remove anomalous data points.

Computer mapping systems produce their best results and operate most efficiently when controlled by people who thoroughly understand the algorithms involved and can, therefore, make reasonable choices between alternative methods presented for use with different data sets.

It is by no means unusual to find would-be practitioners of computer mapping who, given a 3-D seismic data set, will regrid it to other dimensions rather than contour it directly. Regridding would be wasteful in such a situation; it would also lead to a less accurate map than that produced by using the original data! But there are still many people who consider that a fully automatic system is preferable to a system that requires operator intervention. Beware of the maps produced by such people, because no one method is applicable to all geological contouring situations. Indeed, there are many many examples of cases where the same data has produced widely differing maps depending on the contouring system used. There is no correct map in mathematical terms. Surely the interpreter—to save time and computing expense and to save the company from wrong decisions—should choose how the map finally studied for interpretation is created?

A final word: Once all the problems have been overcome and acceptable contour maps produced, a whole new range of options for presenting the data becomes possible—color graphics, isometric projections, etc. Figure 8.18 shows an example of a computer drawn contour map and corresponding block diagram. Similar and more sophisticated displays are likely to become commonplace in the years to come.

MANUAL CONTOURING

The previous section has discussed the mechanical approach to contouring—joining together points of like time with no regard to other geological considerations. In well-folded areas with clear trends, the method is likely to work well; in other areas, where the interpreter needs to bring a consideration of other factors (deeper structural grain etc.) into the contouring exercise, mechanical contouring may not produce such acceptable results. Machine contouring can only consider the immediately available data points and is, thereby, at a disadvantage compared to the interpreter, who can use other outside factors (the obvious trend of a deeper horizon, for example) to aid the contouring. The following discussion describes a rational approach to the problems of manual contouring and suggests some basic rules. It should be stated from the outset that there is no substitute for common sense as an aid to contouring.

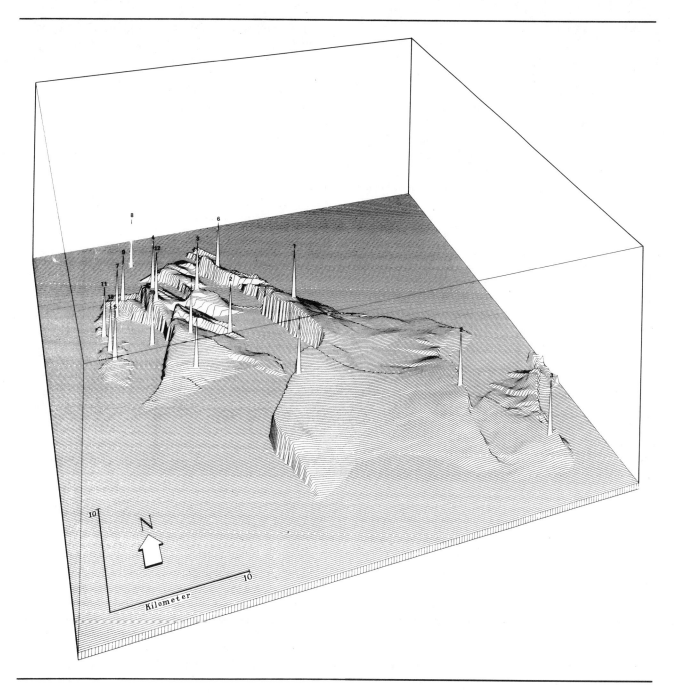

FIGURE 8.18 *Computer-drawn block diagram. Courtesy Norsk Hydro.*

EQUIPMENT AND MAPS

The first requirements for manual contouring are a suitable table on which to place the map and adequate lighting. A selection of pencils, ranging from hard to soft—2H is an ideal hard pencil; H, HB, and B are suitable for producing thicker lines—together with sharp colored crayons (optional) and eraser.

Contouring onto clear plastic drawing film is recommended. It is useful in several ways, making it easier to overlay maps, compare fault trends, contour shapes, etc., and to have a top copy for presentation while a copy is being drafted.

The basis for most seismic maps is the shotpoint map. Shotpoint maps show the position of each seismic line by having a symbol (dot, small circle, cross, etc.) at every 10th, 20th, 50th, or whatever, shotpoint along each line. The shotpoint base maps are drafted either by hand or, more commonly now, by computer. The advantages of the latter are obvious—maps can be edited and plotted at any scale required. The scale of the map to be contoured should be appropriate for the task; that is, the lines should be sufficiently widely spaced for all the values and symbols to be read with ease. For 3-D surveys, a scale of 1:10,000, or a close equivalent, is suitable. For conventional 2-D surveys with a 1 × 1 km grid spacing, a scale of 1:25,000 is adequate, and for wider-spaced grids a scale of 1:50,000 will do. Mapping at 1:100,000 is only advisable for very widely spaced, regional grids. Variations on these scale conventions may be in use locally.

DIGITIZING

The first stage in contouring is to measure the two-way times to the picked horizons on the seismic sections and post these values on shotpoint base maps. The simplest method of digitizing the sections is to read off the values directly using a scale the same as the sections. The horizontal distance between each reading should be sufficient to ensure that a straight-line interpolation between each point will describe the structure adequately. It makes no difference whether sampling is done at regular shotpoint intervals or at regular time intervals, provided that the measurements are made at appropriate intervals. Thus, a long and simple monocline can be specified by just two widely spaced measurements, but a rough, eroded surface requires at least two measurements per cycle of corrugation. Furthermore, an additional step (reconstitution) is necessary before values can be interpolated between the measured values. This is illustrated in figure 8.19a, which shows an anticlinal feature with a faulted crestal area. The black blobs represent the digitized points at regular shotpoint intervals. The intervals are too great; when these values are posted and contoured, the structure appears as shown by the dashed line; and all memory of the

collapsed crest has disappeared. Figure 8.19b shows a major high, a second high, and a small saddle between them; the shotpoint values corresponding to regular intervals of reflection time are represented by black blobs. The intervals are too large; when the values are posted and contoured, it is not possible to determine whether the high is single or double.

To be completely safe, therefore it is necessary to time the reflection at least twice for each cycle of undulation or the reflection surface. It is also necessary to apply the process of reconstitution before interpolating between these times for contouring purposes. This leads to a set of basic rules for marking and digitizing or (if we are using a computerized digitizing system, which should give an excellent representation of the timed surface) when posting the timed values from the sections.

1. During the picking, ignore or smooth trace-to-trace variations judged to be due to noise, poor static corrections, or artefacts of the seismic method; in this, we are applying the criterion of geological plausibility.
2. Then look at the sections overall, in the light of the exploration play, and judge what degree of relief in the reflection surface is material—anything less than this is considered to be of no importance to finding oil or gas.
3. Select a contour interval that provides at least two contours (preferably three or four) over this minimum significant relief.
4. If it is desirable to time the picked reflector at a regular progression of times, do this at the chosen contour interval. In this case, no interpolation of times is necessary in the contouring, and so we are not at risk for failing to reconstitute.
5. If it is desirable to time the picked reflection at a regular progression of shotpoints, look at the sections again, and decide what convenient contour interval corresponds approximately to the contour interval on the steepest flanks of the smallest material relief. In this case, we are at risk for failing to reconstitute. This can be seen in figure 8.19; if it happens that the times at A and B are 1.987 and 2.007 s, respectively, then a simple interpolation of the 2.000 s contour is significantly in error. (As noted above, this problem does not arise if we time and post at the chosen contour interval.) When we elect to time or post on a regular progression of shotpoints we err on the side of caution, and adopt shorter intervals if there is any doubt.

Whether we sample and post regularly in time or in shotpoints, the major protection against flagrant violation of the sampling theory is to mark on the map the position and time of every significant high, every significant low, the position of significant slope breaks, and the position and throw of every significant fault. This step will prevent

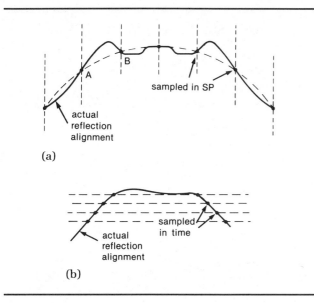

(a)

(b)

FIGURE 8.19 *The inadequacy of coarse sampling, in space and time. (a) The solid line represents the actual surface; black books are digitized points; and the incorrectly reconstituted surface is shown by the dashed line. (b) Sampling at constant time intervals does not correctly depict the crestal area of the structure. Reprinted by permission of IHRDC Press from Badley and Anstey, 1984, fig. A3-1, p. 172.*

us from error in the examples of figure 8.19. The practice is mandatory.

Finally we gain additional protection by marking on the map zones of extended monoclinal dip and of zero dip.

Sensible modification of these precepts may be indicated in practice, depending on the scale of the sections, the eye and hand of the interpreter, the mechanization available, the admissibility of skipping some measurements over featureless zones, and whether the timing is done by the interpreter or by a technician.

Once timed, the readings can be either directly posted onto a shotpoint map of suitable scale or, if more than one horizon is involved, tabulated, and the values posted after digitizing has been completed. The seismic times or depth values are posted against the appropriate shotpoints, together with symbols for faults, truncations, etc. If more than one seismic survey is involved in the interpretation, it is quite probable that there may be consistent static shifts between the surveys. These will have been determined at the initiation of the interpretation but will have played no significant role in the proceedings until now. When the data is digitized, the static shifts should be removed by adding or subtracting appropriate amounts to adjust all values to a common datum. Digitizing by hand is time consuming and tedious. Efficient computer-based systems are now commonly available for digitizing. A typical system consists of an electronic digitizing table, a computer, and a plotter. The seismic sections are placed on the digi-

tizing table; coordinates for the horizontal and time scales are recorded; a check is made for excessive paper stretch; and, once all is in order, the picked horizons (including fault positions, data gaps, etc.) are digitized. The information is stored in a data file where twenty or more horizons might be stored for each seismic section. The data is then available for posting as two-way times. Alternatively, isopachs can be calculated from the data base or, if velocity functions are available, the data depth can be converted and posted as depth values. If a quality control check is required, lists or maps showing mis-ties can be obtained from the data base. When digitized data is combined with survey or navigation data, it is possible to plot and post the contour maps for contouring by computer, saving much time and effort.

SINGLE CONTOUR MAPS—PREPARATION

The following description sets out a suggested procedure for contouring a single map.

ESTABLISHING THE OVERALL STRUCTURE

Attempt to establish the main linear features. Interpretation of faults, fold axes, flexures, and so on, is more reliable than correlation of surfaces. Fault intersections on each line should already be marked with an appropriate symbol, together with values for the up- and downthrown sides. It is useful to review each seismic line in turn at this stage, and to mark on the map suitable color symbols showing high and low axes, breaks in slope, and so forth (see fig. 8.20). The similarity of faults and other structures are thereby systematically correlated from line to line. Nothing in the data will reveal that the faults seen on two cross-sections are, in fact, the same fault. Geological plausibility must be used to test the likeliness of faults correlating—similarity in geological history, direction and amount of throw, structures association with the fault, timing of initiation, end of fault movement, and so on, can be a great help in correlation. Initiation of fault movement is dated by tracing up the fault plane to find the top of the zone with constant throw (allowing for velocity effects on either side of the fault, which can give a thinner time thickness on the downthrown side for identical rock thickness). The shallowest reflection to show the maximum throw dates the initiation of faulting. The shallowest reflection to be displaced marks the end of the main fault movement, though renewed minor movements may induce flexures of still higher levels. It is essential that fault plane dip is correctly portrayed by the intersection of the fault trace and contours, that is, dipping fault planes should "V" into lows and cut into highs. The correlation of fold axes is usually more obvious, but can be difficult in areas where fold axes are en echelon and the grid spacing is relatively wide. A knowledge of an area's structural grain or an understanding of the tectonic style can greatly aid this initial interpretation stage. For ex-

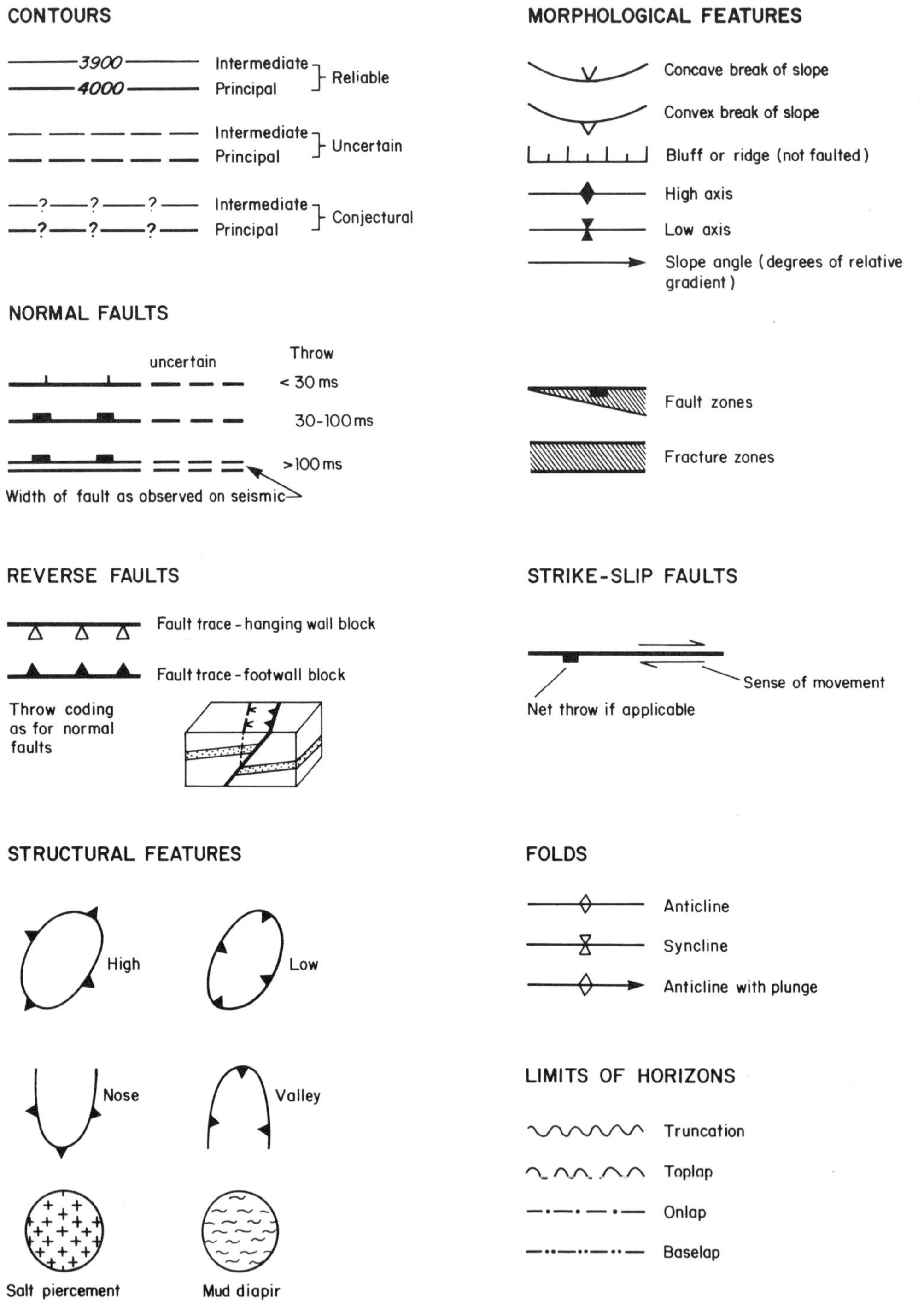

CONTOURS

—3900—	Intermediate	} Reliable
—4000—	Principal	
– – – –	Intermediate	} Uncertain
▬ ▬ ▬	Principal	
—?—?—?—	Intermediate	} Conjectural
▬?▬?▬?▬	Principal	

NORMAL FAULTS

uncertain — Throw

< 30 ms

30-100 ms

>100 ms

Width of fault as observed on seismic

REVERSE FAULTS

△ △ △ Fault trace - hanging wall block

▲ ▲ ▲ Fault trace - footwall block

Throw coding as for normal faults

STRUCTURAL FEATURES

High Low

Nose Valley

Salt piercement Mud diapir

MORPHOLOGICAL FEATURES

Concave break of slope

Convex break of slope

Bluff or ridge (not faulted)

High axis

Low axis

Slope angle (degrees of relative gradient)

Fault zones

Fracture zones

STRIKE-SLIP FAULTS

Sense of movement

Net throw if applicable

FOLDS

Anticline

Syncline

Anticline with plunge

LIMITS OF HORIZONS

Truncation

Toplap

Onlap

Baselap

○ Location

⌀ Drilling (rig on location)

⊕ Hydrocarbon indications

⬦ Dry hole

☼ Gas show

☼ Gas well

◆ Oil show

◆ Oil well

☼ Gas & oil shows

☼ Gas well with oil show

☼ Oil well with gas show

☀ Gas & oil well

☼ Condensate well

⬦ Junked well

Ⓢ Stratigraphic test

Ⓦ Water injected well

Ⓖ Gas injected well

☼ Gas production well

● Oil production well

□ Production platform

⌐⌐ Production platform (planned)

■ Terminal platform

△ Onshore terminal (gas)

▲ Onshore terminal (oil)

FIGURE 8.20 *Map symbols for seismic interpretation.*

ample, if a major strike-slip fault passes through the area, it may be possible to predict the directions of first-, second-, and third-order related structures using knowledge of the stress pattern associated with strike-slip faults.

The fault pattern should be marked using a red (or another color) pencil to make a very faint line joining the main faults. If correlation is in doubt, completion of the fault pattern is best left until the contouring stage. At this stage, assuming that the grid size is dense enough to sample the structures, the map should show the basic fault pattern, fold axes, highs and lows, and major slope changes for the mapped horizon. Traces of the fold axes are a useful guide when contouring, so as to ensure that all contours intersecting them turn along the same axis—as also are the locations of significant slope changes. The latter can often be a distinct linear feature of some significance that can be difficult to locate if only the posted values are used.

CONTOURING RULES

The map is now ready for contouring. Selection of the contour interval will depend on the nature of the mapped surface and map scale. For structural mapping at scales between 1:25,000 and 1:100,000, a contour interval of 20 ms is common. However, for areas with much subtle structural development (e.g., typical Middle East structures, where 5–10 ms may be significant), finer contour intervals are obviously employed. It is a common convention, however, to mark every fifth contour with a bolder line to facilitate a quick appreciation of structure. It is these bolder contours that are traced first, not as a bold line but using a hard (at least 2H) pencil to produce a very, very faint line trace. These initial contours are used as a framework within which the intervening contours will be placed, and to provide the overall structure and identify likely problem areas. Contouring should not consist of driving a pencil point through the data, honoring every value. This would produce a very ragged line containing all mis-ties, and errors inherent in the section marking and digitizing. This noise must be filtered out. Surfaces on seismic sections are generally fairly smooth and rarely violently undulating. Contouring by hand attempts to emulate the knowledge of shapes assumed by folded rocks, peneplaned surfaces, and so forth. Minor mis-ties that become apparent during this and the next stage can be resolved by reference to the original sections. Often the structural trend established by nearby lines will make it obvious which of two mis-tying lines is correct. Following completion of the outline, infill contouring can proceed. This is done using sharply pointed softer pencils (H or HB are ideal) to trace out the intervening first and fourth contours. Use smooth hand movements to produce a single, graceful line of even density—these contours are the finished product. Break the contours into shortish intervals that can be drawn without excessive hand move-

ment. After completing the first and fourth infill contours over a short interval, mark in the second and third contours. Continue this process until the entire map is contoured, completing the fault pattern details as and when dictated by the contouring. Attempt to produce evenly spaced contours over intervals where no dip changes are anticipated. Use the break in slope symbols to guide the contouring. Mark in the final fault pattern, breaks in slope, and so on, using appropriate symbols (fig. 8.20), with soft pencil or colored crayon. Neatly number every fifth contour. The contour values should be easy to read when viewing the map from a southerly aspect (or over its baseline). Using a soft pencil (HB or B) to make a bold line, adjust every fifth contour where necessary, using the adjacent first and fourth contours as a guide to its final location.

Finally, the highs, lows, valleys, noses, no-data areas, and so on, should be marked on the map. Symbols that show the fine detail on a surface can be an extremely important complement to the contours which, for normal contour intervals, do not always convey the message of the detail evident in the seismic sections. For example, subtle breaks in slope on a surface, perhaps very significant geologically, cannot be adequately portrayed using contours; additional symbols are required. It is also important that the map be sufficiently annotated so that the viewer may not only appreciate structure, but also be able to evaluate, on a spatial basis, the degree of confidence that can be placed in the interpretation. This can be done by using differing symbols for the same contour as it passes from a good data area where confidence is high, to poor data areas where confidence is low (fig. 8.20).

In addition to symbols, the following should always be displayed on every map:

Latitude, longitude, and other pertinent map projection values
Map scale and projection
Regional location map
Legend
Labels

The label should include at least:

Map title
Author
Date drawn
Scale
Contour interval

TYPICAL CONTOURING PROBLEMS

The procedure described above works well in most circumstances, but there can be instances where just contouring the values is no longer simple. Briefly described below are some typical contouring problems.

Mis-Ties. It is inevitable that the values at many line intersections will disagree. The problem becomes serious when a discrepancy approaches or exceeds the magnitude of the contour interval. The values can disagree for a number of reasons. There may be a genuine mis-tie of the data, due, for example, to migration between a dip and strike line, poor marking of the section, digitizing error, or processing effects. The majority of errors should be random but some (e.g., those due to migration) could be systematic over areas with similar structural attitude. If serious, a mis-tie should be checked by reference to the sections. In many cases, however, the trend of the contours will indicate which of two values is likely to be correct. It is usual to smooth through small mis-ties to produce a filtered version of the values. Failure to do this will produce a contour map full of noise that will be difficult to interpret. Irreconcilable mis-ties must be handled with common sense and a decision about which value to accept made in the light of acceptable evidence. The map should be suitably annotated where the mis-tie is irreconcilable and significant.

Faults. In the real Earth, viewed in plan, normal faults with hade (fault plane dip) produce a gap in a horizon. There will be a narrow band on the map where the horizon is absent. The converse is true for reverse faults, where the horizon will be present twice within the fault zone. However, seismic reflections do not always display faults with the required clarity. On filtered stack sections reflections at normal faults often appear to overlap the fault. This can be either because it is in fact reversed or because it is a normal fault and the reflections are continued as hyperbolas which intersect in cross-section. In these circumstances, it can be difficult to identify the exact location of the downthrown side of the fault and the fault appears as a single line on the map. Recognition of the downthrown side can also be a problem for major normal faults where noise (diffractions, etc.) on the downthrown side of the fault can obscure primary reflections and make the fault zone appear wider than in reality. Such faults appear too wide when mapped. Caution should also be exercised in interpreting structural closure in the vicinity of faults, because velocity anomalies are commonly associated with faults (figs. 3.31, 3.32, and 3.33). Suggested symbols for marking faults on maps are shown in figure 8.20. Major fault zones and fracture zones can have a separate marking scheme.

Poor Data Areas. An important role of any map is to convey the degree of certainty in an interpretation. The fault symbols shown in figure 8.20 allow for this and so should the contour lines. The same figure shows recommended symbols for contours displaying varying degrees of uncertainty.

Character Change and Leg-jumping. There are occasions when it is impossible to follow a reflection over the entire study area. A reflection can change in character, be recognizable only intermittently, or simply end. If it is important to map the reflection (when, for example, it lies near the top of the main prospective horizon), any changes should be noted on the map. In extreme cases the mapped horizon may not be the same across the entire area. For example, it may be impossible to correlate with certainty across a major fault and a datum change of the mapped horizon may be suspected. These changes should be noted on the map.

Structurally Complex Areas. Often details of local structure cannot be easily resolved using the mapping contour interval. The likely solution can often be found by reducing the contour interval locally until the structure is displayed in sufficient detail for the most likely alternative to be selected.

Summary of Contouring Rules. The following points, taken from Anstey (1977), are good guidelines for all situations.

Recognize trends, establish regional dip, search for dip reversals, and seek a geological rationale for trends in anomalies (folds, faults, reefs, etc.)

Contour from dense data and simple geology toward sparse data and the complications

Locally reduce the contour interval in complicated areas if the structural form is unclear

Be suspicious of a closed high within a low (except for peripheral sinks around piercements)

Be suspicious of closed lows on top of a high

Look twice at a low trend running toward a high

Be wary of like contours that run parallel over considerable distance

Be wary of contours that bear a relationship with the seismic grid (They are likely to correspond to mis-ties.)

Last but not least, check the interpretation against the seismic sections, especially in regions of complex structure

When contouring, it is always important to bear in mind the intended use of the resulting map. This can influence the way the data is contoured. For exploration maps, the objective is to locate potential traps, and so contouring should always be optimistic. This is to ensure that every potential trap is given a reasonable chance of being recognized and evaluated. In an uncertain contouring situation, it is far better to be optimistic, and perhaps kindle enough interest for further investigation, than to be pessimistic, which can too easily lead to a lack of interest and a possible discovery being overlooked. On the other hand, contouring for locating a well or delineating a field should be done with the maximum of objectivity.

CONTOURING MORE THAN ONE HORIZON

For the single contour map the scheme described above works well; but when more than one horizon is to be mapped from the same seismic grid, a further consideration is usually necessary—and that is, the relationship of the surfaces to each other. Except across major angular unconformities, it is rare for successive horizons not to share many common structural features, especially features such as faults and folds. Even overall dip and strike trends, reflected in the contour pattern, often change only gradually with depth. It is essential that the relationship between successive horizons be taken into account when contouring and that the maps be treated as a set—that is, each map is no longer contoured independently, but is contoured with continual reference to the other horizons.

To achieve this goal, a contouring scheme adopted should establish the main fault pattern, fold trends, and other structural elements, on the first map to be contoured. This will usually be the surface showing the greatest structural relief, folding, faulting, and so on. However, the first map contoured should also be on a reliable seismic horizon, since the map will become the standard reference for the subsequent maps. In some complex areas it is possible that the mapped horizons group into two or more structurally distinct sets—for example, an angular unconformity may separate two sequences with quite different attitudes. Each sequence grouping would be mapped as a distinct set. Once completed, the reference map is then used to guide the contouring of the other maps in the set. Mapping in sets can be very helpful when faced with ambiguous data on one of the horizons. Often a trend established at a deeper or shallower level can be used to resolve the problem. It is in such situations that hand contouring scores over machine methods, which always contour independently of what lies above or below, and are completely devoid of geological feeling.

Making maps in sets is best achieved by contouring onto transparent plastic film or, better, using a light table on which the maps can be overlain. The recommended procedure is as follows:

1. Overlay the map to be contoured onto the reference map and with a colored pencil trace out in very fine lines the reference fault pattern or fold axes.
2. Use these lines as a guide to forming the fold or fault pattern on the map to be contoured.
3. Ensure that the fault dip is correct (i.e., that the faults as marked have the correct dip) and, obviously, that the fault pattern agrees with the collective seismic evidence.
4. After the fault pattern has been established, follow the contouring procedure described above, but use the trends (if relevant) of the reference map as a guide.

This procedure should result in a coherent set of maps that display the mapped horizons to their best advantage.

The overlay system is especially useful for making combination maps. Such maps show the combined structure of two or more surfaces. For example, to make a map of a truncated reservoir it is necessary to produce a top reservoir map consisting of both eroded and uneroded parts of the unit. This involves combining maps for top and bottom, reservoir and unconformity maps. Using a light table, it is relatively straightforward to locate the updip limit of the uneroded reservoir and determine its updip truncation limits where like contour lines for top reservoir and the unconformity surface intersect. In complex situations it may be necessary to combine several maps to produce the required map, but this presents no special problem so long as the maps have been methodically contoured as a set.

ISOPACHS

An isopach or an isopach line is a line that joins points of equal thickness of a unit. Strictly, the term should be applied to just that—the true thickness of a unit. However, the term isopach map, together with its synonym isochron map (which is generally used for maps of both time structure and time thickness), are commonly used for thickness maps (of time or depth) derived from seismic data. Only in the very simplest case of flat-lying reflectors and vertical raypaths are isopach and isochron maps likely to be the same. In most cases a dip or structural complication will cause an isochron map to differ from the equivalent isopach map. However, for the following discussion, the term isopach map will be used to describe any seismic map, whether in time or depth, that describes the thickness of an interval between two horizons. In this usage, isopach map also encompasses the term isochore map, which is used to describe a map that expresses the thickness variation of more than one unit, and thus can include the possible effects of one or more unconformities.

Isopach maps have a great many applications and uses in geology and are extensively used in presenting the results of seismic interpretation. Some typical applications (but not an exhaustive list), are described below.

1. Isopach maps can be used to describe the shape of a unit for which some depositional and structural features may be very diagnostic. Thus, isopach maps can be used to predict facies, depositional environment, and so on. For example, an isopach map of a fan or unit within a prograding delta system could be expected to have diagnostic shapes (fig. 8.21). An isopach map of a fan could be used to predict the direction of sediment transport, and thereby be a guide to predicting, for example, potential reservoir properties.

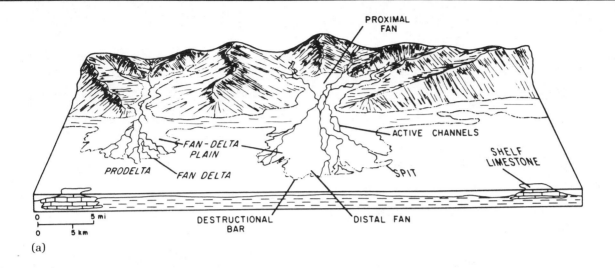

(a)

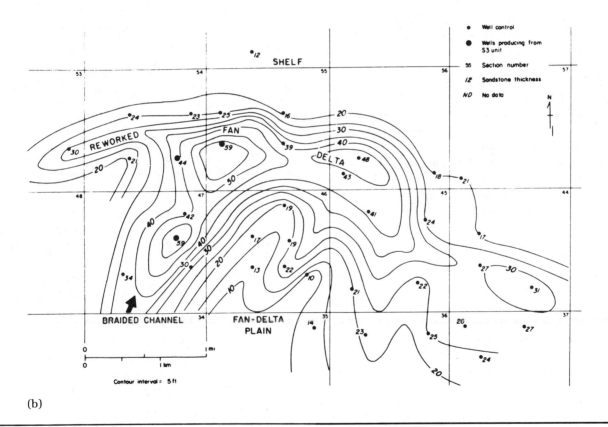

(b)

FIGURE 8.21 *Example of a fan-delta complex isopach map.*
(a) Schematic diagram of a fan-delta system. (b) Isopach
map of the Late Pennsylvania S3 sandstone in the Mibeetle
Field, Texas Panhandle. Reprinted by permission of the
AAPG from Dutton, 1982, fig. 21, p. 406.

232

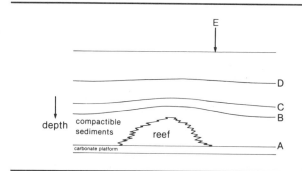

FIGURE 8.22 *Time-interval mapping over a reef, where the flanking sediments are more compactible than the reef. Reprinted by permission of IHRDC Press from Badley and Anstey, 1984, fig. 98, p. 133.*

2. Isopach maps can, in special circumstances, be the main exploration tool. For example, the search for reefs on seismic sections may be simple, or it may be difficult. On occasion, the expression of a reef on a section may be very subtle, even if the seismic line passes right across the reef itself. Typical of such situations are the "patch" reefs of Alberta and the Michigan peninsula. Isopach maps can be used to search for these subtle reefs. See, for example, figure 8.22, in which a patch reef has grown on the carbonate platform and has later become surrounded and buried by clays or lime muds. The latter are more compactible than the reef, so that the differential compaction of later sediments causes the appearance of draping over the reef. Even if the reef is not directly visible on the section, its presence can be inferred by mapping the time interval between the reflections from interfaces A and B—the reef is represented by a thick pattern on the map.

Another special situation is shown in figure 8.23. The actual situation, plotted in depth, is that of figure 8.23a; the resulting seismic section, plotted in reflection time, is that of figure 8.23b. The reef has a higher velocity than that of the surrounding sediments, so that a reflection from below the reef shows velocity pull-up. By mapping the time interval between reflection B and reflection A (or any deeper reflection), it may be possible to infer the presence of the reef from a local thin.

Sometimes the effect of velocity and the effect of differential compaction exist together; the one tends to cancel the other. In this situation, the soundest technique may be to map the interval $B–C$ (or $B–D$, or $C–D$) in figure 8.22 and search for a thin. The techniques of figure 8.22 may be of value even when the reef is clearly visible on the seismic section.

3. Isopach maps can be used to help unravel the geological history or make paleostructural reconstructions. To reveal the early structural relationship, it is often neces-

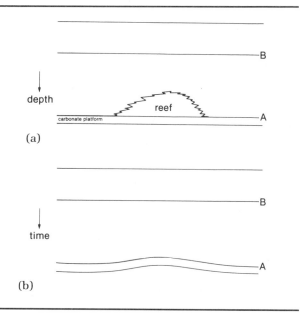

FIGURE 8.23 *Velocity pull-up under a reef, when the flanking sediments have a velocity less than that of the reef. (a) Geological model. (b) Time section. Reprinted by permission of IHRDC Press from Badley and Anstey, 1984, fig. 99, p. 134.*

sary to produce isopach maps that effectively remove the later tilting. This particular application is a very valuable tool in an interpreter's armory and one that sees much use.

4. Isopach maps can be used with structure maps to produce a new structure map. Frequently, seismic reflections are not developed exactly where they are desired—that is, precisely at the top of a reservoir unit. More often the nearest reliable reflection is present some thickness above or below the level required to be mapped. Often, in such cases, the only way to make a top reservoir map is to produce an isopach map of the interval between the top reservoir and seismic horizon and add or subtract the values (whichever is appropriate) to the seismic map. The isopach map can be made by using a combination of well data and any available seismic indications of thickness.

5. Isopach maps are an essential step in detailed reservoir mapping, especially in reserve estimation.

The level of accuracy demanded of isopach maps varies with the type of application. There are two main methods of isopach map construction, one offers speed but poor accuracy and repeatability, the other is time consuming but more accurate. Whatever the method, all isopach values taken from seismic data contain appreciable distortions caused by postdepositional and velocity effects. In some cases compaction can help accentuate a feature. For example, the shape of a clastic fan overlain by a thick shale sequence will be enhanced by subsequent compaction. However, velocity effects dominate seismic data. On a local scale the problem may not be too serious, but for cases where the isopached unit has significant structural relief, velocity effects must be fully evaluated and their implications fully understood. Geologically, the difference between a true isopach (true thickness of a unit) and the seismic equivalent can be significant if appreciable dips are involved.

The least accurate of the two methods of isopach construction involves the simple contouring of thickness values posted on a map. The first interpretive step is to ensure that the fault pattern (if applicable) agrees with the fault locations at the unit's respective boundaries. With this method it is difficult to take into account the trends and/or shape of the bounding surfaces while contouring, and all mis-ties and digitizing errors can be magnified in the isopach values. For example, if at a particular intersection the value for the upper surface was 15 ms too low and at the lower surface was 15 ms too great, the resulting isopach value would reflect both of the errors and be wrong by 30 ms. It is quite easy for levels of error acceptable during structural contouring to become unacceptable when combined into an isopach value. If, for example, in the case of the 30 ms combined error, the contour interval had been 20 ms, the isopach error would have presented contouring difficulties. In the presence of contouring difficulties, it can be difficult to establish trends; and isopach maps constructed in this manner contain much local "noise" due to these effects. However, isopach maps are easy and quick to prepare and, if a coarse contour interval is used, can be very useful in providing the overall shape and trend of a unit. Thus, they are suitable for qualitative assessment of shape and for paleostructural analysis, where reflection relationships rather than absolute thickness values are important. The disadvantage of thickness isopach maps is that they do not necessarily agree with the values obtained by subtracting the structure maps at the top and base of the unit, because the isopach contours are made independently of the other maps.

The second method of isopach construction uses the technique of map subtraction. It is more time consuming but more accurate. Maps for the upper and lower surfaces of the unit are overlain on a light table and an isopach is constructed by subtracting the contours. The method restores the values at the line intersections (assuming mis-ties have been resolved) and creates new values within the grid each time contours intersect. The resulting isopach map is in full accord with the bounding contours. This method is recommended for derivation of new structural maps from a combination of structural and isopach maps, and for maps used in reserve estimates or where accuracy is required.

A word of caution: Any isopach map constructed by contour subtracting will only be as good as the structure maps from which it is derived. If the structure maps have not been contoured as a set, the resulting isopach map is likely to reflect the vagaries of the contouring on each structure map as much as real thickness variations.

The technique of mapping sets described above is the best way to produce a set of maps that reflect the true spatial relationships between mapped events. However, there are occasions when the reliability of the structure maps is in doubt, for example, in areas where the quality of the deeper seismic events is very poor. The validity of the corresponding structure maps would then be, at best, questionable. An alternative approach is to produce structure maps for the good horizons and combine these with isopach maps of the uncertain intervals. This method uses the valid structural information and any relevant geological input to reduce the complex areas to their simplest by isopaching—an isopach will have a simpler form than its associated bounding surfaces and is easier to assess in terms of its geological reasonableness. The method employed is as follows:

1. A structure map is made of the last reliable seismic event.
2. An isopach of the interval between this surface and the next horizon for which a map is required is produced from any reliable seismic information supplemented, in poor data areas, by geological reasoning. The isopach will have a simpler contour pattern than the structure of the deeper, poorly detected event. Some geological control can be exerted over the isopach— for instance, is the shape geologically reasonable?— and in areas of very little or no data it can be much simpler to extrapolate isopach trends rather than those of structure contours.
3. The isopach is added to the shallower structure map to produce a new structure map of the deeper horizon.

The process can be repeated for the next horizon, with the newly created structure map acting as the control surface. The process can be repeated as often as is necessary to produce a structure map of the target horizon. Obviously, there can be no substitute for maps made directly from good seismic data. However, if made with care and geological thoughtfulness, combination mapping using structural and isopach maps can be an invaluable technique. Naturally, care must be taken, especially when significant discordant unconformities are involved.

MAP MIGRATION

The problems inherent in contouring data from conventional 2-D migrated sections have been described. In well-structured areas, migrated dip and strike lines do not tie because of migration effects. True dip lines (assuming the migration is good) will have had the reflections restored

234

to the correct subsurface positions but the strike lines, in which the displayed data in fact lie outside of the plane of the section, will be incorrect. The steeper the dip, the greater the problem. The lines inevitably mis–tie; and, during contouring, greater reliance is placed on data points for the dip lines than for the strike lines.

An alternative approach to using migrated lines and attempting to resolve the mis-ties is to use filtered stack sections for interpretation and contouring and then migrate the resulting map! The resulting map, without any extra effort, will be depth converted as well as migrated. However, as we might expect, this seemingly desirable end product cannot be achieved without considerable effort. Algorithms for migration are based on various approaches, namely, raypath tracing; construction of wave fronts; and downward continuation. All are quite complicated and can only be used realistically with a computer. The most essential information for each of these methods is detailed knowledge of the velocity field. All significant velocity interface above the target horizon must be mapped. In simple cases, such as parts of Texas and the U.S. Gulf Coast, one velocity function may provide an adequate fit for the entire sedimentary section. In other, more structurally complex areas, velocity varies drastically throughout the sedimentary section, both vertically and laterally. In these areas, it is necessary to determine for each formation representative velocity function that also takes lateral velocity variations into account. Faults and other steep features (e.g., salt diapir walls) provide an extra complication. Although such features are common, their presence is usually detected by inference (e.g., the abrupt termination of reflections) rather than by picking a reflection from the interface itself. This presents several problems:

The fault plane (if of large throw) or salt wall is usually an important velocity boundary.

The boundary, unless associated with a reflector, cannot be migrated. It can be moved to its correct position only by using the migration of reflections in the immediate vicinity of the feature.

The position of the feature as a velocity boundary and details of the velocity field associated with the fault, etc., must be known before the reflections can be migrated: A good example of a circular argument!

Obviously, except in the simplest cases, map migration is a major task. For those who need to attempt it, an interactive, computerized, map-migration system that will allow the interpreter to migrate each unit; view the results; and, if necessary try again before proceeding to the next, is very desirable. Several commercial systems are available, but for a very approximate method based on raypath tracing Michaels (1977) and Hubral (1978) give details of a pocket-calculator program for seismic raypath

migration. Using this technique, the map is segmented into cells characterized by relatively uniform dip and strike. Each cell is migrated about its center point using the simple algorithm of Hubral (1978). The map is then contoured using the migrated points. Note that the seismic grid will be distorted after the migration.

Chapter 9

Questions and Answers

QUESTIONS

1. Estimate the dominant frequency content of the seismic section in figure 2.15 below A at 0.48 s, 1.14, and 1.45. Assume that the reflections at these times are relatively free of interference and are representative. The seismic section has been processed to produce a minimum-phase waveform and is displayed with reverse polarity (SEG).

2. Assume that laterally extensive sandstones occur at the times used in question 1 for the calculation of the seismic section's varying dominant frequency. Calculate the minimum thickness of such a laterally extensive sandstone having reflection coefficients of opposite sign at its top and base for:

   a. no interference between reflections from the unit's top and base (half wavelength);
   b. the tuning thickness (quarter wavelength);
   c. the approximate thickness below which a recognizable reflection is not expected (about one-thirtieth wavelength).

   Assume internal velocities for the sandstone of 2000 m/s at 0.48; 3000 m/s at 1.14; 3500 m/s at 1.45 s.

3. Why do the repeated multiples in figure 3.11 show a progressive shift to the right with increasing time in the migrated seismic section?

4. What is the probable lithology between shotpoints 130 and 210 below 800 ms in figure 3.17?

5. In figure 3.27, what is the probable sign of the reflection coefficient of the upper boundary of the synclinal feature A revealed after migration? The section has been processed to produce a minimum-phase waveform and is displayed with normal polarity (SEG).

6. What is the probable reflection coefficient of the on-lapped surface between A and B in figure 4.18? The section has been processed to produce a minimum-phase waveform and is displayed with normal polarity (SEG).

7. Where is the top salt in the crestal part of the diapir shown in figure 4.41? Assume that mapping the top salt in this region is critical in this assessment of the

W   E

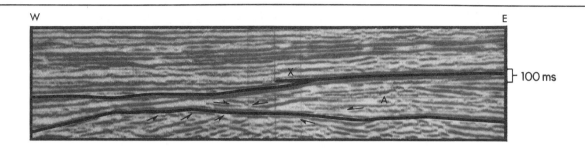

─ 100 ms

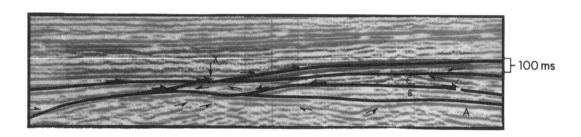

─ 100 ms

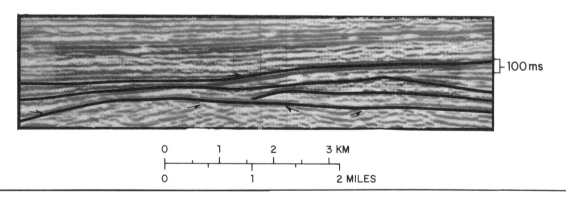

─ 100 ms

```
0        1        2        3 KM
├────┼────┼────┼────┼────┤

0                1              2 MILES
├────┼────┼────┼────┼────┤
```

FIGURE 9.1 *Three versions of a seismic section showing different interpretations. Which interpretation is the most plausible geologically? The seismic section is migrated, processed to produce a minimum-phase waveform, and displayed with normal polarity (SEG). Courtesy Merlin Profilers Ltd.*

likely presence or absence of a potential reservoir interval. Assume an interval velocity of 4500 m/s in the salt; an interval of 3700 m/s in the laterally adjacent sediments; a pull-up of the base salt reflection (A) of 220 ms. What additional assumption must we make in order to estimate where the top salt is located?

8. What are the probable causes of the anticlinal structures affecting reflections A and B in figure 4.49?

9. In figure 4.50 what are the potential pitfalls of interpreting the dim spot (lower reflection amplitude)

over the crestal part of the carbonate mound as being due to

a. the presence of gas;
b. better porosity (and thereby reduced acoustic impedance) in the mound than in the adjacent limestones?

10. What is the display polarity of the seismic section shown in figure 6.6 and what wavelet shape has the processing produced?

11. Where should a pick for reflection A in figure 6.6 be placed, and what is the sign of the reflection coefficient?

12. What is the interval velocity of the intervals between A and B in figure 6.11?

13. In making a well-to-seismic tie, using the sonic log in figure 6.15, is the limestone bed A likely to produce a

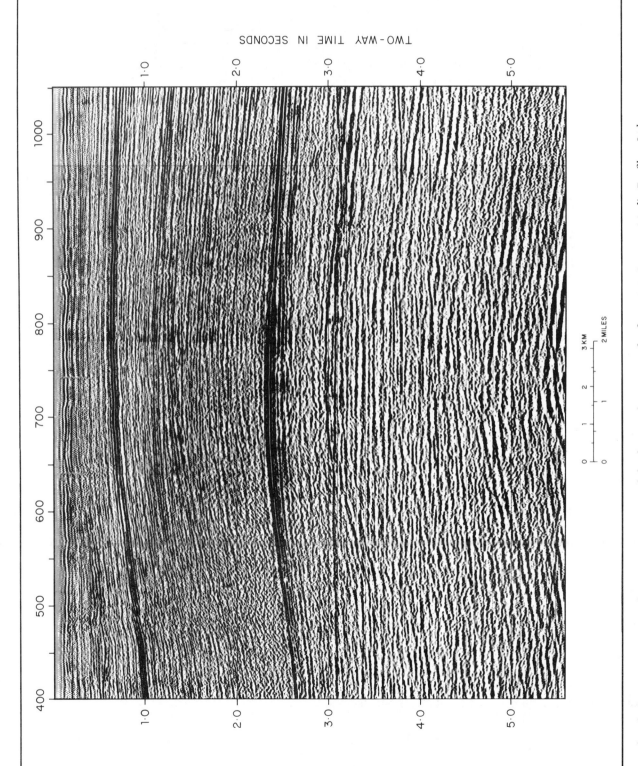

FIGURE 9.2 *Identify the main primary reflections. Processing and display are the same as for figure 9.1. Courtesy Merlin Profilers Ltd.*

238

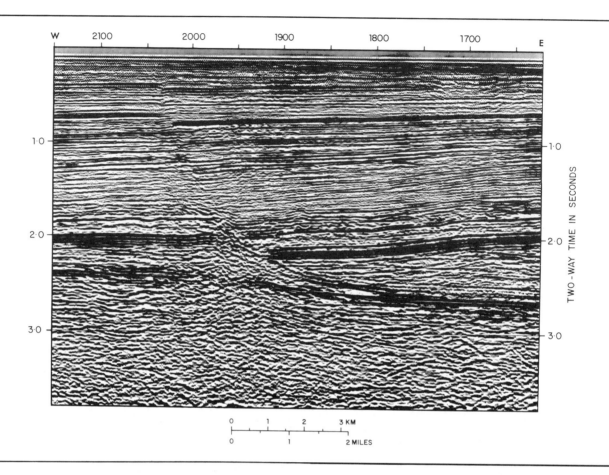

strong reflection in a seismic section? Assume that the limestone has a large lateral extent, the dominant seismic frequency at 2000 m is 35 Hz, and that the sonic log can be used to indicate the limestone's acoustic impedance.

14. Figure 9.1 shows three alternative interpretations: in parts *A*, *B*, and *C*. Which are probably incorrect?

15. Identify the main primary reflections on the seismic section shown in figure 9.2.

16. Is the obvious concave event (e.g., at 2.3 s below shotpoint 1900) in the seismic section shown in figure 9.3 a fault plane reflection?

17. Interpret the seismic section shown in figure 9.4 with emphasis on interpreting the faulting history. On the basis of seismic character and structural associations, what are the likely lithologies of sequences *A*, *B*, and *C*? The seismic section is migrated, processed to produce a minimum-phase wavelet, and displayed with normal polarity (SEG).

18. Interpret the faulting on the seismic section shown in figure 9.5. Is it possible that a curving fault trace intersects the seismic line four times (see the fault trace below the figure)? Is there a more plausible interpretation for the fault pattern? Processing and display are the same as for figure 9.4.

FIGURE 9.3 *A seismic section showing a fault plane reflection? Processing and display are the same as for figure 9.1. Courtesy Merlin Profilers Ltd.*

19. Describe the main aspects of the geology shown by the seismic section in figure 9.6. Assume that the seismic section is a dip line. The seismic section is migrated, processed to produce a minimum-phase wavelet, and displayed with normal polarity (SEG).

20. There is a good prospect in the seismic section shown in figure 9.7. Where is it? Processing and display are the same as in figure 9.6.

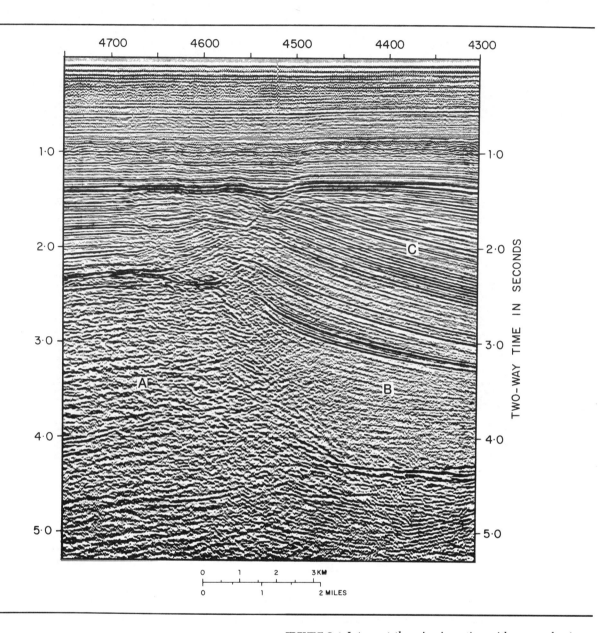

FIGURE 9.4 *Interpret the seismic section with an emphasis on the faulting history. Processing and display are the same as for figure 9.1. Courtesy Merlin Profilers Ltd.*

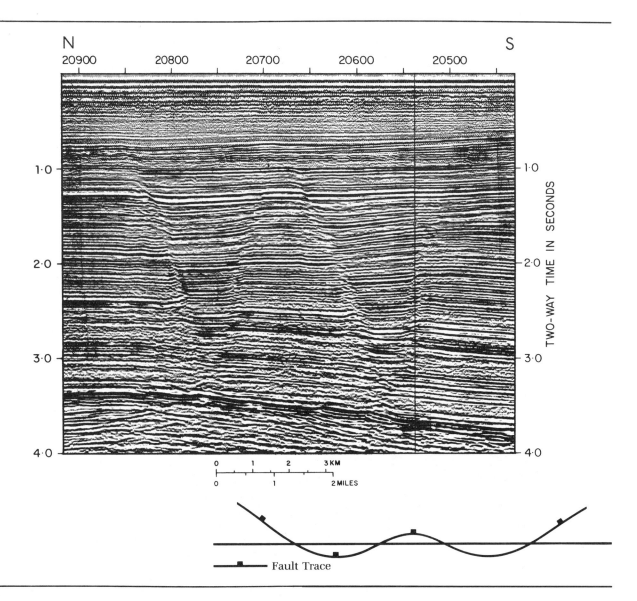

FIGURE 9.5 *The same fault intersecting the seismic section four times as is depicted in the sketch map? Processing and display are the same as for figure 9.1. Courtesy Merlin Profilers Ltd.*

241

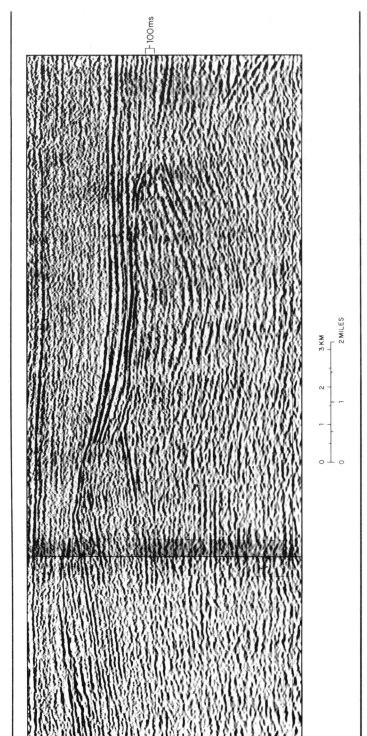

100 ms

0   1   2   3 KM

0   1   2 MILES

FIGURE 9.6 *A seismic section across an interesting structure? Processing and display are the same as for figure 9.1 but are not by the same contractor. Courtesy Saga Petroleum.*

242

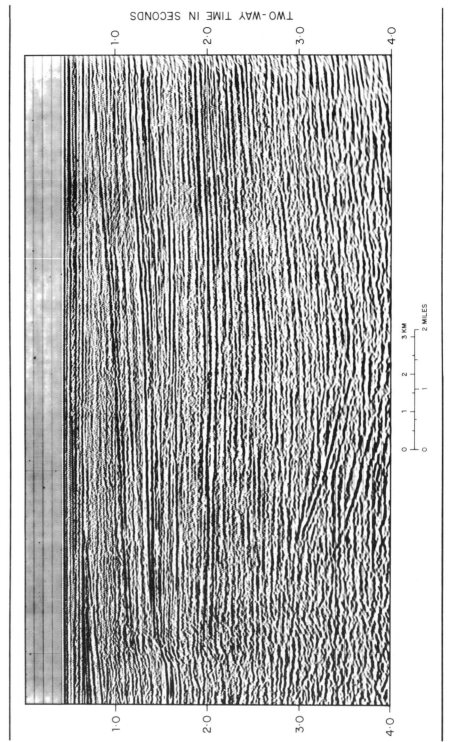

TWO-WAY TIME IN SECONDS

FIGURE 9.7 *A seismic section across a prospect. The seismic section is from the same survey as figure 9.6. Courtesy Saga Petroleum.*

ANSWERS

1. The dominant frequency content at different times in seismic sections can be estimated by measuring the duration (peak-to-peak or trough-to-trough) of individual high-amplitude reflections, and by taking the reciprocal. The reflections should be free of obvious interference with other reflections, and show good lateral continuity of character. The method is not exact, but can provide a good guide to the interpreter of the resolution potential throughout a seismic section. The estimates of dominant frequencies below A in figure 2.15 are

   Time 0.48 s; duration ± 12 ms: frequency 83 Hz
   Time 1.14 s; duration ± 20 ms: frequency 50 Hz
   Time 1.45 s; duration ± 25 ms: frequency 40 Hz

2. Using the frequencies estimated in question 1, the wavelength (λ) can be determined from the internal velocity and the expression

   Wavelength = Velocity/Frequency.

   The following table shows the answers to question 2 (thickness in meters).

Time(s)	λ	$\lambda/2$	$\lambda/4$	$\lambda/30$
0.48	24	12	6	± 0.7
1.14	60	30	15	± 2.0
1.45	88	44	22	± 3.0

3. The seismic section in figure 3.11 shows the sea-floor multiple repeated twelve times. The multiple increases its dip by an amount equal to its original dip with succeeding bounces. The effect of migration on any dipping reflection, primary or multiple, is to increase dip, shorten the reflection's length, and move the reflection in an updip direction. The steeper the dip, the greater the displacement updip after migration. This effect has caused the progressive shift to the right of the multiples with increasing time.

4. It is not usually possible to determine lithology unambiguously from a seismic section. The interval between shotpoints 130 and 210 below 800 ms in figure 3.17 is a seismically opaque interval, free of internal reflections. Only multiple energy has been recorded. Lithologies that commonly produce such a seismic response are salt and shale in diapirs, and igneous intrusions. In this particular case, crystalline basement rocks are responsible for the seismic response.

5. Weak onlap terminations on to the peak of the reflection indicate a negative reflection coefficient for the reflector A in figure 3.27 (see fig. 7.12).

6. The onlap terminations against the peak defining the unconformity surface between A and B in figure 4.18 indicate that the unconformity reflector has a negative reflection coefficient (see fig. 7.12).

7. In a situation where all else has failed, and a commitment to a well to test a possible trap is likely to be made, the interpreter must make some attempt to estimate the location of the top salt. By making the assumption that the apparent base salt time structure is due entirely to a velocity pull-up effect of the overlying salt, the salt structure can be estimated from:

   $$\text{Salt structure} = \frac{t \text{ pull-up} \times V_L \times V_S}{2\,(V_S - V_L)};$$

   where

   t pull-up = assumed pull-up (seconds),
   V_L = interval velocity in sediments adjacent to salt diapir,
   V_S = interval velocity in salt.

   $$\text{Salt thickness (m)} = \frac{0.220 \times 3700 \times 4500}{2\,(4500 - 3700)}$$

   $$= 2289 \text{ m.}$$

   $$\text{Salt thickness (s)} = \frac{2 \times 2289}{4500} = 1.020 \text{ ms.}$$

   The top salt in figure 9.8 is estimated to be 1.020 s above (A) at 1.970 s. Ideally, a range of values should be used to allow for uncertainties in the estimates of interval velocity and pull-up.

8. The structure of reflection A is caused by updoming above a salt diapir. The structure of reflection B can be explained by a combination of velocity pull-up beneath the salt diapir and real structure caused by faulting to both the left and right of the structure (fig. 9.9).

9. The dim spot associated with the carbonate mound is ascribed to the presence of gas in a porous limestone reservoir. More than 5% gas saturation has the effect of reducing acoustic impedance, resulting in a smaller positive reflection coefficient and hence a weaker reflection. Dimming could also be caused if the porosity of the carbonate mound is less than the laterally adjacent sediments. However, on an unmigrated section dimming can also be caused by defocusing of the seismic signal over an anticlinal feature. Geometric effects, and the quality of the migration, should always be thoroughly evaluated before concluding that dimming is caused by higher porosity or the presence of gas.

10. The seismic section shown in figure 6.6 is displayed

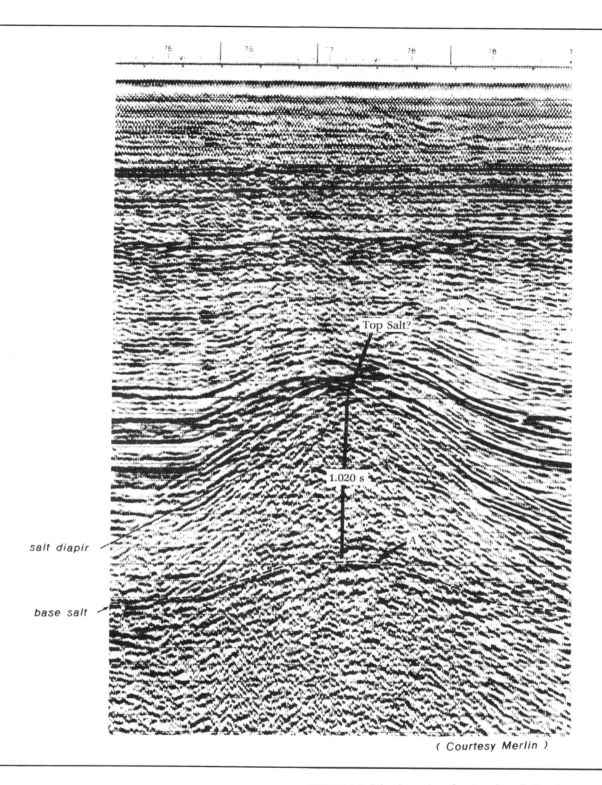

(Courtesy Merlin)

FIGURE 9.8 *Seismic section showing the calculated position of the top salt. Courtesy Norsk Hydro.*

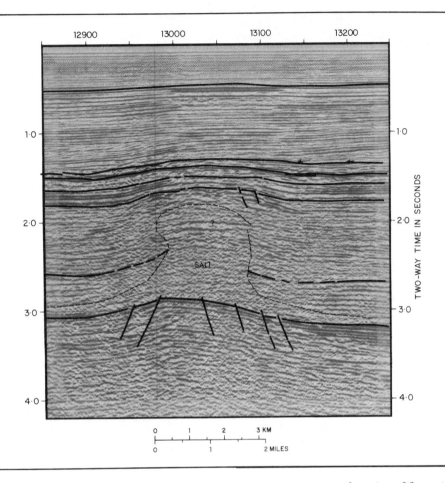

FIGURE 9.9 *Interpreted version of figure 4.49. Courtesy Merlin Profilers Ltd.*

246

with normal polarity (SEG). This can be verified at shotpoint 400 by calculating the anticipated time of the sea-floor reflection using the water depth displayed at the top of the section, and the velocity of sound in water.

$$\text{Time sea bed} = \frac{2 \times \text{water depth}}{\text{velocity in water}}$$

$$= \frac{2 \times 292}{1480} = 395 \text{ ms.}$$

This time (395 ms) corresponds precisely to the center of the trough of the first reflection. The reflection has a high-amplitude symmetric form, with lead half-cycle and follow half-cycle peaks. The sea-bed reflection, with its positive reflection coefficient, would be expected to be associated with a trough on a normal polarity (SEG) seismic section (fig. 9.10). The symmetric nature of the reflection indicates that the seismic section has probably been processed to produce a zero-phase waveform.

11. Since the section has been processed to produce a zero-phase waveform, the symmetric shape of reflection A (with high-amplitude trough, and lead half-cycle and follow half-cycle peaks) can be used to deduce that the reflection is the response to a reflector with positive reflection coefficient. The pick should be placed at the center of the trough (fig. 9.10).

12. The interval velocity of the interval between A and B in figure 6.11 can be calculated using the Dix equation:

Interval velocity

$$= \sqrt{\frac{(T_2 \times VRMS_2^2 - T_1 \times VRMS_1^2)}{(T_2 - T_1)}}.$$

The times T_1 and T_2 corresponding to A and B respectively can be read directly from figure 6.11. The corresponding velocities (taken as $VRMS$) can be found by locating the maximum values of the contoured velocities corresponding to the times for A and B (fig. 9.11). These velocities can be read from the velocity diagram, and internal velocity can be calculated (fig. 9.11).

Interval velocity

$$= \sqrt{\frac{1.680 \times (2250)^2 - 1.030 \times (1800)^2}{(1.680 - 1.030)}}.$$

Internal velocity $= 2820$ m/s.

13. A large acoustic-impedance contrast between the limestone and the overlying and underlying shales is

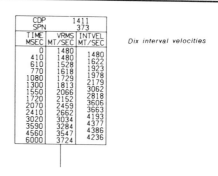

| CDP | 1411 | |
| SPN | 373 | |
TIME MSEC	VRMS MT/SEC	INTVEL MT/SEC
0	1480	
410	1480	1480
610	1528	1622
770	1618	1923
1080	1729	1978
1300	1813	2179
1550	2066	3062
1720	2152	2818
2070	2459	3606
2410	2662	3663
3020	3034	4193
3590	3284	4377
4560	3547	4386
6000	3724	4236

Dix interval velocities

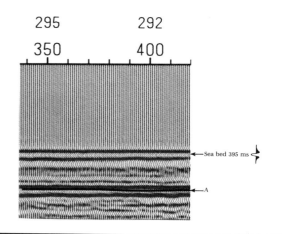

FIGURE 9.10 *Interpreted version of figure 6.6. Courtesy Statoil.*

indicated by the sonic log curve in figure 6.15. However, to produce a strong reflection, the limestone must be thick enough to overcome the effects of destructive interference between the opposing-polarity reflections emanating from its top and base. The minimum thickness necessary to produce a detectable reflection is usually at least one-thirtieth wavelength.

$$X = \frac{V}{f} = \frac{3000}{35} \text{ m/s} = 85 \text{ m.}$$

$$\frac{X}{30} = 3 \text{ m, approximately.}$$

The limestone is only about 2 m thick and so is unlikely to produce a detectable reflection.

14. Interpretation B in figure 9.1 is the most plausible. Reflection relationships have been used to locate sequence boundaries and thereby establish the strati-

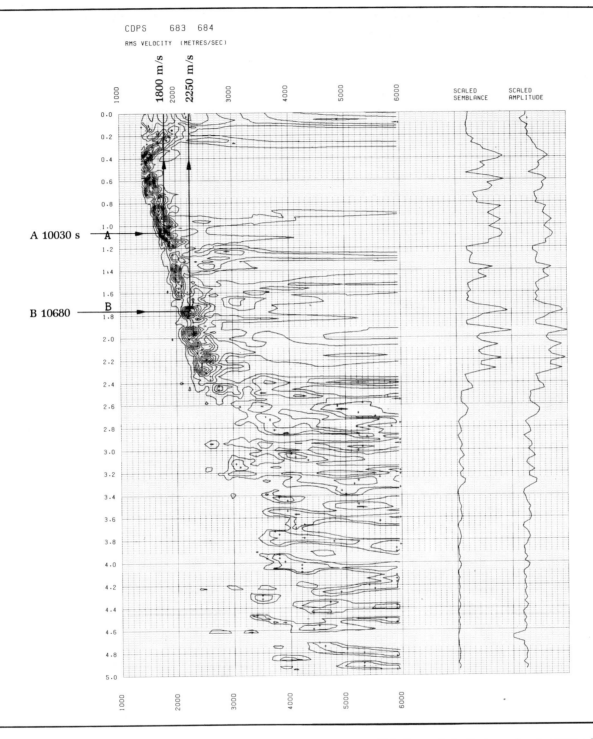

FIGURE 9.11 *Velocity analysis diagram showing RMS velocity for reflections A and B. Courtesy Merlin Profilers Ltd.*

graphic relationships. Onlap terminations provide the best guide for correctly positioning picks on seismic sections for boundaries with sizable reflection coefficients when the processing has produced a minimum-phase waveform (fig. 7.12). It is possible to subdivide the seismic section within the interpreted interval into five sequences, a through e. Furthermore, the onlap relationships over the interval of M-M' (peak onlapping peak) suggest that the sign of the sequence boundary N-N' may locally be negative. The remainder of the surface generally has onlap terminations against a trough, indicating a positive reflection coefficient for most of the sequence boundary.

Interpretation A is less plausible for the following reasons. The upper sequence boundary O-O' is located in a trough. At P the pick stays high and follows the good-continuity trough in a westerly direction. At Q, when the reflection splits, the pick has been carried high. Although the pick O-O' is not necessarily incorrect, that is, it is probably located along an acoustic-impedance contrast, it probably does not correctly portray the geological relationship. Figure 7.14 shows that, in the majority of cases involving onlap, when a reflection splits (as at P and Q), the best choice is likely to be the lower pick. The deeper unconformity R-R', with onlap and downlap above, and truncation below, has been incorrectly picked beneath a high-amplitude good-continuity peak. The reflection terminations indicate that the sequence boundary lies at the onset of the overlying trough and that the truncation reflections terminate against the follow half-cycle peak (fig. 7.13). Only three of the five seismic sequences are recognized by interpretation A.

Interpretation C suffers from the same problems as interpretation A. However, an attempt has been made to further subdivide the sequence. Pick S'S' crosscuts the inclined surface N-N' at T. To the east, the pick S-S' is probably too low (see interpretation B). Pick U-U' is also probably too low, judging from the reflection relationships.

15. Figure 9.12 shows an interpreted version of the seismic sections in figure 9.2.
Reflections A-A', B-B', C-C', and D-D' are the main higher-amplitude primary reflections.
E-E'-E" is the simple multiple of A-A'.
F-F'-F" is the peg-leg multiple, sea-level to reflection A-A' from reflection C-C'.
G-G'-G" is the peg-leg multiple sea-level to reflection A-A' from reflection D-D'.

16. Figure 9.13 shows an interpreted version of the seismic section in figure 9.3. The obvious main fault shows a gentle curved trace, some differential tilt of reflections across the fault, and weak reverse drag

(all of which are indicative of listric normal faulting). However, the deeper concave reflection is interpreted to be the top of a salt diapir and not a fault plane reflection. The reflections to the east of the fault below reflection C, which show an apparent reverse drag relationship with the strong concave reflection, are interpreted to be interbed and peg-leg multiples associated with reflections A, B, and C. The primary reflectors in the interval E to D dip east and are truncated beneath the unconformity C. Early movement of salt, perhaps triggered by faulting, affect reflection F at M and N, and produce the eastward tilt of sequence E-D.

17. Figure 9.14 shows an interpreted version of the seismic section shown in figure 9.4.
The main features of the seismic section are:

a. The major fault M-M', downthrowing E.
b. A sequence (A) in the footwall block with a high-amplitude, good-continuity reflection at its top. The internal seismic character of sequence A, however, is characterized by weak, poor-continuity reflections that dip gently west. This seismic character, when contrasted with the moderate-amplitude, good-continuity, and closely spaced reflectors of sequence C, indicate that although sequence A is probably sedimentary, it consists of sediments with high acoustic impedance but only small acoustic-impedance contrasts between the different lithologies. Such a situation is typical for well-compacted and indurated sediments with low porosity: for example, compacted shales, cemented sandstones, and limestones.
c. A semi-wedge-shaped, largely reflection-free interval, sequence B.
d. Sequence C, a bedded sedimentary sequence (see [b] above).
e. Area D, a structurally complex region with synthetic and antithetic faults, nucleating at the top of fault M-M'.

To explain the reserved configuration only by faulting would involve a phase of down-to-the-east normal faulting on M-M' with syn-fault sedimentation, followed by later transpressional movements that reactivated fault M-M' with reverse movements to produce the uplift of sequence C. The eastward tilting of sequence C would require the fault movement to have had a rotational component and the fault plane M-M' to be curved.

An alternative, and simpler, interpretation assumes that sequence B is a salt-bearing sequence and that salt flowage into the fault zone M-M' occurred after deposition of sequence C. The salt flowage into

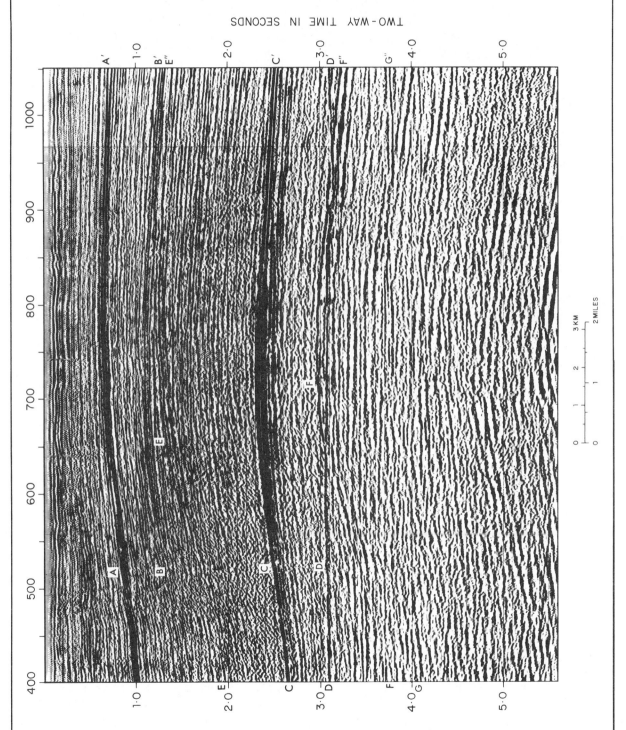

FIGURE 9.12 *Interpreted version of figure 9.2. Courtesy Merlin Profilers Ltd.*

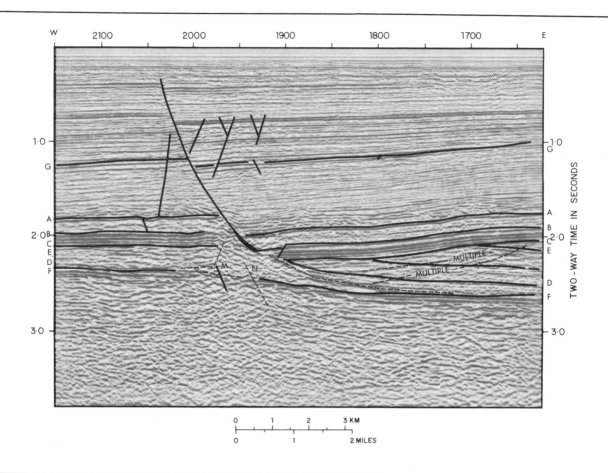

FIGURE 9.13 *Interpreted version of figure 9.3. Courtesy Merlin Profilers Ltd.*

the fault resulted in uplift and eastward tilting of sequence *C* and the development of the synthetic and antithetic faults in the region of *D*. The unconformity developed after the cessation of salt flowage. Compare and contrast the seismic sections shown in figures 9.13 and 9.14. Both involve asymmetric salt structures associated with faulting. Although there are differences in the magnitude of salt movements, note the similarities between the sequences and configurations to the east of the salt in both cases.

18. Figure 9.15 shows an interpreted version of the seismic section in figure 9.5. The variation in throw on the different fault traces makes it unlikely that the fault pattern seen on the seismic section is a single sinuous fault cutting the seismic section four times (see fig. 7.21). Careful inspection of the seismic section reveals that the two groups of faults are present: northerly and southerly dipping, dominantly planar normal faults, forming a conjugate set. The north-dipping faults formed first, and are offset by the southerly dipping faults. Changes in fault dip (refraction of the fault plane), in response to differing rock types, enable dip changes to occur across the otherwise-planar normal faults. Normal drag of the

hanging-wall-block reflections in the immediate vicinity of the fault planes is common. It is more difficult to locate the fault planes below 3.0 s. For example, reflection *M-M'* appears to be flexured (except at *N* where it is clearly faulted), rather than faulted. However, the apparent lack of faulting is likely to be a consequence of the decreasing seismic wavelet frequency with depth (and corresponding increase in wavelength) and higher interval velocities below *M-M'*. The effect of fault throw versus wavelength, and the effect that this has on an interpreter's ability to detect faults, is shown in figure 5.3. Faults with throws of less than half the seismic pulse wavelength generally appear as flexures, rather than offsets of the seismic trace. In practice, especially in the deeper and generally noisy parts of a seismic section, it is probably difficult to detect faults with throws of less than one-quarter wavelength. Assuming a dominant seismic frequency of 50 Hz at 1.0 s and an interval velocity of 2000 m/s, the wavelength is 40 m, and faults with throws between 6 and 10 m are probably

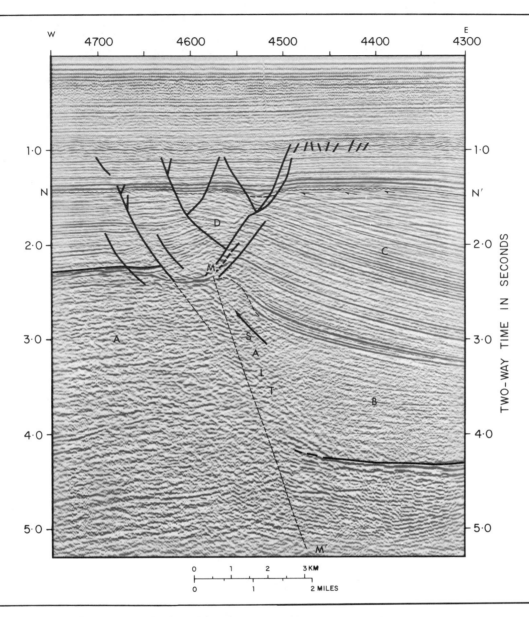

FIGURE 9.14 *Interpreted version of figure 9.4. Courtesy Merlin Profilers Ltd.*

detectable. However, at 3.5 s, with a dominant frequency of 20 Hz and an interval velocity of 4000 m/s (or more), the corresponding wavelength is 200 m, and it may prove difficult to detect faults with throws of 50 m or less.

19. Figure 9.16 shows an interpreted version of the seismic section in figure 9.6. On the basis of the reflection relationships and configuration, the seismic section can be divided into two main sequences, A and B. Sequence A consists of westward-dipping, generally subparallel reflections. Sequence B, overlying sequence A, consists of generally flat-lying subparallel reflections. The overall character of both sequences indicates that they are made up of sedimentary rocks. An unconformity M-M' separates the two sequences. At N, reflection relationships indicate that the unconformity has a negative reflection

coefficient; the onlaps terminate against a moderate-amplitude reflection with a lead half-cycle peak (fig. 7.12). Although the seismic section has been processed to produce a minimum-phase pulse, the nature of the unconformity reflection at N is decidedly symmetrical with a peak-trough-peak form. This symmetric shape indicates that the response at the unconformity is produced by interference between several acoustic-impedance boundaries, or could indicate that the attempt to produce a minimum-phase pulse has not been entirely successful. In such cases caution should be exercised until, if possible, unequivocal reflection relationships can be found that

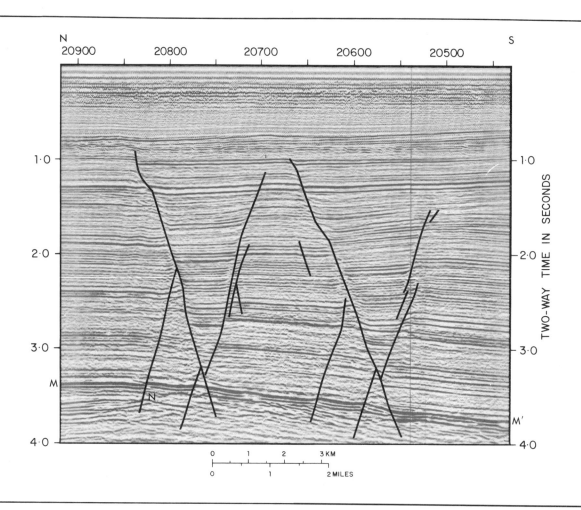

FIGURE 9.15 *Interpreted version of figure 9.5. Courtesy Merlin Profilers Ltd.*

reveal the seismic pulse shape. This is not possible with this particular seismic section. However, even if the seismic wavelet polarity is in doubt, the reflection relationships indicate that to the west of *N* the nature of the unconformity reflection coefficient is variable—changing with the different patterns of onlap above, and truncation below, the unconformity. The dipping reflections of sequence *B* exhibit differences in amplitude and continuity, indicative of a sedimentary sequence. Although the reflection character is indicative of a bedded sequence only, it is not diagnostic of any particular lithofacies or lithology. It is not possible using character to correlate the dipping reflections in the fault blocks *C* and *D*.

Sequence *B*, consisting of subparallel, flat-lying reflections, is typical of a sedimentary sequence and, in this case, the vertical variations in seismic character may be tentatively used to infer possible lithofacies. For example, the contrast between high-amplitude, good-continuity reflections forming sequence *E* and the extremely low-amplitude, very poor-continuity reflections of sequence *F* can be used to infer that here they comprise different lithofacies. For example, high-amplitude, good-continuity reflections are often associated with calcareous shales and limestones. Assuming that sequence *B* is, in fact, marine, we might suppose that sequence *F*, on the basis of its seismic character, is a thick shale sequence. However, without additional data or information, such a supposition would remain very tenuous.

Treating the structural history evident in the seismic section in a similar manner, that is, using a preconceived model to guide our interpretation, we conclude that the overall reflection configuration is suggestive of the type of structural assemblage found in rift basins or on passive margins—tilted fault blocks buried beneath a post-rift or post-drift sequence.

Sequence *A* consists of dipping or tilted reflections

253

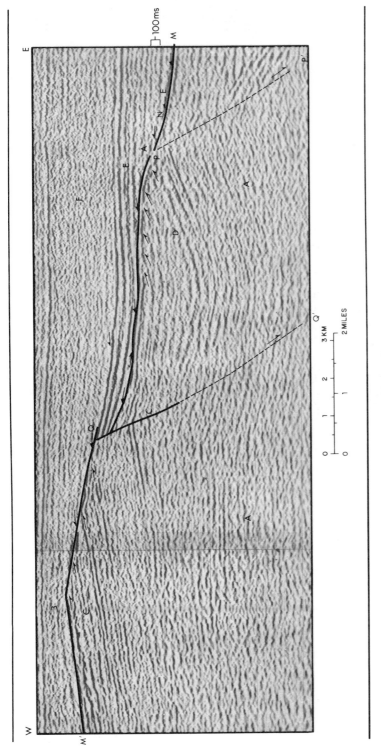

FIGURE 9.16 *Interpreted version of figure 9.6. Courtesy Merlin Profilers Ltd.*

254

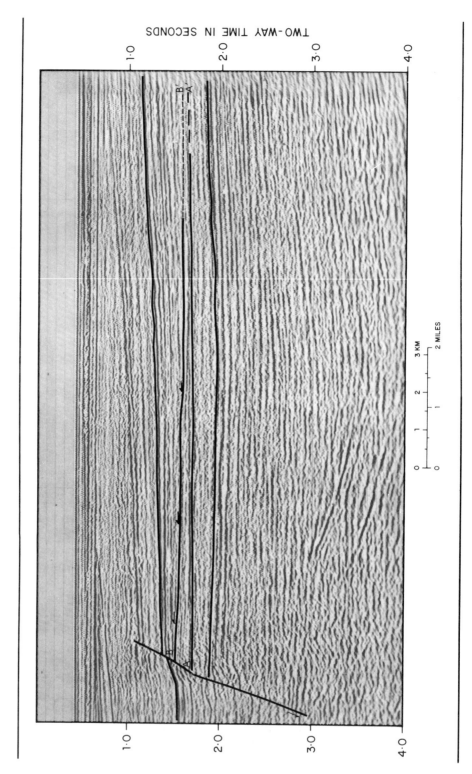

FIGURE 9.17 *Interpreted version of figure 9.7. Courtesy Merlin Profilers, Ltd.*

in two sequences *C* and *D*, separated by a major fault zone *Q-Q'*. If the two sequences are of similar age, sequence *D* has been tilted more than sequence *C*. This could have occurred if fault *Q-Q'*, during the rifting stage, had a curved, or listric, normal fault plane. The relatively small dip difference indicates that the curvature would be on a large scale.

In a rift model, the unconformity *M-M'* would represent the post-rift (or drift) unconformity, separating the pre-rift and syn-rift sequences (not subdivisible on this seismic section) and the thermal-subsidence–dominated post-rift sequence (sequence *B*). The difference in timing of the last fault movements on faults *Q-Q'* and *P-P'*, becoming later toward the structural high, is also characteristic of a rift model. Fault movements on fault *P-P'* ceased before the deposition of sequence *E*. However, fault *Q-Q'* was active practically until the end of the deposition of sequence *E*. Note the normal drag affecting the reflections of sequence *E* in the hanging-wall block adjacent to fault *Q-Q'*. The normal drag is indicative of planar normal faulting. This contrasts with the interpreted earlier listric normal movements in the fault *Q-Q'* during the rifting phase. These conflicting fault kinematics are probably separated in time by several tens of millions of years, with the planar normal faulting utilizing the steeply dipping zone of weakness in the upper few kilometers of the listric normal fault zone.

The use of a conceptual model, such as that applied in the preceding, can be useful to an interpretation. However, great caution should be exercised. No interpretation should be based on a single seismic line—to this extent these exercises are artificial—and any conceptual model is only helpful so long as it is correct. Unfortunately, the fact that a model appears to fit the observations is no guarantee that the model is correct!

20. Figure 9.17 shows an interpretation of the seismic section in figure 9.7. The seismic section crosses the Troll Field, offshore Norway. (The Troll Field reflection configuration is much more clearly shown by the seismic section in fig. 2.8.) The seismic reflection configuration in figure 9.17 is not easy to interpret, nor is the reflection *A-A'* associated with the gas/water contact an initially obvious, direct hydrocarbon indicator. When viewed lengthways at an oblique angle, the reflection associated with the gas/water contact does appear anomalous—a flattish reflection with a triangular-shaped sequence above. The upper surface of the triangle (*B-B'*) is the top reservoir reflection. An unusual geological configuration! It is difficult to explain away the flattish reflection as a multiple, and so it deserves special attention in order to provide an adequate explanation. It is often the unusual, flat or gently dipping reflection, or difficult-to-explain reflection, that can be the key to an interpretation, especially when there is the possibility of encountering reflections from fluid contacts.

References

Ager, D. V., 1983, The nature of the stratigraphic record: Macmillan (London).

Al-Sadi, H. N., 1980, Seismic exploration: Birkhauser Boston Inc.

Anderson, E. J., Goodwin, P. W., and Subieski, T. H., 1984, Episodic accumulation and the origin of formation boundaries in the Helderberg Group of New York State: Geology, **12,** 120–123.

Anderson, R. Y., and Kirkland, D. W., 1980, Dissolution of salt deposits by brine density flow: Geology, **8,** 66–69.

Anstey, N. A., 1977, Seismic interpretation; The physical aspects: IHRDC.

Anstey, N. A., 1980a, Simple seismics: IHRDC.

Anstey, N. A., 1980b, Seismic exploration for sandstone reservoirs: IHRDC.

Aoki, Y., Tamano, T., and Kato, S., 1982, Detailed structure of the Nankai Trough from migrated seismic sections, *in* Watkins and Drake, 1982, 309–324.

Badley, M. E., and Anstey, N. A., 1984, Exploration geophysics; GP501 Basic Interpretation, from the Video library for exploration and production specialists: IHRDC.

Badley, M. E., Egeberg, T., and Nipen, O., 1984, Development of the rift basins illustrated by the structural evolution of the Oseberg feature, Block 30/6 offshore Norway: J. Geol. Soc., London, **141,** 639–649.

Bailey, G. B., and Anderson, P. D., 1982, Applications of Landsat imagery to problems of petroleum exploration in Quidam Basin, China: Am. Assoc. Pet. Geol. Bull., **66,** 1348–1354.

Balch, A. H., Lee, M. W., Miller, J. J., and Ryder, R. T., 1982, The use of vertical seismic profiles in seismic investigations of the earth: Geophysics, **47,** 906–918.

Bally, A. W., Ed., 1983, Seismic expression of structural styles—a picture and work atlas: Studies in Geology series 15, **1–3,** American Association of Petroleum Geologists.

Baria, L. R., Stoudt, D. L., Harris, P. M., and Crevello, P. D., 1982, Upper Jurassic reefs of Smackover Formation, United States Gulf Coast: Am. Assoc. Pet. Geol. Bull., **66,** 1449–1482.

Barry, K. M., and Shugart, T., 1973, Seismic hydrocarbon indicators and models: Teledyne Exploration Company.

Berlanga, J. M., and Harbaugh, J. W., 1981, Use of seismic data for statistical estimation of outcome of probabilities of complexly faulted structures in Tabasco Basin, Mexico: Am. Assoc. Pet. Geol. Bull., **65,** 422–437.

Bishop, R. S., 1978, Mechanism for emplacement of piercement diapirs: Am. Assoc. Pet. Geol. Bull., **62,** 1561–1583.

Blackburn, G., 1980, Errors in stacking velocity—True velocity conversion over geologic situations: Geophysics, **45,** 1465–1488.

Boyer, S. E., and Elliott, D., 1982, Thrust systems: Am. Assoc. Pet. Geol. Bull., **66,** 1196–1230.

Brown, L. F., and Fisher, W. L., 1980, Seismic stratigraphic interpretation and petroleum exploration: Continuing Education Course Note Series, 16, American Association of Petroleum Geologists.

Bubb, J. N., and Hatlelid, W. G., 1977, Seismic recognition of carbonate build ups, in Payton, 1977, 185–204.

Christensen, C. F., 1983, An example of a major syndepositional listric fault, in Bally, 1983, 2, 2.3.1-36–40.

Crutcher, T. D., 1983, Baltimore Canyon Trough, in Bally, 1983, 2, 2.2.3-20–26.

Dahlstrom, C. D. A., 1969, Balanced cross-sections: Can. J. Earth Sci., 6, 743–757.

Day, G. A., and Edwards, J. W. F., 1983, Reflected refracted events on seismic sections: First Break, Sept. 14–17.

De'Ath, N. G., and Schuyleman, S. F., 1981, The geology of the Magnus Field, in L. V. Illing, and G. D. Hobson, Petroleum geology of the continental shelf of north-west Europe: Heyden & Son, 342–345.

Dix, C. H., 1955, Seismic velocities from surface measurements: Geophysics, 20, 68–86.

Dobrin, M. B., 1960, Introduction to geophysical prospecting: McGraw-Hill.

Dobrin, M. B., 1976, Introduction to geophysical prospecting: 3rd ed.: McGraw-Hill.

Domenico, S. N., 1974, Effect of water saturation on seismic reflectivity of sand reservoirs encased in shale: Geophysics, 39, 759–769.

Dott, R. H. J., 1983, Episodic sedimentation—how normal is average? How rare is rare? Does it matter? 1982 SEPM Presidential address: J. Sediment. Petrol., 53, 5–23.

Dutton, S. P., 1982, Pennsylvanian fan-delta and carbonate deposits, Mobeetie Field, Texas Panhandle: Am. Assoc. Pet. Geol. Bull., 66, 389–407.

Evans, G., and Bush, P., 1969, Some oceanographic and sedimentological observations on a Persian Gulf lagoon: Man. Simp. Internat. Lagunas Costeras. UNAM UNESCO, Mexico (1967), 155–170.

Gal'perin, E. I., 1973, Vertical seismic profiling: Spec. Pub. no. 12, Society of Exploratory Geophysicists.

Gardner, G. H. F., Gardner, L. W., and Gregory, A. R., 1974, Formation velocity and density—the diagnostic basis of stratigraphic traps: Geophysics, 39, 770–780.

Gatliff, R. W., Hitchin, K., Ritchie, J. D., and Smythe, D. K., 1984, Internal structure of the Erlend Tertiary volcanic complex, north of Shetland, revealed by seismic reflection: J. Geol. Soc., London, 141, 555–562.

Gibbs, A. D., 1983, Balanced cross-section construction from seismic sections in areas of extensional tectonics: J. Struct. Geol., 5, 153–160.

Gibbs, A. D., 1984, Structural evolution of extensional basin margins: J. Geol. Soc., London, 141, 609–620.

Girty, G. H., and Parrott, B. S., 1983. Upper Cenozoic Unconformity, Gulf of Mexico: in Bally, 1983, 1, 1.2.2-1–2.

Halbouty, M. T., 1976, Application of Landsat imagery to petroleum and mineral exploration: Am. Assoc. Pet. Geol. Bull., 60, 745–793.

Halbouty, M. T., 1980, Geological significance of Landsat data for 15 giant oil and gas fields: in M. T. Halbouty, Ed., Giant oil and gas fields of the decade 1968–78: Am. Assoc. Pet. Geol. Mem., 30, 7–38.

Hammond, R. D., and Gaither, J. R., 1983, Anomalous seismic character—Bering Sea Shelf: Geophysics, 48, 590–605.

Hancock, J. N., and Taylor, A. M., 1978, Clay mineral diagenesis and oil migration in the Middle Jurassic Brent Sand Formation: J. Geol. Soc., London, 135, 69–72.

Harding, T. P., and Lowell, S. D., 1979, Structural styles, their plate tectonic habits, and hydrocarbon traps in petroleum provinces: Am. Assoc. Pet. Geol. Bull., 63, 1016–1058.

Hedberg, H. D., 1976, International Stratigraphic Guide; A guide to stratigraphic classification terminology and procedure by international subcommission on stratigraphic classification of IUGS Commission on Stratigraphy: John Wiley & Sons.

Hein, J. R., Scholl, D. W., Barron, J. A., Jones, M. G., and Miller, J., 1978, Diagenesis of late Cenozoic diatomaceous deposits and formation of the bottom simulating reflector in the Southern Bering Sea: Sedimentology, 25, 155–181.

Horsfield, W. T., 1977, An experimental approach to basement controlled faulting: Geol. Mijnbouw, 56, 363–370.

Howard, M. S., and Danbom, J. D., 1983, Random noise example: in Bally, 1983, 1, 25.

Hubbard, T. P., 1979, Deconvolution of surface recorded data using vertical seismic profiles: 49th Annual SEG Meeting, New Orleans, November 4–8.

Hubral, P., 1978, Discussion—seismic raypath migration with the pocket calculator: Geophysics, 43, 1024.

Hubral, P., and Krey, T., 1981, Interval velocities from seismic reflection time measurements: Society of Exploration Geophysicists.

Jackson, J., and McKenzie, D. P., 1983, The geometrical evolution of normal fault systems: J. Struct. Geol., 5, 471–482.

Jaunich, S., 1983, The South-western African continental margin, velocity anomalies: in Bally, 1983, 2, 2.2.3-108–117.

Jenyon, M. K., 1984, Seismic response to collapse structures in the southern North Sea: Mar. Pet. Geol., 1, 27–36.

Jones, M. E., and Addis, M. A., 1984, Volume changes during sediment diagenesis and the development of growth faults: Mar. Pet. Geol., 1, 118–122.

Kennett, P., Ireson, R. L., and Conn, P. J., 1980, Vertical seismic profiles; their applications in exploration geophysics: Geophys. Prospect., 28, 676–699.

King, G., and Brewer, J., 1983, Fault related folding near the Wind River thrust, Wyoming, USA: Nature (London), 306, 147–150.

Kvenvolden, K. A., and Barnard, L. A., 1982. Hydrates of natural gas in continental margins: in Watkins and Drake, 1982, 631–642.

Lambert-Aikhionbare, D. O., and Shaw, H. F., 1982, Significance of clays in the petroleum geology of the Niger Delta: Clay Miner., 17, 91–103.

Larner, K., Gibson, B., and Chambers, R., 1983, Imaging beneath complex structure: in Bally, 1983, 1, 26.

Larsen, V., Aasheim, J. M., and Masset, J. M., 1981, 30/6—Alpha structure, a field case study in the silver block: in Norwegian Symposium on Exploration (NSE–81), Norsk Petroleumsforening, 122–141.

Lohmann, H. H., 1979, Seismic recognition of salt diapirs: Am. Assoc. Pet. Geol., 63, 2097–2102.

McClellan, B. D., and Storrusten, J. A., 1983, Utah-Wyoming Overthrust line: in Bally, 1983, 3, 3.4.1-39–44.

McKenzie, D. P., 1978, Some remarks on the development of sedimentary basins: Earth Planet. Sci. Lett., 40, 25–32.

McQuillin, R., Bacon, M., and Barclay, W., 1979, An introduction to seismic interpretation: Graham and Trotman, London.

MacLeod, M. K., 1982, Gas hydrates in ocean bottom sediments: Am. Assoc. Pet. Geol. Bull., 66, 2649–2662.

Mandl, G., and Crans, W., 1981, Gravitational gliding in deltas: in K. R. McClay, and N. J. Price, Eds., Thrust and nappe tectonics: Blackwell, 41–54.

Mathur, S. P., 1976, Relation of Bouguer anomalies to crustal structure in southwestern and central Australia: BMR Journal of Australian Geology & Geophysics, 1, 277–286.

May, B. T., and Covey, J. D., 1983, Structural inversion of salt dome flanks: Geophysics, 48, 1039–1050.

Meckel, L. D., and Nath, A. K., 1977, Geological considerations for stratigraphic modelling and interpretation: *in* Payton, 1977, 417–438.

Michaels, P., 1977, Seismic raypath migration with the pocket calculator: Geophysics, **42**, 1056–1063.

Mitchum, R. M., Vail, P. R., and Sangree, J. B., 1977, Seismic stratigraphy and global changes of sea level; Part 6, Stratigraphic interpretation of seismic reflection patterns in depositional sequences, *in* Payton, 1977, 117–133.

Mitchum, R. M., Vail, P. R., and Thompson, S., 1977, The depositional sequence as a basic unit for stratigraphic analysis: *in* Payton, 1977, 53–62.

Morgan, L., and Dowdall, W., 1983, The Atlantic continental margin: *in* Bally, 1983, **2**, 2.2.3-30–35.

Musgrave, A. W., 1967, Seismic refraction prospecting: Society of Exploration Geophysicists.

Nath, A. K., 1975, Reflection amplitude, modelling can help locate Michigan Reefs: Oil and Gas Jour., **73**, 180–182.

Neidell, N. S., and Poggiagliolmi, E., 1977, Stratigraphic modelling and interpretation—geophysical principles and techniques: *in* Payton, 1977, 389–416.

North American Commission on Stratigraphic Nomenclature, 1983, North American stratigraphic code: Am. Assoc. Pet. Geol. Bull., **67**, 841–875.

P'an, C. H., 1982, Petroleum in basement rocks: Am. Assoc. Pet. Geol. Bull., **66**, 1597–1643.

Payton, C. E., Ed., 1977, Seismic stratigraphy—applications to hydrocarbon exploration: Am. Assoc. Pet. Geol. Mem. 26.

Phelps, E. H., and Roripaugh, C. C., 1983, Carbonate shelf, Central Louisiana: *in* Bally, 1983, **1**, 1.2.4-1–5.

Pieri, M., 1983, Three seismic profiles through the Po Plain: *in* Bally, 1983, **3**, 3.4.1-8–26.

Ramsayer, G. K., 1979, Seismic stratigraphy, a fundamental exploration tool: Offshore Technology Conference, Houston, paper 3568.

Roberts, M. T., 1983, Seismic example of complex faulting from the north-west shelf of Palawan, Philippines: *in* Bally, 1983, **3**, 4.2-18–24.

Robinson, E. A., 1983, Seismic velocity analysis and the convolutional model: IHRDC.

Ryder, R. T., Lee, W. L., and Smith, G. N., 1977, Seismic models of sandstone traps in Rocky Mountain basins: Methods in Exploration Series, American Association of Petroleum Geologists.

Sadler, P. M., 1981, Sediment accumulation rates and the completeness of the stratigraphic section: J. Geol., **89**, 569–584.

Sangree, J. B., and Widmier, J. M., 1977, Seismic interpretation of clastic depositional facies: *in* Payton, 1977, 165–184.

Schlee, J. S., and Fritsch, J., 1982, Seismic stratigraphy of the Georges Bank Basin Complex, offshore New England: *in* Watkins and Drake, 1982, 223–252.

Sengbush, R. L., 1983, Seismic exploration methods: IHRDC.

Seni, S. J., and Jackson, M. P. A., 1983, Evolution of salt structures, East Texas Diapir Province, Part 1, Sedimentary record of halokinesis: Am. Assoc. Pet. Geol. Bull., **67**, 1219–1244.

Sheriff, R. E., 1973, Encyclopedic dictionary of exploration geophysics: Society of Exploration Geophysicists.

Sheriff, R. E., 1975, Factors affecting seismic amplitudes: Geophys. Prospect., **23**, 125–138.

Sheriff, R. E., 1977, Limitations on resolution of seismic reflections and geologic detail derivable from them: *in* Payton, 1977, 3–14.

Sheriff, R. E., 1980a, Seismic Stratigraphy: IHRDC.

Sheriff, R. E., 1980b, Nomogram for Fresnel-zone calculations: Geophysics, **45**, 968–992.

Sheriff, R. E., 1982, Structural interpretation of seismic data:

Education Course Note Series, 23, American Association of Petroleum Geologists.

Shipley, T. H., Houston, M. H., Buffler, R. T., Shaub, S. J., Macmillen, K. J., Ladd, J. W., Worzel, J. L., 1979, Seismic evidence for wide-spread possible gas hydrate horizon on continental slopes and rises, Am. Assoc. Pet. Geol. Bull., **63**, 2204–2213.

Society of Exploration Geophysicists, 1971, Elementary gravity and magnetics for geologists and seismologists. Spec. Pub. No. 1, the Society.

Stone, D. S., 1983, Seismic profile—South Elk Basin: *in* Bally, 1983, **3**, 3.2.2-20–24.

Surlyk, F., 1977, Mesozoic faulting in East Greenland: Geol. Mijnbouw, **56**, 311–327.

Suzuki, U., 1983, 1.3 Igneous structures: volcanic mound: *in* Bally, 1983, **1**, 1.3-15–18.

Taner, M. T., and Sheriff, R. E., 1977, Application of amplitude, frequency, and other attributes to stratigraphic hydrocarbon determination: *in* Payton, 1977, 301–328.

Telford, W. M., Geldart, C. P., Sheriff, R. E., and Keys, D. A., 1976, Applied Geophysics: Cambridge University Press.

Trusheim, F., 1960, Mechanism of salt migration in Northern Germany: Am. Assoc. Pet. Geol. Bull., **44**, 1519–1540.

Vail, P. R., Todd, R. G., and Sangree, J. B., 1977, Chronostratigraphic significance of seismic reflections: *in* Payton, 1977, 99–116.

Watkins, J. S., and Drake, C. L., Eds. 1982, Studies in continental margin geology: Am. Assoc. Pet. Geol. Mem. 34.

Watts, A. B., 1982, Tectonic subsidence, flexure and global changes of sea level: Nature (London), **302**, 134–136.

Wells, A. T., Moss, F. J., Sabitay, A., 1972, The Ngalia Basin, Northern Territory—Recent geological and geophysical information upgrades petroleum prospects: APEA Journal, **12**, 144–151.

Index